# Sweet Mountain Water

Oregon Pulp and Paper Company in the 1950's where Pringle Creek empties into the Willamette Slough. All of Salem's 1856 water rights were purchased from this company or its successor, Boise Cascade. (Now the Boise Corporation.) The plant's water power is from the Mill Race.

# Sweet Mountain Water

*The Story of Salem, Oregon's Struggle to Tap
Mt. Jefferson Water and Protect the
North Santiam River*

Frank Mauldin

Upper Bennett Dam on the North Santiam River: The dam diverts a major part of the river to a north channel where Salem's water intake is located. A fish ladder is in the background and a boat slide is in the foreground. This dam is necessary for the continued operation of the Geren Island water treatment system but is not loved by the those who fish the river.

Published by Oak Savanna Publishing, 1962 Beaver Loop, Salem, Oregon, 97304.
Printed in Salem, Oregon
Front cover photograph of Mount Jefferson. Copyright © by Ron Cooper.
Back cover photograph of Little North Fork Santiam River from City of Salem Public Works Department.
First Printing
ISBN 0-9748668-0-6

# Contents

# Glossary

The abbreviations and acronyms used throughout this book can be tedious for the general reader. The good news is that these terms have been minimized. This is not an engineering book full of technical jargon, but rather, a general history of Salem's watershed and drinking water sources.

First, the abbreviations defined and explained:
<u>cfs</u> (cubic feet per second) and <u>cf</u> (cubic feet). Cfs is a measure of the rate of flow of water in a pipeline or waterway. A flow rate of 1 cfs is a lot of water flow compared to normal household use such as the flow from a bathroom shower of say 2.5 gpm (gallons per minute). A 1 cfs flow rate is 448 gpm, or 2.5 gpm is 0.00558 cfs.

<u>mgd</u> (million gallons per day). Mgd is also a measure of the rate of flow and is commonly used interchangeably with cfs. One mgd = 1.55 cfs.

In this book I have tried not to use cfs and mgd interchangeably but use cfs only to define water rights. (Salem purchased 60 cfs of 1856 priority water rights from Oregon Pulp and Paper Company in 1951.) Mgd is used in this book to define the capacity of pipelines or treatment facilities. (The 54 inch transmission pipeline has a maximum capacity of 50 mgd.)

Second, the acronyms defined:
<u>BLM</u>  United States Bureau of Land Management
<u>DEQ</u>  Oregon Department of Environmental Quality
<u>ESA</u>  United States Endangered Species Act
<u>GAO</u>  United States General Accounting Office
<u>NMFS</u> National Marine Fisheries Service or NOAA Fisheries National Oceanic And Atmospheric Administration Fisheries (recent name change not used in this book)
<u>ODF</u>  Oregon Department of Forestry
<u>ODFW</u>  Oregon Department of Fish and Wildlife
<u>OWWSC</u>  Oregon-Washington Water Service Company
<u>USFS</u>  United States Forest Service
<u>USGS</u>  United States Geological Survey
<u>USFWS</u>  United States Fish and Wildlife Service

# Introduction

In the 1930's Salem residents voted in a Mountain Water Party to develop a drinking water source on the North Santiam River and discontinue use of the polluted Willamette River water source. City residents were demanding a clean, unpolluted water supply. The title of this book, *Sweet Mountain Water*, reflects that desire. But it would be a while before Salem's water could truly be described as being "sweet" or clean and having a pleasant taste.

Developing the North Santiam River as a sweet mountain source demanded that the city overcome numerous obstacles along the way. The current situation where fish are exerting their rights on the North Santiam is the latest challenge the City of Salem is encountering to preserve its water supply (and legal water rights granted by the State of Oregon) for a growing state capital.

Over the years Salem has developed a truly excellent water system. How did this happen? Did the city stumble upon it without effort? Was it blind luck? Why is the finished water quality equal to, or better than, the cities of Eugene and Portland? Can we continue to provide excellent quality drinking water and supply the quantities of water demanded by a growing city? Is the City of Salem committed to continuing the evolution of this high quality drinking water system?

These are questions I am sure every health-minded person in Salem has an interest in. These questions should also be of prime interest to citizens who desire a sustainable community, because Salem's water system could be a critical factor for a vibrant and nonpolluting local economy.

In 1840 when Jason Lee and the "major reinforcement" of Methodist missionaries moved the mission from the original site north of Salem to a site on Mill Creek at Boones Island (at the present Broadway Street bridge over Mill Creek), the Willamette River was pristine and the pioneers could safely drink its waters. Jason Lee and the Methodist missionaries knew the "Chemeketa Plain" contained excellent water resources for many uses. One of these was Mill Creek which would later serve as an excellent power source for local mills, fueling Salem's early economy.

But as the pioneers quickly found out, the Willamette River did not stay pristine and the waters did not flow abundantly in Mill Creek year around. The pioneers soon discovered, after constructing a small dam and erecting a sawmill and flour milling plant, that Mill Creek almost dried up in most summers. So, to their dismay, there was no year around power for their mills. They did continue the luxury of drinking clean water from the Willamette River but only for a short time.

The discovery in the 1850's that Mill Creek's low summer flows were inadequate to power a growing, prosperous state capital was disheartening to many local business men. They decided to embark on an incredibly ambitious project: construct a canal for diverting water from the plentiful North Santiam River to Mill Creek (at a point just upstream from what is now Stayton). The canal was completed by Chinese laborers using plows and shovels. When completed, Salem was power wealthy. The diverted water provided water power for several industries. It even provided power for a pumping station to pipe drinking water from the Willamette River.

In the mid 1850's as more and more pioneers arrived, the Willamette River started showing signs of pollution from human and industrial waste. The solutions for cleaning up the river were very long in coming (even with the turn of two new centuries the Willamette remains polluted, and, at the start of the twenty-first century, it takes extraordinary technology to treat this water to federal drinking water standards).

Prior to 1870, Salem residents and businesses depended on shallow wells and dipping water from the Willamette River and Mill Creek. A small business was created by an industrious Chinese resident who hauled water from the Willamette and sold it to businesses and homes that did not have shallow wells. In 1870 two business men saw an opportunity to make a few bucks by building a piped water system for the downtown area and close by residential areas. The system would also provide fire flow capacity for a growing city that was plagued by frequent structure fires. The system built for Salem's 1200 residents was an 80 foot high wooden water tank filled from the Willamette River with a steam powered pump.

The water tank was located on the banks of the Willamette where the Riverfront Park is now located. The 80 foot elevation of the tank provided ample pressure for the downtown area from about Union Street to Mission Street and about 12th Street to the Willamette River.

This first privately owned water system was just what a growing state capital needed. It provided the required water pressures to serve buildings of up to three stories. The pressurized water system created a building boom in the downtown area. Several multistory buildings were constructed as a result.

Unfortunately, over the years the Willamette River also became a very convenient place to dump wastes. Salem's first sanitary sewers discharged directly to the river (as did all of the other cities and industries in the Willamette Valley). By the 1880's the river was dangerously polluted and not suitable as a drinking water source. However, Salem continued to use it and suffered the ridicule of residents, visitors and state legislators who feared they would get sick from drinking the foul water (and many probably did).

Until the 1930's private water companies in Salem tried to create better drinking water systems. After the raw Willamette River water was found to be an unacceptable source, one private water company developed a new source on Minto Island. They pumped Willamette River water with a water powered pump and treated it by primitively filtering it through the natural soils on the island. However, the finished water remained polluted. At this point the citizens of Salem were suffering water borne diseases such as typhoid, and they desperately needed a clean, healthy source of water.

Public pressure for developing a healthy water system started about 1910 and continued unabated until the City Council finally acted in the early 1930's. They purchased the private water system and sold bonds to build a new mountain water system using the North Santiam River at Stayton Island as the source. This was a daring step by the City Council even though the citizens had voted to approve the bonds. A very vocal minority thought the mountain water system was far too expensive and felt we should stay with what we had, because it was cheap.

The mountain water system was built in 1936 and 1937. It consisted of an intake and a buried perforated pipe for filtering the river water through the pervious cobble and sands on Stayton Island. The system was called an infiltration gallery. The island was located a short distance upstream of the City of Stayton. A 13 mile, 36 inch concrete pipe was laid from the island to a new 10 million gallon reservoir on Fairmount Hill in the City of Salem. When completed, the first mountain water system was the beginning of a water infrastructure that had the potential to provide excellent and plentiful water for a quickly growing city.

In 1957 the water system was greatly improved by the construction of a 54 inch water transmission line and the construction of state-of-the-art slow sand filters that provide polishing of relatively pure North Santiam River water. The system produces the high quality drinking water demanded by Salem residents and industries.

A major achievement was securing the legal rights to divert the North Santiam River water and use it for municipal purposes. Since 1951 the City has acquired most of the earliest water rights on the river and has hopefully ensured an adequate long term water supply. Or has it?

The quality of Salem's water in the future now depends, to a great extent on the quality of the watershed. Sixty eight percent of the watershed is owned and managed by the United States Forest Service (USFS). The remainder of the watershed is Oregon State forest land, forests managed by the Bureau of Land Management (BLM), and a small amount of agricultural and urban lands.

During the 1980's the USFS sold huge amounts of old growth timber, clear-cut thousands of acres on steep mountain slopes, and built hundreds of miles of logging roads. This created the potential for massive erosion with major negative consequences for continued high quality water in the North Santiam watershed. However, the Clinton Forest Plan in 1993 created very high standards for logging practices and targets for more sustainable forest yields. Due in large part to this new forest plan, the watershed has more recently been in a state of recovery.

To safeguard this important resource, city officials and the elected federal representatives need to continue their aggressive vigilance in protecting the watershed from logging practices detrimental to excellent water quality.

The last chapter, "Fish Exert Their Rights" explains the unprecedented problem and challenge with the Endangered Species Act (ESA) requirements being imposed on urban area water supplies where fish have been listed as either endangered or threatened. This is a situation that exists today and could compromise the early water rights that Salem has worked hard to obtain.

A major indicator of the health of a river system is the health of the biological life in the river. Recently the federal government listed the Oregon chub as endangered and two salmonid species as threatened in the upper Willamette basin. The two salmonid species are: spring Chinook salmon and winter steelhead. The North Santiam River, however, could be an anomaly in the region because it still has very good runs of the threatened fish. This is due to the excellent habitat the North Santiam provides for spawning and rearing of juvenile fish. The continued health of these fish will depend to a great degree on the quantity of water in the river. But demands on river water for both instream and out-of-stream uses continue to mount as population increases and recreational uses of stored water in Detroit Reservoir become a higher priority.

The federal agencies charged with regulating the threatened and endangered species are very concerned about the amount of water Salem diverts from the river. Two federal agencies, the U.S. Fish and Wildlife Service (USFWS) and the National Marine Fisheries Service (NMFS), are particularly concerned about the amount of water Salem can divert in the future because of the extensive water rights it owns. The future therefore becomes very cloudy due to the threatened and endangered fish. This may create a major long term challenge to the city in continuing to provide water from the North Santiam River far into the future.

Limiting the amount of water diverted from the North Santiam River by greatly increasing conservation will undoubtedly be one of the city's main priorities in future years. During several drought years between 1994 and 2001, the city successfully reduced peak water use through aggressive public education campaigns. Whether this will work in non-drought years remains to be tested.

It seems clear the future will require a new direction for the city in managing its water system. In the near past a major effort went into expanding and modernizing the treatment system. Management emphasis in the future has to be directed to conserving water so as to keep as much water in the river as possible and to provide leadership and resources in preserving the habitat of the threatened and endangered fish. However, this new direction could very well seriously affect the economy and future growth of the city. Regardless, it is very likely this new direction will become a much debated political topic.

The city could follow a direction of pressuring the federal fish agencies to look at a long list of options within their powers to implement, which does not unduly limit the city's use of North Santiam River water. The City of Salem owns most of the earliest water rights on the river and could argue that other users of river water should limit their use of water first. The city could argue that diversions of water does not "take" fish as defined in the ESA and, therefore, the diversions are legal under the ESA. The city could argue that the fish agencies are pressuring the "deep pockets" of the City of Salem to provide most of the resources for recovering fish.

Regardless of the future direction the city follows in meeting legal requirements under the ESA, management of the watershed will continue to be a point of conflict between the city and federal and state regulatory agencies. It is the belief of many city officials that the federal and state agencies have their own technical point of view and have little patience or sympathy for the problems of providing basic services for a city within the ability of residents to pay for those services.

As the story of Salem's evolving water system unfolds, it will become clear that Salem's political leaders and staff have been extremely committed to supplying high quality water for Salem's residents and businesses. In the past, the city has also felt confident in knowing the quantity of water needed will be there for many years into the future. Now that future has become clouded. How the conflicts over water supplies will be resolved is of major importance to the city. Will future leaders be up for these challenges? We can surely hope so.

# Chapter 1
# Salem's Early Water Systems

The settlement of Salem and the subsequent development of the city is clearly linked to Mill Creek, the North Santiam River and the Willamette River. Without these incredibly rich water resources, Salem would be far different from the present day capital city.

Salem's topography was created by geologic conditions and the powerful actions of the Santiam River. This river once flowed through a narrow opening in the basaltic hills southeast of Salem, called the Turner gap (a natural break in the Columbia River basalts which created the South Salem hills). It then flowed through what is now downtown Salem and northward through the present area of Keizer before joining the Willamette River. Over thousands of years the Santiam River laid down rich alluvial deposits along its path until changing conditions and catastrophic flood events moved its course to the present alignment south of Salem's southern hills.

The first domestic water supplies in Salem were shallow wells in the alluvial deposits. Wells of only a few feet deep were possible during the early years of settlement, but as residents were soon to find out, these very shallow wells were easily polluted from activities on the surface.

Salem's earliest inhabitants were the Kalapuya Indians who occupied the entire Willamette Valley prior to settlement by Canadian trappers and American pioneers. The Kalapuya were dependent on the common camas plant (*Camassia quamash*) which grew in and near the luxuriant wetlands in the valley. Meriwether Lewis's journal describes a meadow of camas seen from the distance as "resembling a lake of fine clear water."[1] The Kalapuya subsistence economy was based primarily on the collection of camas roots which were ground into flour and other wild plant products such as Oregon white oak acorns and various berries. Wild game, insects and salmon were also part of their diet but of secondary importance to these staples.

Since the Kalapuya were dependent on wild plants, they managed their environment by improving the plant's growing conditions through periodic burning of competing  brush and young trees. This helped to maintain open meadows and oak savannas which produced plentiful growth of edible plants and made them much more easy to harvest. It also provided open range land for large game.

The first settlers to the Mid-Willamette Valley area were retired trappers from the Hudson Bay Company whose base of operation was at Fort Vancouver. Unfortunately for the Kalapuya, these first settlers brought a wide variety of European diseases from which the Kalapuya had no natural immunity. Most of the Kalapuya died from smallpox and malaria in the 1820's and 1830's prior to arrival of the first American settlers.

Jason Lee, a Methodist missionary, started the first mission in 1834 for Christianizing the Kalapuya on the east side of the Willamette about 10 miles to the north of present Salem. (The Willamette Mission Park was created over a century later by the State of Oregon to honor this historic site.) However, the Lee mission found the site to be very flood prone and unhealthy.

On arrival of the "great reinforcement" in 1840 which included about 40 additional missionaries along with machinery for a flour mill and sawmill they moved the mission to the "Chemeketa Plain" (now the City of Salem).

They then constructed their water powered flour mill and sawmill on Mill Creek close to its confluence with the Willamette River, at what was called Boones Island. (The original site was located about where Broadway Street crosses Mill Creek today.) Figure 1-1 shows a present day Marion County Historical Society sign on Broadway Street where Mill Creek crosses under the street.

The missionaries also built a school for the Kalapuya called the "Manual Labor School". This school later evolved to Willamette University, the oldest college west of the Mississippi River.[2]

From 1840 through 1844 the Methodist Church in Boston sponsoring the mission became increasingly dissatisfied with the progress and the great expense of the Manual Labor School. Jason Lee was recalled back to Boston and the church then sent Reverend George Gary to liquidate the holdings of the mission. Since the flour mill and the sawmill could only operate during the high water period on Mill Creek, it had become an uneconomical operation. Reverend Gary then sold the mills to John Force in 1844 for $6,000.[3]

Force soon realized he needed a reliable source of water year around in Mill Creek to power his new flour mill. Mr. Force being a person with vision and apparently deep pockets, had the idea that North Santiam River water could be diverted to Mill Creek at about

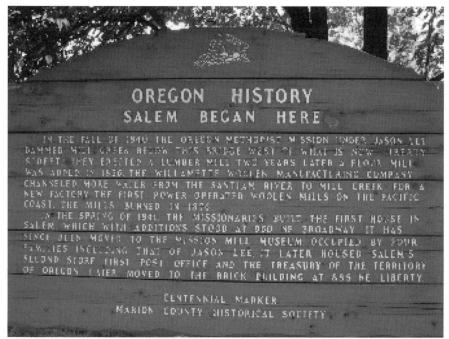

FIGURE 1-1: A Marion County Historical Society sign describing Jason Lee's Methodist Mission and the location of a saw mill and flour mill powered by Mill Creek water.

the present location of the City of Stayton.

In 1850 Force hired laborers to start digging a ditch of about six miles connecting the North Santiam and Mill Creek upstream from Salem. However, Force forgot to get the approval of the residents in the area, and once word got around, they protested this farsighted venture by a business man from the "big" village of Salem. Apparently the protests were especially caustic, because even though Force obtained easements from the property owners along the route, he eventually abandoned the project.

In other ways Force's venture was well planned. He had obtained a water right for his diversion from the Oregon Territorial Government which on March 3, 1849 replaced the provisional government. Specifically why Force gave up on his project to construct the diversion ditch is unknown to the author. Perhaps he ran out of funds to complete this highly ambitious project. Force, however, continued to operate his flour mill until 1856 when the Willamette Woolen Manufacturing Company purchased the site. Joseph Watt, one of the owners, immediately pursued construction of the North Santiam River diversion. Supposedly he hired Chinese laborers to dig the ditch.

James Watt paid John Force $400 for both his claimed water right and the right of way of Salem Ditch to Mill Creek, even though the legality of the water right was in dispute.[4]

Watt, a person of considerable business acumen and with political connections, proposed to the Oregon Territorial Government the incorporation of the Willamette Woolen Manufacturing Company and a diversion water right of 254 cubic feet per second (cfs) from the North Santiam River to Mill Creek. On December 7, 1856 the Oregon Territorial Government approved the incorporation of the woolen mill, and of utmost importance to the future of Salem, the water right diversion with a priority right of 1856.

In August, 1857, construction of the diversion ditch, named appropriately "Salem Ditch", was completed and North Santiam River water started flowing in Mill Creek through Salem. The entire village celebrated this great event in anticipation of industrial prosperity, because at this time water power was the key to industrial development. Ben Maxwell a Salem historian reported: "Whiskey was passed, a cannon boomed and nearly every pioneer felt a little richer."[5]

And, Salem truly became richer. For the next 20 years Willamette Woolen Manufacturing Company was Salem's largest industry employing 100 people. The entire factory was powered from two water turbines in Mill Creek. A small dam upstream of the site created a small water drop. Inside the factory the machinery to weave thousands of yards of woolen material per day was powered by an elaborate set of belts from the water turbine shafts. (Obviously something Oregon's Occupation Safety and Health Administration would never allow today!)

In March, 1861 a committee of three City of Salem aldermen started negotiations with Willamette Woolen Manufacturing Company to use part of their Mill Creek water rights for city use. The city was growing and the individual shallow wells that businesses and residences relied on were generally unsatisfactory. However, the negotiations stalled but continued again in 1866.[6]

The historic record has not been found to explain why the city was denied the use of Mill Creek water. After all, once the water had passed through the water power wheel it was no further use to the woolen plant. This was a huge missed opportunity for the city, because the water quality in Mill Creek was much better than the Willamette River, which was quickly deteriorating as the growing valley started using it as a convenient place to discharge sewage and industrial waste.

In the early 1860's, the year of Salem's incorporation, there was a growing need to deal with ever increasing structure fires. Firefighting capacity was needed which required a reliable source of water. This need, along with the planned construction of a flax oil plant called the Pioneer Oil Company (located at the present Mission Mill site) plus a large flour mill and a new woolen mill to be located on Willamette Slough (where Boise Cascade is now located) required additional water resources for power.

The plan was to construct a dam on Mill Creek (now named Waller Dam) and divert Mill Creek water down a Mill Race to begin at the dam and flow to Pringle Creek. The new Mill Race would supply the industrial water and power for the proposed new industries. In 1864 the construction of the Mill Race was completed.

The new Mill Race had a drop in elevation of about 30 feet about where the present Liberty Street crosses the Mill Race. The City installed a hydraulic ram (a water powered pump) at this location and laid pipe to four large underground cisterns located in downtown Salem.

It is not known by the author how the city acquired the right to use this water. There is no known record of the city acquiring water rights, so this use  probably resulted from the legal water right holders making a hand shake deal with the city (probably not unusual in the the early 1860's).

The four cisterns, 22,000 gallons each, were located at Commercial and Ferry Streets, Commercial and State, Commercial and Court, and Liberty and State. The cisterns were for the purpose of providing fire pumping reservoirs and were not intended as a drinking water supply. The cisterns were kept full at all times and were the responsibility of the city's street superintendent.[7]

On January 15, 1861 the city  appointed Wiley Kenyon as the first fire warden. Later that year the city's Board of Aldermen gave official standing to the volunteer "Alert Hook and Ladder Company" and ordered payment of all previous indebtedness incurred by the company.[8]  Obviously the volunteer fire companies swung a lot of political weight for such largess from a penny pinching Board of Aldermen. The good thing is that the city has had a reliable fire protection service ever since.

The four cisterns made fire fighting in the downtown core much more efficient. Prior to construction of the cisterns, the volunteer fire company would have to use bucket brigades to carry water to a burning structure. Using such primitive methods, only the smallest structure fires could be extinguished. The cisterns and the fire company's first hand-pumpers were put into service in 1865, shortly after construction of the mill race and the pumping system for filling the cisterns.

The cisterns, the hand-pumpers along with highly motivated volunteer fire companies made fire protection a reality in the downtown area. This ended an era in the downtown where fires were frequent with little hope of saving a building or its contents.

Figure 1-2 is a photograph of one of the first volunteer fire companies, the "Yew Park Hose Team" and their mascot.

FIGURE 1-2: The Yew Park Hose Team, one of the first volunteer fire companies in Salem.

Figure 1-3 shows a fire pumper typical of the later generation of steam powered pumps used in the late 19th century.

In 1865 with the start up of a fire protection service, Salem had taken a first step in creating a city water system and a large step in moving from a primitive pioneer village to a modern full service city. However, one more very large step had to be taken to create a piped city drinking water system. Residents and businesses at this time depended on shallow wells or strong backs to haul water from the Willamette River or from the nearest creek.

The strong back was supplied in 1868 by an enterprising Chinese resident, Lee Tong. Tong had a vision that the city needed to find a better water source than the hodgepodge of shallow polluted wells scattered around the downtown and adjacent residential neighborhoods. Water was supplied directly to homes and businesses by Tong and his helpers by filling discarded oil tins and carrying the water to customers. We can only hope for the customers sake the tins had been thoroughly cleaned first, but in the 1860's that could have been a nicety that was not very important.

FIGURE 1-3: A steam fire pumper all decked out for a parade in the late 19th century parked in front of the Marion County Court House.

Regardless, Tong's business grew and grew and it soon attracted some local business men who saw the water supply business as potentially very profitable.

Clark Moor Will, a longtime Salem water utility employee, wrote in 1958 about Salem's early water system. Following in Mr. Will's own unique style is a description of the takeover of Lee Tong's enterprise:[9]

It is highly probable that Lee Tong, a China man, [sic] influenced the promotion of piped water to Salem. Late one afternoon on a very warm summer day in 1870 three men were discussing the events of the day in Martin and Allen's Trading Store on Commercial Street between State and Court. The two principals of the discoursing trio were Martin and Allen, proprietors of the past dealing in groceries, provisions and produce.

"There's a change coming when the gap is closed between here and Frisco" remarked the third party of Martin and Allen on that summer afternoon." [The gap referred to completing the railroad between San Francisco and Portland.]

"Yes", responded Allen, "Dependable rail transportation will bring development. People are coming."

"And we are stuck here in a grocery provisions retail business. Can't we do better than that, Allen?" responded Martin.

"What's that China man [sic] doing across the street there?" asked the stranger.

"Why that's Lee Tong, our water boy", said Allen." He brings water up from the river in those old oil tins and peddles it out to such as have no wells here in the village."

Martin and Allen decided to "horn in" on the Chinaman's water delivery business.

Construction of the Salem water works started early in 1871 under the direct supervision of W. F. Boothby, who was invited into the promoting group because of his experience.

Thus from a point on the river on Front Street between Court and State water mains were extended to the finer homes, hotels and business buildings. It was a costly undertaking. The streets were wide, the settlement scattered.

The coming of piped water into Salem homes created some excitement. Old timers say many large wood and tin tubs made their last trip to the center of the kitchen floor during the winter and spring of 1871. Small bedrooms and large closets became bathrooms and few homes without bathrooms were found in the social registry. It was the dawn of a new day for many Salem housewives.

The Chemeketa House, now known as the Marion Hotel, opened its doors to the coast traveling public late in 1870. That the water company was prepared to meet the demand for water delivery two to three floors above street level is evidenced by an early statement dated July 12, 1871: Salem Water Company's G.W. Rhodes plans called for an open fifty foot square wooden tank to be erected on piling and to be located somewhere near the foot of State Street not far from Salem's Iron Foundry.

An early photograph in the Salem Public Library dated 1875 shows the location of the plant and square water tank on the river bank between Court and State Street. The exact location is further pin pointed by a warranty deed dated May 2, 1871 from John G. Wilson and Sarah Wilson as being Lot 2 of Block 63.

Later this location was corrected by Mr. Will that the water tank was built on Lot 3, Block 63 and a large brick lined cistern was built on Lot 2, Block 63.

It is doubtful that Mr. Will's dates are correct as to when the owners of Salem Water Company first conceived their business plan. Because the owners of the Reed Opera House built in 1869 and the Chemeketa House built in 1870 probably knew as early as 1868 that a water system would soon be built that would serve multi story buildings. Without this piped water system these buildings would probably not have been built as multi story buildings.

David Allen and J.M. Martin proposed to the Board of Alderman a franchise for supplying water to certain parts of the city. The Board approved the franchise on December 30, 1870. Salem Water Company was incorporated on February 21, 1871 with J.M. Martin, W.F. Boothby, N. Stapleton and David Allen as principals. Boothby was elected president and Allen as secretary. Salem Water Company agreed to furnish city uses for $1800 per year, lay a mile of pipe the first year and charge rates no higher than other cities in the area of comparable population and, additionally, build an elevated tank to enhance fire fighting capabilities.

Salem Water Company's plan for obtaining the best water quality possible was to dig a brick lined infiltrating cistern near the rivers edge and to take advantage of the natural filtering action of the alluvial soils. The cistern was 12 feet in diameter and 45 feet deep. It was planned to pump water from the cistern to the elevated tank with a 2500 gallon per minute (gpm) steam powered pump. It is possible the pump was fueled by coal, but it could have been powered by wood, which was very plentiful and cheap at the time. (A coal gassification plant was started in 1871 on the riverfront very close to the water tank. The coal gas was used to light city street lights in the downtown area.)

The water tower was constructed of wooden piling and timber supported on a masonry foundation. The water tower was 80 feet high and held 270,000 gallons. Figure 1-4 shows an artist's drawing of Salem in 1876. The water tower can be seen to the right of the upper-most steamboat on the Willamette River. Minto Island is also shown as well as the Marion County Courthouse and the State of Oregon Capitol.

After a short period it was found, to the chagrin of the water company owners, that the infiltrating cistern was not capable of supplying a sufficient amount of water and had to be abandoned. (Much later in 1929 Clark Moor Will remembered he had visited the abandoned cistern. He found the old cistern located in the basement of the Cliff and Brown Mohair Warehouse at 171 Front Street.)

Salem Water Company, with the failure of the well to supply sufficient water, installed an 8 inch suction pipe 75 feet into the Willamette Slough near its confluence with the river channel. The suction pipe was weighted at the inlet end to hold it in place during high water in the Willamette. Water was then pumped directly to the elevated tank.

In writing this history it would be very easy to criticize the decisions of the Salem Water Company. First, it was a good decision to pump from an infiltration cistern, since the waters of the Willamette River and especially the Willamette Slough were already showing signs of pollution. However, it was a huge mistake to assume the cistern would supply sufficient water without testing it before building the water tank and installing the steam powered pump. When the cistern failed, another mistake was made in not ending the suction line upstream in the main river channel instead of in the Willamette Slough.

The slough was already polluted because of the industrial waste from the flour mill and woolen mill located at the foot of the Mill Race plus domestic waste from Pringle Creek. Another major mistake was related to the failure of the infiltrating cistern. If it was known the cistern would not supply sufficient filtered water, then another water source should have been investigated before building the water tower.

In 1871 Mill Creek with its banks full of water diverted from the pristine North Santiam River should possibly have been considered as the primary water source. But, in 1871 the owners of Salem Water Company were in a hurry to sell water and in their haste they overlooked better options for the water source.

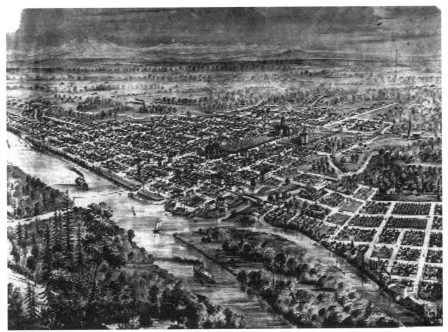

FIGURE 1-4 Salem in 1876 showing several prominent landmarks as well as the Salem Water Company water tower on the east bank of the Willamette River

Regardless of the decisions which I can now label as mistakes, the owners of the Salem Water Company overcame extreme financial, political and technical obstacles to provide Salem with its first water system which the public in 1871 greatly appreciated.

Getting back to our story, the water tower was a huge success because it allowed construction of multiple story buildings with sufficient water pressure for up to about three stories. It also gave an elevated platform for land developers to show visitors and investors a birds eye view of the growing city. A circular stair was built around the structure to access the top of the tower. However, the tank soon started leaking and this probably discouraged most of the sightseers.

A short decade after construction the water tower had outlived its usefulness. The leaky tank was regarded as an unsightly landmark.

Vegetation flourished around its well irrigated base. With increasing public criticism the water company decided to demolish the water tower in the 1880's. The steam powered pump then pumped water directly into the water lines. This required the pump to be operated full time to maintain acceptable pressures and created an increased operating expense for the water company.

Salem Water Company incurred a considerable capital cost in constructing the city's first water system. The Company produced no profits for the owners initially. The first year the Company suffered losses. The Company reported expenses of $21,096 while cash received was $20,812. All of the cash received, except $948, was from assessments to property owners for laying the water pipes. In essence the assessments were hookup charges. It appears the Company after this first year became profitable with its agreement with the city supplying $1800 per year and ongoing water rate fees received from customers. It also appears the company's initial capital costs of constructing the system were almost totally recovered with assessment charges.

During the period of 1874 to 1878 a competing water company, the Santiam Water Company, started operations by laying wooden water pipes in developing areas north of Mission Street and east of High Street. (The Salem Water Company in contrast was laying metal pipe in downtown and adjacent residential areas.)

The Santiam Water Company system consisted of about four miles of wooden pipe and a water powered pump. A 48 inch water wheel installed at the drop in the Mill Race between High and Liberty Streets supplied the power. This power system was not capable of supplying the high pressures needed for multiple story buildings but apparently it was sufficient for residential purposes at the time.

Santiam Water Company certainly had the right idea as far as water source. The water source was the Mill Race with its supply of water diverted from the North Santiam River.

Santiam Water Company was owned by three men: a Mr. Wealdon, a Mr. Edwards and a Mr. Griswald. The water wheel pumping system was housed in the Pacific Agricultural Works Building at the corner of Trade and Liberty Streets. This building had originally housed a flour mill and was owned by Mr. Griswald.

Apparently Mr. Griswald borrowed money to construct the Santiam Water Company system. However, revenues were insufficient to service the debt and his creditors foreclosed. In 1878 Salem Water Company purchased the Santiam Water Company system.

Along with the water system, Salem Water Company acquired the very valuable  Mill Race water power rights. Mr. Griswald's right to the Mill Race water came from an Act of the Territorial Legislator in 1856 that conveyed 254 cfs of rights of diverted water from the North Santiam River. Griswald was  largely responsible for defining water and power rights by deeded description for the several power right holders on the Mill Race. It was James Watt, one of the owners of Willamette Woolen Manufacturing Company, that obtained the original 254 cfs of water rights. However, his woolen mill on Mill Creek did not use all of the 254 cfs of allowed rights.  Instead he built another mill at the present Boise Cascade site and transferred part of the original 254 cfs water right to the Mill Race. This opened the door for properties upstream on the Mill Race to use the water for power as well. Mr. Griswald took advantage of this as well as did Kay Woolen Mills further upstream. (Chapter 4 includes an explanation of the complexities of power water rights  for both the Mill Race and Mill Creek.)

The purchase of the Griswald property and the Santiam Water Company gave the Salem Water Company a huge opportunity for creating a more economical water powered system. However, it took a few years of continuing to take water from the Willamette Slough on Front Street before it was finally realized that it was too polluted to use as Salem's water source. A cleaner source was needed.

The obvious alternative source of drinking water for Salem was the Mill Race which at the time consisted primarily of diverted water from the North Santiam River (much later Mill Creek was not an appropriate water source because of extensive upstream farming). But Salem could have been drinking water from the North Santiam via Mill Creek as early as 1878, but it was not to be. Salem would have to wait an additional 59 years to start drinking North Santiam River water.

# Chapter 2
# Improvements Are Made
# Discontent Grows

In 1885 after 14 long hard years of owning and operating the water system, Salem Water Company was sold to R.S. Wallace. The sale was a private affair and the selling price was not made public. The Salem City Council approved the purchase recognizing the financial limitations of the original owners to make the large improvements which were sorely needed. The Willamette Slough's water quality was becoming progressively worse and a change of the water intake using a cleaner source was needed.

Mr. Wallace recognized the extreme limitations of the Front Street water intake and started planning a more energy efficient system with a cleaner source. Putting his plan into action, he purchased the property at the southeast corner of Trade and Commercial (the present site of Fire Station No. 1). In 1886 he constructed a 14 inch suction line into the Willamette Slough upstream of the pollutants discharged by the flour and woolen mill. The suction line crossed part of the Willamette Slough and rested on a wooden crib which in turn rested on the bottom of the slough.

It was estimated the suction lift was only about 10 feet due to a deep below-the-ground pump pit constructed at the southeast corner of Commercial and Trade Streets. The pump pit was 32 feet in diameter and 24 feet deep, constructed of brick, and probably waterproofed to keep out the groundwater. The steam pump which was originally installed in 1871 by Martin and Allen on Front Street was moved and installed in the pit. The steam pump was wood powered. In addition to the steam power, the pump was also powered by the water wheel located at the Mill Race fall near Liberty Street. Power was transmitted by a unique rope drive system.[10] The transmission ropes were covered by a wooden house 600 feet long.

Figure 2-1 is a photograph taken in 1895 of the pump house and the wooden covering of the rope drives stretching from about Commercial Street east to the water wheel between the present High and Liberty Streets. Figure 2-2 is a photograph of the pump house near Commercial Street.

FIGURE 2-1: Pump house and rope drives to a water wheel installed in the Mill Race looking east. Trade Street is to the left.

In 1887 operators realized improvements were needed to equalize pressures to the two discharge lines that served areas to the north and east. An air chamber was installed which was five feet in diameter and 20 feet high enclosed in an octagonal building on a heavy concrete foundation. The air chamber connected both discharge pipes leading to the service mains.

In 1890 improvements were made to the round house because the water wheel powered pump was insufficient to meet the ever growing demands of water for a growing city. A Smith steam powered pump was added to the round house to provide additional pumping power. This additional power allowed the construction of a two million gallon reservoir on Fairmount Hill. The reservoir was 176 feet above the pumping system. A 10 inch main was constructed to connect the reservoir to the pumps.[11]

In 1893 J. M. Wallace took over management of Salem Water Company after his brother R.S. Wallace died. That year J.M. Wallace made three major improvements to the water system. Because the Willamette Slough's water quality was becoming more and more polluted with industrial and human waste, he decided to extend the suction line to the Willamette River across Minto Island. The Willamette River was somewhat better in quality than the water in the slough. This created a suction line of about 2200 feet and the need for a much more powerful pumping system.

FIGURE 2-2: Front view of pump house. Commercial Street is in the foreground.

The second major improvement was the required improvement of the main pumping system. The Smith steam pump was retired and a Dow triplex plunger pump was installed in the west round house. This 70,000 pound pump had a capacity of 2.5 million gallons per day (mgd) of pumping capacity at 80 pounds of pressure. The pump was steam powered from wood with assistance from the water wheel. The pump was able to create sufficient suction pressure for the new

Minto Island intake.

The third major improvement was to build a primitive filtration system on Minto Island, because the raw water quality in the Willamette River was not suitable as a drinking water source without filtration. J.M. Wallace sought to find a solution to this water pollution in the Willamette River. A filtering system was needed.

To accomplish this, a wooden crib of 20 feet by 60 feet was buried in a sand bar of the Willamette at an elevation below the river bed. The top of the crib was sealed water tight which forced all the water entering the crib to be filtered by the gravels and sands below the river bed. The end of a new 24 inch suction line extension was placed in the crib below river bed elevation. This very early infiltration type filter system provided improved water quality in the winter when the river was naturally turbid. It probably did very little to remove colloidal and dissolved pollutants, including river pathogens.

Figure 2-3 is a 1898 photograph of the beginning stages of crib construction.

The construction of the crib started in 1898 and was completed in 1899. Salem Water Company was very proud of this treatment system and published the following information:

> There was a time when the purity of Salem's domestic water supply could be questioned, but that time has passed. The Capital City is now supplied with the purest quality of cold, crystal water that is in many respects superior to that of which the people of Portland and Astoria boast. This supply is furnished by the Salem Water Company.
>
> It is not every city that possesses an efficient water system by which an adequate and never failing supply of water of great purity and unvarying temperature is furnished continuously through out the year. To this acquisition and to these conditions is largely responsible to the absence of any great amount of sickness in this locality, making the Capital City an ideal home for home seekers, of whom many annually locate here, being largely influenced terested [sic] in the ownership and managing their selection of a home by reason of these existing conditions.[12]

Figure 2-4 shows an end view of the timber constructed crib.

Obviously, Salem Water Company was interested in telling their customers they were buying clean, healthy water. They certainly overstated their product with such statements as: "purest quality of cold, crystal water." The Willamette River was just not that pure and the filtration system just wasn't very efficient. The tragedy is that the Willamette River would become more and more polluted every year as population and industry increased.

The technology available to Salem Water Company to truly produce water of the "highest purity" from the Willamette River was not available in the late 1800's. If the technology had been available Salem Water Company did not have the capital resources to make the necessary huge investments. And additionally, Salem residents even though they were complaining about water quality, would probably not have been willing to pay the costs of treating Willamette River water to its highest purity.

FIGURE 2-3: Construction of the first timber water inlet crib on Minto Island.

In 1909 further improvements were made to the infiltration system to increase its capacity. Apparently the original crib and under drain percolation system were incapable of supplying sufficient amounts of water during peak demand periods. To increase the capacity, an area above the crib was diked to create a reservoir. Water was then pumped from the Willamette River to the reservoir. The increased height of water on the infiltration crib apparently did increase the flow through the crib. However, this was  probably done at the expense of good water quality since the faster the infiltration rate through a filter the more pollutants can pass through the filter.

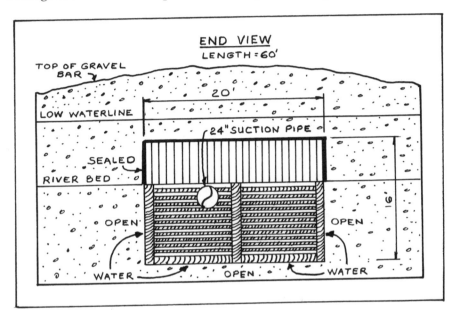

FIGURE 2-4: Water inlet crib on Minto Island.

Figure 2-5 shows a plan view of the pump house, the water wheel site, the suction lines to Minto Island and the infiltration crib and pond.

In 1911 a new parallel 24 inch suction line was built from the main pumping station to the infiltration and filtering area. This new line north of the original line, which starts as a 14 inch line, was interconnected by valves to the old suction line. Because leaks developed in this new line, and they were never able to be fixed, the new suction line crossing the slough was never made serviceable. The old line continued to be used.

Although Salem Water Company attempted  major improvements, the water quality delivered to their customers still continued to deteriorate. The water was thought to be contaminated with water borne bacteria and viruses. Typhoid was probably endemic in the city at this time. The general mood of the citizens of Salem was that the water was unhealthy and caused just about every ailment anyone suffered from.

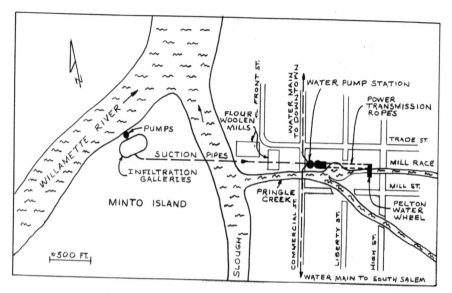

FIGURE 2-5: Salem Water Company system of pumping water from its water inlet on Minto Island in 1909.

By 1909 there was general citizen unrest and the belief that a new and healthy water source must be developed was gaining momentum. Many citizens started thinking about tapping the North Santiam River as the water source. There was talk  that a gravity system of supply could be built from the North Santiam River near Stayton to the city because there was a drop in elevation of about 200 feet.

In 1910 the City Council appointed a Mountain Water Committee of three city councilors and the mayor. The committee recommended and the City Council voted to approve a special election on August 15, 1910 to authorize the city's purchase of the Salem Water Company and to lease water power rights on the Mill Race. The voters that year approved the measure to buy the water company for $205,000 in cash and assume outstanding debt of $125,000 for a total sale price of $330,000. The water company also agreed to lease to the city the rights to water power on the Mill Race for $3000  per year with an option to purchase the rights for $44,000 in cash.

This final negotiated sale price of $330,000 was achieved after a long period of negotiating and wrangling between two City Council appointed committees that started meeting in late 1909 and completed their recommendations in February, 1910. There was a Citizen Committee of three members and an "Engineers Commission" of three members including John Lewis, State Engineer; J.H. Cunningham, private engineer representing the city; and, R.L. Donald, representing Salem Water Company. The Engineers Commission recommended a sale price of $422,595 but the Citizens Committee thought the price was greatly inflated. In a final showdown the Citizens Committee prevailed. (Obviously there was more than a little bit of conflict of interest with the Engineers Commission.)[13]

Salem Water Company became reluctant sellers. They were not pleased with the recommendation that was made to the City Council regarding the sale price. On March 12, 1910 Salem Water Company sent the Citizens Committee the following letter:

To:     John A. Carson, Chairman
        Gideon Stolz
        Isadore Greenbaum
From: Salem Water Company

Gentlemen:
We trust that the whole of the following will be taken by your honorable committee in the spirit in which it is submitted. On our part, we are making it in a spirit of concession and in an effort honestly to meet public sentiment. Almost nine months ago, we were requested to submit our property to the appraisement of a Committee of Engineers. We readily consented to this, not wishing in any way to oppose what the people of our city thought would tend to its development.

Our stockholders feel and know that it is not a desirable time to sell their water plant. They foresee large development for Salem and consequently increasing revenues for their property. They know the long struggle it has been in the past to meet public sentiment in the conduct of their business, and at the same time to get some small return upon the investment. A sale at this time under the present conditions, means that they will get no reward for the years of poor business and unfavorable returns during which they gave the best service to the city which was possible for them to furnish. Should the sale be made now it will deprive them of the profits which should begin to accrue with the rapid development of the city. The stockholders of this company recognize however that they are furnishing a public utility and are, in a large measure, subordinate to the wishes of the community, and the price we now make upon the plant is for the acceptance by the City of Salem only, and for this period of time and open only for so long as is reasonably necessary for the city to take proper action to consummate the purchase, and is not a general offer of sale.

After several meetings with your committee, and after giving the matter careful consideration from our viewpoint and from the viewpoint of the City of Salem, we see the following alternatives: first, the possibility of the municipality bringing in a gravity water system; second, the possibility of the municipality desiring to continue the present pumping system, but to change the source of supply from the present gravel bar to some other point.

Under the first condition, it would not be necessary for the city to acquire permanently the water power now in use. This, therefore, being an unnecessary expenditure of the city's funds, it has occurred to us to submit an offer which will eliminate this water power from the purchase price and agree to rent it to the municipality until such time as their future plans have fully matured.

Under the second heading, should the city retain the present system of furnishing water but change the source of supply to some other point further up the river, it would also be unnecessary for the city to expend its funds in purchasing the present water right on the gravel bar from which the supply is now taken. For this reason, we are willing to keep this water right and rent it to the city for such period as they find necessary.

Under the above conditions we make the following offer: We will accept $205,500 in cash, the City of Salem to assume the bonded debt of $125,000. The Salem Water Company will lease to the city, as long as required, all the water power which can be developed with the equipment on the present site for a sum (payable monthly) equal to ninety per cent of the cost of the cheapest power which can be delivered or generated at that point. this cost to be determined at the time of purchase and on January 1st of each succeeding year, and we will lease the water right for such period as the city retains this source of supply for the sum of $120 per month.

After the successful vote to purchase the water company, the mayor, George F. Rodgers, proclaimed on October 18, 1910 that an ordinance had been passed by the City Council that allowed the city to sell $400,000 in bonds called the "Water Bonds of the City of Salem." The ordinance's preamble stated, "the electors of the City of Salem at a special election on August 10, 1910 by a majority vote authorized the city to purchase the Salem Water Company, to maintain and operate the plant and to authorized a water bond to pay the costs."[14]

On November 28, 1910 the City Council appointed a Water Board of four city councilors which included Charles McNary. (McNary was to become the most successful politician in Salem's history. He was later elected to the U.S. Senate where he was a leader and in 1940 ran on the Wendall Wilkie ticket as Vice President. After Wilkie lost to Franklin Roosevelt, McNary resumed his long distinguished career in the U.S. Senate.)

With the appointment of the Water Board, it is unknown by the author what the relationship this board had with the Mountain Water Committee which was appointed earlier that year with different City Councilors. Apparently all the Councilors wanted to be part of this historic event of purchasing the private water system and creating a mountain water source.

The city had received bids on the water bonds and the water board opened them on November 28th. The winning bid came from a consortium of Emery, Peck & Lockwood, Blodgett and Company, and Easterbrook and Company, with G.W. Peck being the principal in charge. The city had specified the interest rate on the bonds would be 5%, so the winning bid was a low bid fee for selling the bonds, which was $25,200. This was an unusual way in modern terms of bidding a bond sale. (Today the potential buyers of the bonds bid interest rates and the lowest interest rate wins.)

At this point it appeared that the city's purchase or condemnation of Salem Water Company was a done deal. However, a deal is not done until its finally done because in early 1911 a new mayor and City Council took office. It was rumored right from the start of this administration that the new mayor was not pleased with the cost of purchasing Salem Water Company. There was still one more step the new City Council needed to pass and that was an ordinance that approved the final sale of the bonds.

The City Council took no action for several months and finally on April 14, 1911 G.W. Peck wrote C.A. Parks, President of Salem Water Company and said the city was not cooperating in proceeding with sale of the bonds.

Salem Water Company's C.A. Parks responded on August 18th to Mr. Peck as follows:

Your letter received. Since your visit several ill informed councilmen have been elected who have delayed proceedings and are attempting to force us to accept price much lower than what we quoted to city which price we regard as low and which is our minimum. Cannot give you all details satisfactorily by correspondence. Believe a visit by you necessary for a full understanding of situation and think such a visit at this time will result in much good. You know the offer we made to the city.
What do you think of a visit?[15]

G.W. Peck at this point seemed to believe the bond sale was now going nowhere, but he did confer with his attorney and partners to determine how to proceed. After conferring the partners decided they had enough of the city's endless negotiations and foot dragging. The following letter was then sent:

Chicago, Illinois
April 22, 1911
Hon. Louis Lachmund, Mayor
Salem, Oregon

Dear Sir:
On November 28, 1910 with our associates, we submitted an offer of $400,000 for your water bonds. By the time you have received this letter practically five months have elapsed since the offer was made. We might revise the various dates on which we write to you for additional information to complete this record, and the dates on which this additional information, both complete and incomplete, was received, but you, of course, know them, and regardless of these dates, the fact that five months has elapsed, though we think no fault of our own, is sufficient in itself.
You, of course, realize that the bond market is subject to innumerable conditions which determine the value of securities and because of this in general when a banking house bids for municipal bonds, they count on having them ready to deliver to their clients at a time not over thirty days from the date of the purchase. In the majority of cases the legality of an issue is determined within thirty days, but occasionally, due to an incomplete legal record, it may run slightly over

this. This, however, is quite unusual.

In making a bid for your bonds, our purpose was to get them ready to sell in December and early in January markets. Which are usually the best months in the year for municipal bonds, but as you were unable to deliver them at that time, we still held the hope that at almost any time you might be able to deliver the bonds and we would try and market them. However, conditions in the municipal division have continued to get worse, and at the present time the bonds would not be salable at any price as they would have been in December or January.

We have discussed this matter very carefully with our associates and the result is that we now formally advise you that we withdraw our bid for the bonds.

If you eventually get your difficulty with the Company [Salem Water Company] adjusted and the legality of the issue established and care to then offer us the bonds, we shall be very glad to consider them and will hope to be able to offer you an attractive price. We have instructed our associates to return to you all papers incident to this issue that they may have.

Assuring you that we regret very much that the legality and regularity of the issue could have been straightened out so that we could have secured delivery of the bonds, we are:

EMERY, PECK & LOCKWOOD[16]

In the meantime the drama deepened. On May 1, 1911 the City Council voted to go ahead with the purchase with basically the same price and conditions as negotiated previously. They then passed an ordinance authorizing the sale of the bonds and the purchase of Salem Water Company.

The City Charter at that time allowed the mayor to veto any ordinance he disagreed with, and this was one he did not like. On May 8, 1911 Mayor Louis Lachmund vetoed the enabling ordinance to sell the voter and City Council approved bonds. Following is the mayor's letter to the Council with his reasons for the veto:

Salem, Oregon
May 1, 1911
To the Common Council of the City of Salem

Gentlemen:
I herewith return Ordinance 822-930 with my veto, advancing

the following reasons therefore.

At the outset I desire to state that I am an earnest advocate of Municipal Ownership of Water Works, but after making a careful investigation of the reports covering the plant now owned by the Salem Water Company, I have come to the conclusion that the price asked is excessive and furthermore considering its present condition and inadequacy it is my belief that the taking over of this property by the city would not be justified.

From investigations and information derived from numerous sources the company's present mains and connections are totally inadequate to furnish a sufficient supply of water during the summer months and were the city to take over by purchasing the existing water works, the first step would be the installation of pipe of sufficient size to meet the requirements and demands of the entire city. It would mean the prompt construction of a reservoir of triple the capacity of the present one and finally a modern filtration plant.

A bond issue as contemplated of $400,000 would be but a beginning and before the plant could be brought up to date and sufficiently large to meet the requirements of the present and future, $1,000,000 or more would be invested, which investment would then consist of a plant about 1/2 obsolete and 1/2 modern.

The responsibility for the passing of this ordinance seems to rest with my signature but after giving the subject my best attention and looking at it from every angle, I feel that I would be derelict in my duty to this city and its citizens by affixing my name thereto.

City taxes have reached a maximum and to increase this burden would work an unnecessary hardship upon a class least able to stand it. The city is making rapid strides along the lines of progress and while the acquisition of the water works would be desirable, it is not absolutely necessary at this time.

I therefore return Ordinance No. 822-930 with my veto.

[signed] Louis Lachmund, Mayor[17]


Mayor Lachmund apparently believed the water system was adequate and the city had higher priorities for scarce tax resources. Its interesting to note he believed it would take $1,000,000 of additional funds after purchase to partially modernize the plant. The city at this time was aware of the possibility that a source on the North Santiam with pristine water quality was available and that an economical gravity piped system to the city was probably possible. However the city had not done detailed engineering investigations of this potential new source. That would have to wait until the early 1930's.

Mayor Lachmund's veto, however, was not a popular decision. Salem's newspapers were critical about the veto.[18 19]

Thus ended, temporarily, the efforts of Salem's Mountain Water Committee and the Water Board to buy the private water system and to create a clean source on the North Santiam River.

As we will see later, because the city had not done their homework on the location of a new water source, nor the cost of developing the source and constructing a transmission line to the city, it was probably a wise move by Mayor Lachmund to veto the bill. However, the cost of buying the privatized water system in 1911 was a bargain since later the price would more than double.

Meanwhile, the Minto Island water source and the suction lines to this facility continued to deteriorate. The suction lines leaked and drew in very polluted water from the slough. By 1920, Oregon Pulp and Paper Company was producing paper immediately west of the city's main pumping station and discharging huge amounts of waste into the slough, which was an additional source of pollution.

And the Minto Island infiltration system proved inadequate to treat the polluted Willamette River water. The Willamette Valley was experiencing a progressively increasing pollution of the Willamette River from industries and cities dumping their wastes directly into the river without treatment. In the 1920's taking water from the Willamette without extensive treatment was a public health disaster. The Oregon State Board of Health and the U.S. Public Health Service began studying the river and warning the public of its pollution and hazards to health.

It was not until 1967 when Tom McCall was elected governor that an aggressive program for cleaning up the Willamette River was started. McCall was committed to the environment and in his inaugural address he made it very clear his intentions as follows:

> Health, economic strength, recreation, in fact, the entire outlook and image of the state are tied inseparably to environment. Water, air, land and scenic pollution threaten these and other values in Oregon.
> The overriding challenge—the umbrella issue—of the campaign and the decade is quality of life in Oregon.[20]

City residents in the 1920's were loudly complaining about the bad drinking water in the city. Salem Water Company, already deeply in debt decided they were unable financially to make any major improvements to the Minto Island facility or the leaky suction line. They prudently decided to sell the system in 1927 to the private Oregon Washington Water Service Company (OWWSC). The new owners promised better service and immediately started making improvements.[21]

In 1929 they built a new 24 inch steel suction line from the pump station across the slough to the infiltration system. This solved the problem of the suction line leaking and bringing in extremely polluted slough water. In 1929 and 1930 they also built a much improved infiltration gallery by diking off a large area next to the existing pond and laying perforated concrete pipe back filled by fine sand and gravel. Willamette River water was then pumped into the diked area and discharged to the suction pipe after being filtered. This system, however, was totally ineffective in removing pollution that was finely suspended or in solution, pathogenic bacteria, and heavy metals.

The water quality produced by the new infiltration gallery was greatly improved over previous systems but still insufficient to provide healthy drinking water. So, in 1930 OWWSC started the construction of a modern rapid sand filtration plant, adjacent to the Salem Water Company office. (this building was razed in 1973 to construct the, new Fire Station No. 1 at Commercial and Trade Street). However, the new filtration plant was never completed because of city interest in purchasing the system.

Clark Moor Will, a long time employee of the water system recalled an incident in 1958 in which the old abandoned partially constructed filtration plant was uncovered. In Mr. Will's own words:

> My first day with the then Oregon Washington Water, Light and Power Company was April 1, 1929.
> One of the world's most unusual rope [power transmission systems that] Washington Water, Light and Power dismantled and a large filter bed was being built. This old filter bed, prepared by the Oregon Washington Water Company and later abandoned when municipal ownership was brought in, came to light some weeks ago. A cave-in suddenly made its appearance in the main water plant car park and equipment yard at 304 S. Commercial Street. The old filter bed by this freakish incident was brought to mind; as I peered into the depths of the cave in, I saw water. My ten foot plastic tape almost touched the water. A steel rod twenty one feet long stood only eight-

een inches above the yard level. There were nine and one-half feet of water in the hole below me. Some six and one half feet of rock and dirt covered the old filter bed built in 1929. Rotting planks cover a large hole in reinforced concrete caused the cave in, revealing the old filter bed. The incident brought back memories to the senior members of the department.[22]

So, in 1958 prior to the construction of the Salem Fire Department's Station No. 1, there still existed the remains of a rapid sand filtration plant, covered over and forgotten. Did Salem miss the opportunity to complete this plant after they purchased the water system in 1935? How far did OWWSC get in completing this plant? In all likelihood, not very far.

Also in 1930, OWWSC removed the old water wheel and built a hydroelectric plant of 156 KVA capacity. At the same time, the steam engines for the main pumping plant were replaced with electric motors. The hydroelectric plant furnished about 50 percent of the total electrical demand of the pumping station.[23]

In 1931 Salem voters elected a new City Council who ran on the ticket of the "Mountain Water Party." They pledged to buy the OWWSC water system by purchase or condemnation and to bring in "mountain water" from the North Santiam River. This political movement started the process of finally creating a plentiful, healthy source of water for Salem residents.

# Chapter 3
# Mountain Water, Finally

As early as 1909 there were many citizens in Salem who wanted to tap the North Santiam River as a healthy drinking water source. With the city's failure of purchasing Salem Water Company in 1911, this issue continued to simmer. The water supply from the Willamette River in the early 1920's was probably highly polluted and contained water borne pathogens. Even though the water was chlorinated at that time, we now know chlorination is only effective if organic matter in the water is very low. The primitive Minto Island filtration system was incapable of effectively removing suspended organic matter. Therefore the water could not have been properly disinfected for pathogenic organisms.

In May, 1923 with the Willamette River becoming more polluted by the day, Mayor Giesy appointed a committee to investigate drinking water conditions.[24] The committee reported to the City Council on July 2, 1923. They recommended the city file water rights applications with the State Engineer for rights to a "pure and adequate supply of water for the future use of the City of Salem."[25]

The City Council accepted the recommendation and authorized that the appropriate applications be filed. On July 16, 1923, the committee further recommended a "competent engineer" make a survey of the filings made by the committee. In addition the engineer would study a pipeline route to the North Santiam River and make an estimate of the expense for constructing a complete water system for Salem.[26]

The City Council agreed with this recommendation. They, however, thought the engineer would be too expensive and failed at that time to authorize any funds to hire one. Later in 1930 the City Council finally did agree to hire an engineer. Obviously they were in no hurry. In the meantime residents of Salem continued to get sick from drinking the bad water.

The committee, not discouraged, kept working on water right applications. Because the committee had no idea where the best source on the North Santiam might be, they made sure they covered a large area by shot gunning several applications up and down the North Santiam River and its tributaries. The water right applications filed by the committee were numbers one through four. A new City Council committee, the Public Utilities Committee, made the 1930 filing. The water right applications filed were:

1. July 5, 1923 - Applications for three separate diversions at 40 cfs for municipal purposes each on the North Santiam from two to four miles below the mouth of the Breitenbush River.

2. December 4, 1923 - Application for 50 cfs for municipal purposes from the Little North Fork Santiam River about five miles above its confluence with the North Santiam River.

3. July 24, 1924 - Application for use of Marion Lake and other lakes as storage reservoirs to the extent of 25,000 acre feet.

4. July 24, 1924 - Application for 300 cfs for municipal, irrigation and power purposes from the Marion Lake Fork about six miles below Marion Lake.

5. August 26, 1930 - Application for domestic, municipal, irrigation, and power purposes covering two separate diversions of 500 cfs each from the North Santiam below Whitewater Creek and at a point near Gates, Oregon and also 150 cfs from the Breitenbush River about four miles above its mouth.[27]

Figure 3-1 is a map of the upper North Santiam River and shows the locations of the water right applications.

From today's perspective, it is obvious the committees were trying to anticipate all possibilities for a future water diversion from the North Santiam or the Little North Fork. However, the committees missed the most economical option, Stayton Island just upstream from the City of Stayton and adjacent to the diversion point for Salem Ditch. This was also the shortest pipeline route to Salem. How this glaring omission occurred is anyone's guess.

In 1928, shortly after the 1927 purchase of the private water system by Oregon Washington Water Service Company (OWWSC), the drinking water went bad and it went very, very bad. It was foul tasting and had color suggesting serious pollution. Some city residents speculated it was from algae in the Willamette River. Others suggested it was from bacteria in the pipelines, and still others said it was leaky suction lines crossing the slough and sucking in paper mill wastes from the Oregon Pulp and Paper Company plant just upstream. In all likelihood, it was probably a combination of all three possibilities. OWWSC did repair the suction lines crossing the slough which improved the water to some extent. [28] Can you imagine drinking water that was contaminated with algae, bacteria, and pulp and paper waste? Well, that's exactly what the citizens of Salem were provided to drink at this time.

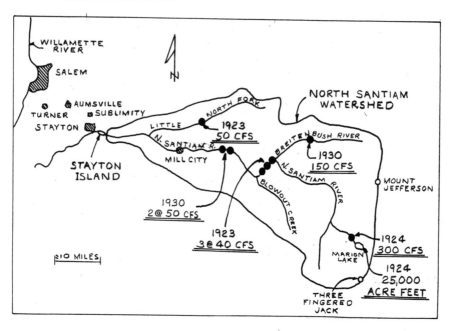

FIGURE 3-1: Water right applications filed in 1923, 1924, and 1930 by the City of Salem.

Bad drinking water gave Salem a horrible reputation. Legislatures while in session in Salem, demanded spring water be specially supplied to them. The city was probably fortunate that the state kept the capital in Salem!

Salem citizens were also in an uproar. As previously discussed, OWWSC, in a step of desperation, decided to build a modern rapid sand filtration plant on their property at Commercial and Trade Streets. They retained expert consultants from the east coast to design the plant and started the construction in 1929. However, they did not finish the construction because of the obvious intention of the city to buy the private system and create a mountain water source.

Early in 1930 the City Council finally reached agreement to hire an engineering firm to plan the mountain water system. They hired Barr and Cunningham, civil engineers from Portland. On August 31, 1930 Barr and Cunningham submitted their report, "Appraisal and Valuation of Salem Waterworks System."[29] The report was requested by the Salem Public Utilities Committee as necessary information to negotiate the purchase of the water system from OWWSC. The engineer's estimate for replacing the water system in kind was $426,713 and the depreciated value was $324,741.

Mayor, P.M. Gregory and the City Council, politically elected to create a mountain water system, approved a special election of voting for bonds to both buy the private OWWSC system and to build a pipeline to the North Santiam River for a mountain water source. In December, 1931, the voters of Salem approved $2,500,000 in bonds for both buying the private system by negotiation or condemnation and developing the new water source. This time, the City Council handled the selling of the bonds without controversy. Now the money was in the bank and everyone in Salem was anticipating a new water supply very quickly. However, it was not to be.

Time was wasting and citizens of Salem were still drinking bad water, as the wheels of government turned very slowly, at least in Salem, in the 1930's. Negotiations began with OWWSC and they went on and on and on. The city started with an offer to purchase the private system for the depreciated value of about $325,000. OWWSC thought that was a joke and countered with a sale price of $2,000,000. For three and a half years negotiations dragged on. Finally, in 1935, the city condemned the private water system. On July 31, 1935, Judge James Alger Fee signed a decree that transferred ownership of the OWWSC system to the City of Salem for a price of $1,003,042.98 for everything including the water power system on the Mill Race.[30 31]

The newly created and elected Salem Water Commission then took possession of the existing system on August 1, 1935, under the staff leadership of Cuyler Van Patten, water department director. He had a young assistant, Karl Guenther, who in the coming decades would lead the department in a rapid evolution to an outstanding water system. However, in 1935, no one knew what the future might hold and what was possible for Salem.

Because of uncertainty whether or if a mountain water system was possible, Van Patten decided to rebuild the Minto Island filtration system that consisted of a wooden crib and a pipe infiltration system.

The system between the impoundment dikes was totally rebuilt by city crews. Figure 3-2 is a photograph of crews installing the infiltration lines in 1936.

FIGURE 3-2 Installation of infiltration system on Minto Island by city crews in 1936.

The quality of the water from this rebuilt system was probably improved which made everyone in the city happier. But residents were still anticipating the pristine waters from a mountain water system.

Political wrangling started immediately on where to locate the new water source. The optional sources were narrowed down to four and there were proponents favoring each one.

Previously, in 1931, Barr and Cunningham had prepared a preliminary analysis of the options for a new water source. Their brief report covered the options well but with a bias that bad water can be made into excellent water if you apply enough engineering technology.[32] Other than that, the report moved the city in the right direction. The following excerpt from the report provides a strong recommendation and economic incentive for Salem to do something about their bad water:

The selection of a permanent source of supply is the major problem before the city. If the choice is correct any reasonable investment is justified. If it is not, costly supply works may have to be abandoned in the course of time to correct the mistakes of the past. Salem is a city with a population in excess of 26,000, and the metropolis of a large and famous valley with room for many times the inhabitants it now supports. It seems the trend of the times for cities to grow more rapidly than in the past while smaller common cities barely hold their own. The automobile has greatly enlarged the trading radius of the farmer, to the benefit of the city and at the expense of the country towns. As the population and activity of the Willamette Valley increase, Salem more than any other city seems destined to reap the benefit by reason of its strategic location and the many advantages it offers. Its only handicap today appears in the reputation for an abominable water supply, vastly inferior to those offered by rival cities. The far reaching effects of this must not be under estimated especially in the northwest where competition between cities is keen and exceptionally fine water supplies are common.

Barr and Cunningham were experienced with the water supplies that other cities in the Willamette Valley had developed by the 1930's. Portland had its Bull Run water source which was the drainage from the west side of Mount Hood and was at the time the finest water source that could be obtained anywhere. Eugene, in the southern end of the Willamette Valley, obtained its water from the McKenzie River, with its source the western slopes of the Cascades. Salem, the capital city, was far, far behind these other comparable Willamette Valley cities.

Barr and Cunningham briefly described three possible optional water sources. The first option, deep wells, they dismissed quickly because of the high cost of pumping and the possibility of depletion. (In the 1980's, the City of Keizer, on Salem's northern border, proved this assumption wrong. They were able to stop buying water from Salem and developed a deep well system in the Mission Bottom aquifer that supplies large amounts of excellent water. Salem had this same opportunity in the 1930's but passed it up because of lack of knowledge of the potential of this aquifer. Salem is now (in 2003) trying to tap this same aquifer as a back-up water supply.

Barr and Cunningham's second option was a Willamette River supply. Their brief analysis follows:

The Willamette River is an unquestioned source as to quantity. The quality of the water is good [?], excepting for pollution which has now reached a degree to make it unsafe for human consumption and corrective treatment is necessary, as sterilization alone to be effective would require the application of such heavy doses of chlorine or other agents that would make the water unpotable. The valley is still sparsely populated and as its development increases, pollution will increase. The industrial wastes contributed by Salem and the cities above present a most serious problem. So long as we seek to attract industries to the state we must permit the disposal of their wastes without placing them under a handicap that does not exist elsewhere. There is no check on stream pollution, nor is there any assurance that it will come in the near future. No matter what remedial steps are taken pollution will increase, as science has not as yet discovered (nor do they appear on the horizon) means for elimination from large rivers, all pollution at costs which the public could bear, and we will have accomplished a great deal when stream pollution is checked to a degree not harmful to fish life which is a long way from a wholesome sparkling water supply conforming to modern standards for drinking water.

There is an esthetic side which must also be considered. The cities and communities upstream all discharge their sewage into the river. There is no question that the Willamette River water, by means of filtration and possible after treatment can be made a sparklingly clear, polished and absolutely sterile water supply. Processes have been developed and are now in extensive use by which sewage can be converted into safe and potable water, but the very thought of drinking it is repulsive.

The cost of producing a filtered water supply from the river in its present condition can be estimated with reasonable accuracy provided the raw water is taken a safe distance from the wastes contributed by local industries. What the costs might be should the degree or nature of pollution change for the worse is more difficult to predict but we can say safely that they would increase materially. It will be shown later in this report that the cost of a pumped and filtered supply from the Willamette River compares favorably with the cost of a mountain water delivered by gravity, so the deciding factors are the esthetic question and to a lesser degree the uncertainty of future costs in case of increased pollution.

Barr and Cunningham obviously thought that the Willamette River water could be treated to the same "sparklingly clear" quality as North Santiam River water. We know today that "sparklingly clear" or in technical terms "zero turbidity" is only the most basic water treatment requirement. Industrial and human wastes contain dissolved toxins and pathogenic bacteria and viruses. The Willamette in the 1930's was polluted and the North Santiam was pristine with few people and no industrial waste upstream of the City of Stayton. Following is the engineers' evaluation of the North Santiam River option:

> The third possible source of supply is the North Santiam River, tributary of the Willamette originating in the west slope of the Cascade Mountains. The minimum recorded flow of the stream at suitable diversion points is over 400 cfs which is equivalent of 275,000,000 gallons per day, and this could be materially increased by creating storage in the watershed. The quality of the water is excellent and pollution so slight that simple clarification when the stream is in flood and sterilization by light doses will produce a supply of mountain water of the first class at all times.
>
> Any point of diversion considered would be above the town of Mehama which is near the upper end of the main Santiam Valley. Above Mehama the population is sparse, the watershed largely mountainous and heavily timbered so that the possibilities for agricultural or industrial development and consequent pollution are very limited.
>
> The North Santiam River is the principal tributary of the Willamette River between Oregon City and Eugene and the only adequate source of gravity water supply from which Salem and a larger portion of the Willamette Valley can be conveniently and economically served. If it is selected, all unapropriated water should be reserved and conflicting water rights extinguished for the benefit of Salem and other communities or a possible future metropolitan water district which would serve the entire territory through a common system.
>
> Aside from a source of water supply the North Santiam River has great merit as a source of power. The potential possibilities are considerable and power developments could be made which would also improve it as a source of water supply provided both projects are under the same control. The City of Salem has initiated power rights and as these are perfected the way is clear for an orderly program of development in the future.

Barr and Cunningham made no recommendation for a new source

but their analysis of the three options implied strongly that the North Santiam River was by far the best water source option.

They also saw the economic benefit of Salem developing the power potential of the North Santiam. Salem in 1924 and 1930 had already applied for water rights to develop power on the river. However, in the late 1930's, Congress preempted those ambitions by authorizing the Detroit Dam system which took advantage of the power potential on the North Santiam. (Chapter 5 tells the sad story of the city trying to buy stored water from Detroit Reservoir.) Obviously the federal government took away a huge opportunity for the City of Salem to develop power and use stored water for municipal purposes on the North Santiam. (We can now only speculate how the economy of Salem would have been benefited if they had developed this power source instead of the federal government.)

In 1935, the city chose to not hire Barr and Cunningham for design of the new water source. Instead the engineering firm of Stevens and Koon of Portland was retained to both design and manage the construction of the new system. However, no decision had been made on which source option to design and build. At this time there were four options still under consideration and there were passionate proponents of all four, so the final decision was a difficult one for the City Council. The four options still on the table were the Willamette River, the Little North Fork tributary of the North Santiam, the main stem of the North Santiam, and wells in or close to Salem.

Shortly after purchasing the private water system, the City Council delegated the task of determining the best option to the newly elected Water Commission. But, the Commission was not accepting the delegation. They said that under the city charter it was the responsibility of the City Council to make this determination. Obviously this was a political hot potato because there were determined groups pushing for each of the four options.[33]

A political action group, the Taxpayers League, pleaded to the City Council that no water source should be adopted by Salem that creates higher water rates. They believed in-city wells or the Willamette River option would satisfy their requirement but the Little North Fork and the North Santiam River options would substantially increase fees and, therefore, were not acceptable.[34]

To satisfy advocates of a deep well system, the City Council authorized testing of several wells in and around the city. The wells did not produce the desired quantities and the option was eliminated by the City Council. Also to the displeasure of the Taxpayers League the City Council eliminated the Willamette River option because of the obvious pollution problems and the need for an ultra sophisticated filtration plant. The Council also knew that if they chose to treat Willamette River water given the voter approved bond issue, which had promised a mountain water system, they would all be recalled. Salem residents had already had enough of the polluted Willamette River water!

At this time a tremendous stroke of good fortune intervened that demanded a new plan. On December 13, 1935, the City Council received a letter from Mr. A.D. Gardner of Stayton. Mr. Gardner was the owner of a water right of 811 cfs with an 1866 priority date to divert North Santiam River water to his power canal in Stayton. Gardner sold both power and water to industries in Stayton using the river water to generate power. But, of interest to the City of Salem, Gardner also owned an island between the main stem of the North Santiam and a north channel from where his power canal was diverted (and coincidentally, also close to where Salem Ditch was diverted). The name of the island was Stayton Island. In Gardner's letter to the City Council, he offered to sell Stayton Island to the City of Salem. Also in his letter he stated the island would be an ideal location for the City of Salem's water intake and treatment system. He contended the island was of high enough elevation to allow the construction of a gravity pipeline all the way to Salem.[35]

Gardner's offer was checked out by the engineers who confirmed the island was a good location and a gravity pipeline could be built to a new reservoir in Salem to be located on Fairmount Hill. The overflow elevation of a new 10 million gallon reservoir would serve all the lower elevations of Salem with adequate pressure. The land sale of the eastern upstream 240 acres was agreed to at a sale price of $2300. So, Mr. Gardner's offer provided the vital missing piece of the puzzle of where to locate the water source.

The engineers helped the City Council decide between the Little North Fork and the main stem of the North Santiam. They determined a gravity pipeline could be constructed to the North Santiam within the city's budget whereas the budget would not allow a pipeline to the Little North Fork. That decided it. At their meeting on February 17, 1936 the City Council on a 9 to 4 vote with two councilors absent (Salem at that time had seven wards with two aldermen each and a mayor) chose the Stayton Island location on the North Santiam River. The engineers' initial plan was completed. It was to divert the raw water from the North Santiam, transport the water to Salem by pipeline, then treat the water in Salem. However, the engineers intended to investigate the feasibility of treating the water also at Stayton Island.

Even so, not everyone was happy. And it appeared to the City Council that many of Salem's finest were unhappy over this decision. The *Capital Press* gave a very negative opinion in an editorial on February 14, 1936 that was apparently anticipating the City Council's final decision on February 17th. Excerpts from the editorial follow:[36]

> Not only is the Santiam practically as bad as the Willamette, but it will get worse when the super highway is constructed along its banks [Highway 22] and it becomes lined with summer cottages. On the other hand the Little North Fork is now almost entirely free and pure and will get more so......
>
> Construction of the Little North supply line would cost less than one million dollars.....
>
> The Capital Press is ready to back its statements with real figures—not some special as the Mayor is carrying around in his pocket and reciting to service clubs and the Chamber of Commerce, but real figures that will stand investigation.....
>
> In the meantime the Water Commission should try to understand that it has absolutely no right or power to do anything except manage the water plant. It has no power to dig wells or send engineers into the mountains or buy land on which to build reservoirs. All such expenditures on its part are unlawful. It should not put its trust in shaky alibis. The City Council can not lawfully delegate its powers to the Water Commission or anybody else.

Exactly how this extreme criticism influenced the City Council is not known, but it appears they ignored it.

The controversy over in-city wells versus a mountain water system at Stayton Island was also not over. On March 10, 1936, the Taxpayers League invited Roscoe Moss of Los Angeles to Salem to present an offer of developing a well system as the city's water source. At a special conference attended by Mayor V.E. Kuhn, members of the Taxpayers League and the press, Mr. Moss proposed for a fee of $90,000 he would guarantee a well system that would produce 10 million gallons per day (mgd). He believed this system would meet all state board of health requirements.

At the conference, the mayor stated the North Santiam option was estimated to cost $750,000 for a transmission line and $185,000 for a filtration plant.

A Mr. Durbin of the Taxpayers League emphasized the necessity of the City Council to listen to the league which represented 300 large holders of real estate in Salem. He emphasized the North Santiam River source was too expensive for the city.[37]

On April 16, 1936, a "Well Committee" of the City Council reported the findings of a field trip they had just completed. They said after visiting the City of Olympia and several other Washington cities with well water supplies, they found the cities were very pleased with their wells, and several had abandoned river systems in favor of wells.

The Well Committee recommended the well option be investigated more thoroughly before the city spends a large amount on studies and engineering for the Stayton Island system.

On May 2, 1936, Salem Water Manager, Cuyler Van Patten, reported to the City Council that a Stayton Island gravity water source would cost $30,000 per year less to operate than a well system. This estimate was based on a savings of $20,000 per year in power costs and $10,000 less in labor costs. Van Patten stated the well drillers proposal to deliver 10 mgd for $90,000 did not include pumping equipment or new mains to interconnect to the existing distribution system.[38]

At the May 2nd meeting the City Council authorized the start of the new water system, including: 1) further field work at Stayton Island, 2) exercise the option to purchase Stayton Island from Gardner, and 3) develop the Stayton Island system as the city's permanent water supply.

The City Council thus made a final decision and the opponents of the Stayton Island system were sent packing.

There was general approval of this decision by the press in Salem. On May 3, 1936, the *Oregon Statesman* published a large article that was very positive. The article included a fair amount of technical detail supplied by the city's engineers and good maps of the transmission line route and Stayton Island. The article's headline on page one read: "Report Favors Stayton Island". Obviously the decision by the City Council was big news in Salem.

The engineers immediately proceeded to make both aerial photographs of the island and extensive surface surveys. Many test pits were dug and groundwater was pumped down in each one to determine what the yield of a subsurface collection system might be if the intake of water would be ground water instead of surface water. Ground water was found at about the same elevation as the surface of the river surrounding the island. River run cobbles and gravel were found to be the characteristics of soil on the island. The water pumped from the pits was clear and was tested to be without pollutants. The State Board of Health approved the groundwater as meeting all the drinking water standards but did require the water  be chlorinated to eliminate any possible bacterial contamination.

After completing their exploration, the engineers concluded it was possible to obtain the desired amount of water by burying perforated pipes as collectors in the porous soils.  They would produce an excellent quality of water which would make it unnecessary to further filter the water in Salem. The engineers also concluded, that if the groundwater was insufficient to meet demands, a filtration system could be built on the island at some future date.

Construction on the island began in the summer of 1936 by Slate Construction Company of Albany on a force account contract with an estimated cost of $150,000. The city was anxious to move ahead with the construction and did not want to take the time to prepare complete contract bid documents. On the island several components of the system were built. First, a collection chamber was built for the three infiltration lines radiating out in three directions. The infiltration line running east toward the upper part of the island was a 30 inch perforated pipe made of galvanized corrugated iron. The perforations were 3/8 inch in diameter and spaced 1 1/2 inches apart. Only the lower 1/3 of the pipe was perforated. A second 30 inch infiltration line ran northeast and the third line, an 18 inch line, ran southeast of the collection chamber. A total of 4800 feet of infiltration lines were laid. The lines were laid about five feet below the lowest groundwater levels to ensure a constant supply of water filtered by the natural subsurface sands and gravels.

A second control structure was built near the downstream end of the island. The structure was a combination sand trap and flow control structure. It also had a bypass to the river.  The bypass was necessary when the downstream lines needed to be dewatered for maintenance. The sand trap was needed because fine sand could pass through the 3/8 inch openings in the perforated infiltration lines. The sand traps were cleaned by hand but it was only necessary every several years.

The two control structures were connected by a 42 inch creosoted wood pipe. The logic of using a wood pipe was political, because the pipe was made locally and the City Council desired to assist the local economy by purchasing the wood pipe. (The City Council had previously turned down a request from the local union that requested the city use creosoted wood pipe for the full 13 mile length of the water transmission line.) The wood pipe remained in service on the island until the early 1980's.

Figure 3-3 shows Stayton Island and the treatment system constructed in 1937.

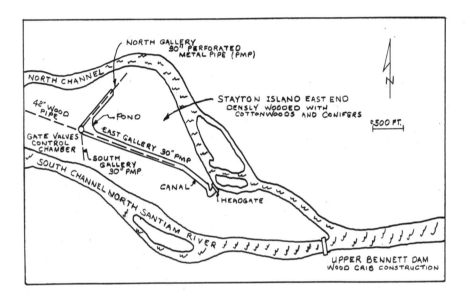

FIGURE 3-3 The City of Salem's first Stayton Island treatment system consisted of infiltration galleries constructed in 1937.

The under crossing of the north channel of the river was the most difficult part of the project. The water in the river was not diverted, but the work was done in the early fall when the river level was at its lowest. A trench was excavated five feet wide and to a depth of six feet below the river bed. It was necessary to blast the lowest two feet of the trench, because cemented gravels were encountered. This provided an excellent foundation for the pipe, but the blasting must have done some damage to fish life in the river. The under crossing was 300 feet long and consisted of a 36 inch welded steel pipe.

The pipe manufacturers were issued a force account contract to lay 3700 feet of 36 inch welded steel pipe from the river to the City of Stayton. This section of line crossed two power canals. In October,

1936, a separate contract was let after bids were received for the construction of the main section of the transmission line. It consisted of 6.3 miles of 36 inch concrete pipe and 10.1 miles of 36, 30 and 27 inch welded steel pipe. This construction completed the transmission line to the new 10 million gallon Fairmount Reservoir in the City of Salem.

At the same time construction was not going well on Stayton Island. The contractor installing the infiltration pipes, as they proceeded to the upper part of the island, ran into more and more groundwater and sloughing sands that made excavation difficult and expensive.

After completion of construction of the infiltration system, a major crisis soon became obvious. The completed infiltration system would not supply the necessary 7 million gallons per day of water. So, engineer R.E. Koon recommended to the Water Commission that a canal be constructed on top of the infiltration pipes and a river water inlet be constructed to feed the canals. This was a major change in direction because the plan was now to use river water instead of ground water. (This decision will rear its ugly head later.)

Koon justified his decision by saying "the result would be an increased flow of water through the underground gravels into the perforated infiltration pipe and water of the same quality as that of a strictly underground supply."[39] He estimated the new canals would cost $10,000 and the intake structure $25,000.

Koon was fully supported by Mayor Kuhn in this new proposal. The mayor said: "I would vote for the canal if a vote were being taken. I draw that conclusion from the understanding I have had from the island plan from the beginning. I am confident we will get the class of water that we understood we would get in the first place."[40]

But not everyone was happy, as usual. On May 14, 1937 the *Capital Press* printed a scorching editorial critical of the entire Stayton Island system. Excerpts from the editorial follow:[41]

> The locoed Salem water commission is whistling in the dark to keep its courage up, and apparently the prediction of the Capital Press that the Stayton Island water supply would prove unsatisfactory in quality and insufficient in quantity is coming true sooner than expected. In fact it is true right now. The water is not there. It never was there. There was no reason in thinking it was there. There was nothing to indicate that it was there. Yet engineer Koon and the water commission made reports and gave interviews stating that there was a plentiful supply to be found through "natural filtration" down in

the bowels of Stayton Island, and it would be equivalent to sparkling spring water. So they proceeded to lay pipe down in the ground on the island, and from it they extended prongs of smaller pipe punched full of holes, and assured everybody that lots of water would be gushing into the mains here in Salem.....

The present situation of the water project is not encouraging. Of the $2,500,000 voted by the taxpayers for the purpose, $2,100,000 has been spent or contracted with practically nothing to show for it, and Salem is no nearer to a satisfactory water system than it was before the bonds were voted. In fact we are worse off than ever, for the money is gone and we can hardly afford to start over again and take on another such financial load.

Apparently the criticism did not affect the direction of the Water Commission. They approved the $10,000 expenditure for the construction of the canals. Later they approved the $25,000 for construction of the water inlet.

Even with the canals, the infiltration galleries would produce only about 6 to 6 1/2 mgd when river levels were low. The city's peak daily demand in 1937 was about 7 mgd so a slight drawdown of Fairmount Reservoir was required. But it was obvious there needed to be an increased output from Stayton Island.

Engineer Koon then recommended shallow wells be drilled at the island. Three wells were then developed with a combined output of 2.75 mgd. This increased the water output from Stayton Island to about 9 mgd. However, on a peak day the city had the opportunity to sell up to 10 mgd because Oregon Pulp and Paper Company desired to purchase 3 mgd. When river levels were higher, the output from Stayton Island increased significantly, but also peak demands usually decreased.

Before deciding to drill wells on Stayton Island, the Water Commission seriously considered building a concrete settling tank and a conventional water filtration plant at Stayton Island. However, the capital and operating costs for the filtration plant greatly exceeded the cost of the wells, so the filtration plant idea was dropped.

In late 1937 the transmission line and reservoir construction were completed. The Minto Island source was shut down and water started flowing on October 30th in city mains and homes from the North Santiam river. Mountain water had finally arrived in Salem! No longer would the city be ridiculed for having the worst water in the state. Because now they had the best quality, many believed. But, would it remain that way?

An unusual feature of the new Stayton Island water treatment system was that there was no vehicular bridge to the island. The operators crossed the north channel of the North Santiam River by way of a new foot bridge shown in Figure 3-4. Any required heavy construction or maintenance equipment had to cross the flowing channel in the low flow summer period.

Over time the output from the infiltration galleries greatly increased to about 13 million gallons per day in the 1940's. With the three wells the summer peak output from Stayton Island matched the transmission line capacity of 16 million gallons per day. This increased capacity was probably due to the fine sands being washed out of the subsurface gravels and a more porous media resulted in increased flows. This also probably resulted in a decrease of water quality, especially turbidity and algae which produced off tastes and perceptions of poor water.

So, as soon as 1938 the water quality was becoming a disappointment to many Salem residents. And again the *Capital Press* was quick to point out this obvious problem. On September 16, 1938 they published another scathing editorial. Excerpts follow:[42]

> "Engineer" Koon and the members of the water commission and Manager Van Patten are at last in perfect agreement with the people of Salem. They agree that the fantastic and ridiculous water system for which they have spent so much money is a flop. There is not enough water and the quality is nauseous.

Again, the *Oregon Statesman* put a positive spin on the situation. Excerpts from their editorial on September 18, 1938, follow:[43]

> At the water board meetings in the past week it was agreed that an underground water was the most desirable; that river water, unless mechanically filtered would always have the unpleasant "river taste" in late summer...A mechanical filter built at great expense at Bend, did not eliminate the algae taste of Deschutes river water, and the community abandoned the river in favor of "mountain water."

So, to the disappointment of many, the Stayton Island system did not produce the pure sweet spring water taste the citizens of Salem desired. But it was free from pathogenic organisms and on most days it did produce some of the finest water in the state. However, the desired quality every day of the year would have to wait until the 1950's when the city finally built "natural filtration beds".

FIGURE 3-4: Footbridge over the north channel of the North Santiam River was the only bridge crossing to Stayton Island treatment system until 1957. All heavy vehicles had to portage the river during low flow periods.

Again, the *Oregon Statesman* put a positive spin on the situation. Excerpts from their editorial on September 18, 1938, follow:[44]

> At the water board meetings in the past week it was agreed that an underground water was the most desirable; that river water, unless mechanically filtered would always have the unpleasant "river taste" in late summer...A mechanical filter built at great expense at Bend, did not eliminate the algae taste of Deschutes river water, and the community abandoned the river in favor of "mountain water."

So, to the disappointment of many, the Stayton Island system did not produce the pure sweet spring water taste the citizens of Salem desired. But it was free from pathogenic organisms and on most days it did produce some of the finest water in the state. However, the desired quality every day of the year would have to wait until the 1950's when the city finally built "natural filtration beds".

Only one other little problem remained. The city had no water right to divert North Santiam River water at Stayton Island through the new water inlet. At the time of construction this diversion had not even been applied for. Perhaps the city and their engineer consultants thought those rights would be automatically granted. After making the huge investments of the transmission line and the Stayton Island system they hoped they were right. Will good fortune shine on Salem and allow them to get their water rights?

# Chapter 4
# Water Rights Through 1951

The City of Salem was fortunate that water right applications were made to the State Engineers Office (predecessor of the Oregon Water Resources Department) for diverting North Santiam River water to the City of Salem. As discussed previously, the city had a very poor understanding of where the water could economically be diverted and piped to the city. In 1923 a shotgun approach was used but still failed to hit the final target.

Three water right applications were made in 1923, each being 40 cfs, with the diversion points varying from two to four miles below the confluence of the Breitenbush and North Santiam Rivers. In hindsight it was later found that a pipeline of this length (approximately 50 miles) was not financially feasible. However, the applications for these rights did create a priority date.

Since Oregon's water laws are based on the principle of prior appropriation, it is most important to have a right with the earliest possible priority date. Prior appropriation means the first person to obtain a water right on a stream is the last to be shut off in times of low stream flows. In most cases the date of application for a permit to use water is the priority date of the right.

Prior to construction of the Stayton Island water source facility, the city applied to the State Engineer for a "supplement" to its application in 1923 for three 40 cfs water rights. The supplement amended the 1923 application from three 40 cfs to a single 22 cfs water right and also amended the point of diversion from downstream of the Breitenbush River to Stayton Island.

The obvious question is why did the city apply for 22 cfs instead of the original total application of 120 cfs (three applications of 40 cfs each)? The reason is that at the time the estimated capacity of the 36 inch pipeline to Salem was 22 cfs. It was later determined the maximum gravity capacity to be 16 mgd or 25 cfs. Still it could have been argued that 120 cfs should have been applied for in 1936 as a reserve for future growth of the city. (However, even the very modest application for 22 cfs of water rights would not go unchallenged in the early 1950's.)

Meanwhile in 1942, Carl Guenther, manager of the Salem Water Department, requested an opinion of Percy Cupper, private attorney and consultant to the city, on the legal status of the various water right applications made in 1923 and 1924. His recommendations, all agreed to by the city, were as follows:

1. Application 9055 filed July 5, 1923 on the North Santiam River just below the mouth of the Breitenbush River, should be amended with a point of diversion at Stayton Island. If approved this 40 cfs will increase the water right diversion from 22 cfs to 62 cfs.

2. Application 9057 filed July 5, 1923 for an additional 40 cfs on the North Santiam River near the Breitenbush should be canceled because it has no further value to the city.

3. Application 9289 filed December 4, 1923 for 50 cfs on the Little North Fork should be canceled because it has no further value to the city.

4. Application 9713 filed July 24, 1924 for use of Marion Lake as a 25,000 acre feet storage reservoir appears to be impractical as a way of supplementing the city water supply during the low water season. This application should be continued until a more definite determination is made regarding the construction of Detroit Reservoir.

5. Application 9714 filed July 24, 1924 was for a power application and municipal uses right above the proposed Detroit Reservoir. This application should be canceled because it appears to have no further value to the city.

6. Application 13694 filed August 26, 1930 was for power purposes with one diversion below the proposed Detroit Reservoir. The State Engineer should continue this application until the Detroit Reservoir issue has been determined.

Finally in 1956, City Manager J.L. Franzen completed the above water right transactions.[45]

The feasibility of constructing the federal Detroit Reservoir system received final approval by Congress in the late 1940's, and Detroit and Big Cliff Reservoirs were constructed in the early 1950's. This invalidated any city attempt to establish power use water rights on the North Santiam.

Shortly after the city submitted their recommendations for supplements to the existing water right applications, the State Engineer Charles Stricklin issued a new permit, number 15164, for an additional 40 cfs water right diversion at Stayton Island with a 1923 priority date.

However on October 10, 1945, Stricklin changed his mind about the additional 40 cfs water right diversion. He told Carl Guenther there was no proof the city required the full 40 cfs applied for in 15164. Stricklin left the door open for justifying the need for this right by allowing an extension of time before canceling the application. Much later in 1956 this application was canceled after the city was successful in acquiring much better rights with an 1856 priority date.

The early filing and management of 1923 through 1930 water right applications was obviously less than efficient but it was a warning signal that the City of Salem must get its act together in applying for and managing invaluable North Santiam water rights.

The city was soon to endure a major embarrassment regarding North Santiam River water rights. Beginning in 1937 with completion of the infiltration gallery filtering system on Stayton Island, the city started using the system to supply city needs through the 36 inch pipeline to a new 10 million gallon Fairmount Reservoir. This reservoir was filled by gravity from Stayton Island. It was soon apparent, however, that the underground infiltration galleries on Stayton Island were insufficient to supply the consumption demands of the city. The city then began diverting surface waters of the North Santiam to an open channel that was immediately above the infiltration pipes buried in the gravels below. This artificial charging of the infiltration system increased the supply to the city.

The embarrassment was that a Mr. Bennett, successor to A.D. Gardner, filed suit in Marion County Circuit Court charging that the city's diversion of surface waters with a 1923 priority date interfered with the power rights of A.D. Gardner who held a priority date of 1866 for 812 cfs.

Bennett was correct that the North Santiam River water adjudication proceedings of 1945 awarded to A.D. Gardner water rights of 812 cfs with a priority date of 1866. The Gardner water was being diverted at the Gardner power canal (slightly downstream of the Salem Ditch diversion on the north channel of the North Santiam River). The use of the Gardner diversion was for the development of power and for other manufacturing purposes.

Gardner's power right dates back to 1866 due to his predecessor, Dray S. Stayton, whose first diversion of waters of the north channel through a canal carried waters to his mill just upstream of the present City of Stayton. Later, after Dray Stayton's death in 1890, the canal was purchased by A.D. Gardner. Gardner formed a corporation for maintaining and operating the canal for the purpose of furnishing water to various industries for power purposes. The Gardner corporation received payments for the use to the diverted water.

The City of Salem in 1955, with the assistance of a law student intern, Warren Culver, prepared a comprehensive history of all water rights on the North Santiam River and Mill Creek. The Culver report contended that the Gardner Ditch was only capable of diverting 700 cfs and therefore 112 cfs should be lost due to nonuse.[46]

In 1950 Bennett's suit against the city was awarded in favor of Bennett. The Marion County Circuit Court on September 27, 1950 held Gardner's prior power right of 812 cfs was senior to the city's 1923 right of 22 cfs. The court issued an injunction restraining the city from diverting surface waters from the North Santiam River when there would be insufficient water to supply the water rights of Gardner-Bennett. The city appealed to the Oregon Supreme Court, but the court affirmed the decision of the Circuit Court.

The decision of the Circuit Court in this case had no practical impact on the city's diversion of surface waters. Bennett was incapable of diverting his full water right as was discovered by Culver in 1955. Only in an extreme drought, where the flows in the North Santiam dropped below about 700 cfs, would the city's right be impacted. As it turned out, a situation never existed after the courts ruling where the city could not divert surface waters of the North Santiam. But, the possibility that surface waters could not be diverted to the city resulted in a frantic attempt to obtain earlier water rights.

In seeking additional water rights two possibilities existed: first, purchase of power and manufacturing water rights of 60 cfs owned by Oregon Pulp and Paper Company along the North Power Canal (Mill Creek in Salem downstream from Waller Dam) with a priority right of 1856; and, second, purchase of power and manufacturing rights of 812 cfs owned by Bennett in Stayton with a priority date of 1866. Because of the legal skirmishes with Bennett, it was quickly decided that the Oregon Pulp and Paper rights would offer the best possibility. Also this right had the earliest priority date on the North Santiam, and, if the right could be obtained, the city would always be assured of being first in time and last to be cut off. An enviable position worth fighting for!

How Oregon Pulp and Paper Company acquired its ownership of 60 cfs on the North Power Canal was complex. In 1856, Willamette Woolen Manufacturing Company was granted by an act of the Oregon Territorial Legislature the right to use, rent, assign or lease 254 cfs of waters diverted from the North Santiam River. Willamette Woolen Manufacturing Company obtained this water right by digging a ditch known as Salem Ditch which connected the North Santiam River by gravity to Mill Creek. This brought the 254 cfs of North Santiam River water to Salem along the natural channel of Mill Creek. In 1865 Willamette Woolen Mills, a successor to Willamette Woolen Manufacturing Company constructed Waller Dam near 19th Street in Salem and a mill race, named South Power, to its new mill site on the Willamette Slough (the present Boise Cascade site).

However, their acquisition of easements from property owners was a tiny bit sloppy. Culver documented his problems with researching deed records to determine the legality of easements for the Mill Race (South Power).[47]

In the year 1856, as heretofore mentioned, the Willamette Woolen Mills [actually the Willamette Woolen Manufacturing Company] was incorporated by Territorial Legislative Act and given authority to bring water from the Santiam River to any place or places in or near Salem, to be brought as far as practicable through the channel or the valley of Mill Creek. Since the waters of Mill Creek flow in a northwesterly direction at 19th Street, Salem, and whereas the woolen company [the Willamette Woolen Mills] was located at a place west of said 19th Street, it was necessary for the concern in order to impound North Santiam waters so brought into Salem through the channel of Mill Creek to construct a raceway, often referred to as South Power, which would channel the waters in a westerly direction to the location of the woolen mill.

Construction of the power race [South Power] was completed in about the year 1865. The exact date of completion of the canal is not known, but it is believed to have been finished after the time of the platting of the City of Salem, in 1850, and before the platting of University Addition, in 1889. Testimony given in 1926 by several persons between the ages of 85 and 90 established, insofar as their memories are reliable, that the canal was completed in 1865 with water flowing therein. One such person, a former sheriff, testified he remembered the day well, since it was the first time in the history of Salem that a public hanging had taken place. Perpetrator was perched on top of a building. and as the hanging was taking place he became so excited that he fell over backward into the raceway. The above hanging and dunking having taken place in 1865.

A check of Marion County deed records of this period indicates that the woolen company [Willamette Woolen Mills] was not particular about securing easements or rights of way for their proposed canal. Extensive search of such early deed records disclose only four instances where the company obtained in writing the consent of property owners to dig a canal through their lands. In at least one of the above four instances permission was obtained after the canal was started.

After construction of the canal and prior to 1889 the University Addition was plotted over the canal [South Power]. If any easements or rights of way were obtained the deed records pertaining to the University Addition failed to show it. A few sample properties were traced back to 1909, but it was impossible to go any further without long index searching, which did not seem justifiable when none of the records heretofore examined mentioned any easements or rights of way.

The Salem Flouring Mills, successor in interest to the Willamette Woolen Mills, along in 1880 or 1890 widened and lengthened the race way. The flouring company as in the case of its predecessor, did not bother to secure permission to do so from adjoining landowners.

The fact that few easements were obtained does not, however, cast any legal cloud over the rights of Salem power owners to the use of the raceway, since what was not secured by proper conveyance has not through continuous use ripened into an adverse prescriptive right, inextinguishable except through nonuse. So long as waters are carried through the raceway and are appropriated for beneficial use the right is inviolate. The enjoyment and use of the canal [South Power], however, carries some responsibilities in that the owners must maintain and keep in such condition that it does not become hazardous or a menace to public health and welfare.

In 1945 the North Santiam River adjudication proceeding affirmed the early priority date of 1856 for the 254 cfs power and manufacturing right. The adjudication proceedings further allocated the 254 cfs between North Power and South Power. The amount of water needed to supply the power sources for the North and South power was then used to proportion the water right. North Power was allocated 82 cfs and south power 172 cfs. In further allocating water rights on North Power, Oregon Pulp and Paper, being a successor to Willamette Woolen Manufacturing Company, received 60 cfs and Salem Ice Works received 22 cfs. Salem Ice Works was located where the Methodist Retirement Home is now located and used Mill Creek water for power and manufacturing. Figure 4-1 shows a photograph of the original Willamette Woolen Manufacturing Company which was destroyed by fire in the 1870's

Figure 4-1: Willamette Woolen Manufacturing Company, the original holder of all 1856 water rights diverted to Mill Creek from the North Santiam River.

In allocating South Power rights, Oregon Pulp and Paper Company (being the successor of Salem Flouring Mills), the City of Salem, and Thomas Kay Woolen Mills were each entitled to undivided equal interest in the 172 cfs power and manufacturing right. Figure 4-2 shows an early photograph of Salem Flouring Mills with the Mill Race clearly shown as a wooden flume.

Undivided equal interest did not mean that each of the three parties owned rights to one third of the 172 cfs of water. It meant, because this was a power and manufacturing right, each of the three parties owned a right to use the entire 172 cfs of water as a noncomsumptive use.

Figure 4-3 shows the location of all water right holders in 1951 on both South and North Power.

The City of Salem acquired its power right through the succession of: first, Pacific Agricultural Works first using the Mill Race drop at about present High Street to produce power by a water wheel; second, by Salem Water Company using the water power to pump city water; third, Oregon Washington Water Service Company modernizing the power site with an electric turbine; and last, the Mill Race power site was acquired by the City of Salem when they purchased the water system in 1935. The site continued to produce power at this site until the 1960's.

The Salem flour mill in Salem in the 1870's.

FIGURE 4-2: The above postcard shows the Salem Flouring Mill which was water powered by the Mill Race, called South Power. The Mill Race is the wooden flume entering the plant. This site was later occupied by Oregon Pulp and Paper Company.

After a prolonged negotiation that could have been the envy of professional diplomats, the three parties entered into an agreement dated May 28, 1951. The parties agreed that Thomas Kay Woolen Mills can continue to use the 172 cfs for power generation and pay a pro rata share of maintaining the Mill Race. However, the main part of the agreement was between the City of Salem and Oregon Pulp and Paper. The two parties agreed to the following:

1. Oregon Pulp and Paper will sell the City of Salem 60 cfs of 1856 water rights on the North Power and join the city in applying for

transfer of the right to the city for municipal purposes with a diversion at Stayton Island.

2. In exchange for the 60 cfs water right the city agreed to convey to Oregon Pulp and Paper a deed to 9.88 acres on Minto Island and to eliminate the easements for three suction pipelines crossing the property of Oregon Pulp and Paper Company.

3. The City of Salem could use 25 cfs of water from the South Power for emergency municipal use.

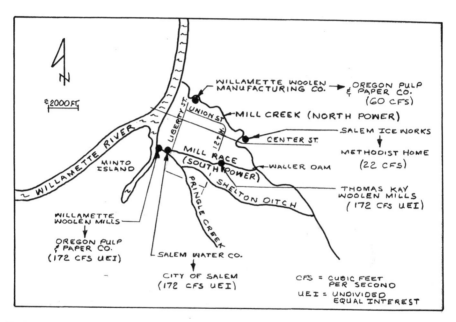

FIGURE 4-3 North and South Power rights existing in 1952 showing how the original 254 cfs of 1856 water rights of Willamette Woolen Manufacturing Company was allocated to its successors.

The agreement was signed by Al Loucks, Mayor of the City of Salem, Niles G. Teren, President of Oregon Pulp and Paper Company, and E.W. Kay, President of Thomas Kay Woolen Mills.

On June 11, 1951, the City Council passed Resolution 6061 approving the agreement. The Resolution because of its stated importance to the city is reproduced in full as follows:

WHEREAS, in 1935, the City of Salem acquired from the Oregon

Washington Water Service Company 9.88 acres of land, more or less, situated upon and being a part of Minto Island, and at the same time acquired easements over adjoining lands for the laying and maintenance of pipelines for the conveyance of water from the filter beds upon said 9.88 acres tract to the water distribution system in the City of Salem and on the east side of the Willamette River, and for the transmission of power from the city to such tract for the operation of a pumping plant, the said tract and easements being at the time of acquisition a part of and used in connection with the water system purchased by the city from the said Oregon Washington Water Service Company; and

WHEREAS, heretofore the City of Salem acquired the privilege and right to remove gravel which might from time to time form accretions to part of Minto Island; and

WHEREAS, the 9.88 acre tract of land and easements above mentioned are no longer needed by the City of Salem for the supplying of water to the city and its inhabitants, and have not been needed or used for such purpose since 1938 when the water from the North Santiam River was brought to the city, but have been retained as a stand by plant, and said right or privilege to take gravel forming accretions to a part of Minto Island has not been used or exercised for more than thirty years, and there now are no such accretions that could be removed; and

WHEREAS, the Oregon Pulp and Paper Company, a corporation, desires to acquire from the City of Salem the title to said tract and desires to acquire the interest of the city in and to the easements and privileges above mentioned; and

WHEREAS, the City of Salem desires to acquire of the Oregon Pulp and Paper Company the exclusive right to 60 cfs of water which is brought to the City of Salem from the North Santiam River through a ditch or canal which connects the said river and Mill Creek and thence down said creek, being a part of the water allotted and adjudicated for use in or along Mill Creek below Waller dam in the said City for power and manufacturing purposes, generally referred to as the North Power; and

WHEREAS, the said water right has priority of 1856, and the acquisition by the city of the right to use 60 cfs of such water for municipal purposes will afford the city an abundant water supply under a right having priority over other existing and allegedly conflicting rights, provided the change of use from power and manufacturing purposes to municipal purposes be allowed by the state engineer, and such officer allow a change in the point of diversion; and

WHEREAS, it would appear to be in the public interest of the City of Salem, and the inhabitants thereof that the city convey and transfer to the said Oregon Pulp and Paper Company the aforesaid tract of land, easements and privileges in consideration of a transfer by the said company to the city of 60 cfs of the waters aforesaid, and in consideration of the city having an emergency standby service in the said Mill Race above the point where the Oregon Pulp and Paper Company treats or filters the water it uses in its plant on the banks of the Willamette River, such exchange to be contingent upon allowance and approval by the state engineer of such exchange and such change of use and point of diversion of such amount of said waters.

The Agreement was concluded with a summation of the Whereas statements. The Agreement was adopted by the City Council on June 11, 1951. Now the parties had the task of convincing the State Engineer that a change of the diversion and the change of use from a non consumptive power and consumptive manufacturing use to a consumption municipal use was possible under State of Oregon water rights laws.

In September, a momentous occasion occurred for the City of Salem. The State Engineer Charles Stricklin ordered the change in use and point of diversion of the 60 cfs 1856 water right to municipal use with a point of diversion at Stayton Island to be conveyed to the city by pipeline. He further ordered that the necessary construction work to change the point of diversion be made before October 1, 1962, or within such extensions of time as may be granted by the state engineer.

This decision by the State Engineer created a precedent of diverting a once pristine river in a watershed with drainage from Mount Jefferson and its huge wilderness area to a city for consumptive purposes with the earliest water right priority on the river. This decision was made after the huge Detroit Reservoir system was built which completely changed the hydrology of the river from wild to controlled. Maybe this greatly influenced the State Engineer in approving this use and diversion, because now with Detroit Reservoir the infrequent droughts with extremely low flows in the summer and fall would be a thing of the past. The Detroit Reservoir would in the future ensure minimum flows at about 1000 cfs as opposed to natural drought flows of about 450 cfs. So, this may have given the State Engineer much more freedom to allow diversions for consumptive use.

As it turned out, the city required several time extensions to complete the construction and fully utilize the 60 cfs of water. Finally, James Sexton, State Water Resources Director issued a water right certificate on April 14, 1983. The water right certificate was the final step in acquiring the legal use of water by certifying the city had fully put this right to use.

# Chapter 5
## The Detroit Dam Fiasco

This sad story begins in November, 1947 when the City of Salem was desperate for additional water rights. That year the city had only 22 cfs, or 14.2 mgd, of rights to the North Santiam River with a priority date of 1923. Those rights as described previously were challenged by Mr. Bennett in the early 1950's.

In 1947 the city's first city manager, J.L. Franzen, in his first year on the job, wrote to Colonel O.E. Walsh, District Engineer of the Corps of Engineers in Portland. Franzen's letter follows:[48]

Colonel O.E. Walsh
District Engineer
U.S. Army Engineers
Portland, Oregon

As verification of our recent conversation regarding the water supply of the City of Salem, we wish to again present the following figures.

The capacity of the present pipe line is 16 mgd. The maximum 24 hour use period during 1947 is 13.5 million gallons. The maximum use for a 4 hour period was 22 million gallons.

Using a curve indicating the increase in population for the years during the war and since the war would indicate that the population of Salem might be 100,000 within 25 years, and on the same basis of use per capita as during the past year, it would require 50 mgd and I believe that we should figure 65 mgd or 100 cfs.

It is contemplated that a pipe line be installed from our present head works at Stayton up the river to the dam, of sufficient size to carry the required amount of water. From Stayton into Salem there would be installed an additional line to be used in conjunction with the system of reservoirs. Therefore we would make application for the above mentioned quantity of water to be obtained from the reservoir created by the construction of the Detroit Dam, and would request that the necessary outlet be included in the design of the dam, of sufficient size to take care of the future needs of the water supply for the City of Salem.

Thanking you for your interest in this matter, I am yours very truly.
J.L. Franzen
City Manager

Franzen's letter implies that he is concerned about future pollution in the North Santiam from Detroit Dam to Stayton Island. Otherwise he would not have proposed an expensive pipeline from the dam to Stayton Island. That could have been a real fear, because the State of Oregon at that time was not requiring cities and industries to treat their wastes. If the North Santiam River canyon area had experienced heavy development and no pollution controls, a pipeline as Franzen proposes would be required. (However, Franzen's fears have not materialized due to later environmental rules, and the upstream North Santiam River is still of excellent quality at the start of the 21st century.)

Franzen's letter preceded by several years the design and construction of the Corp's Detroit and Big Cliff Dams. His letter showed clearly the plight of the city in 1947. Peak four hour use in 1947 was at a rate of 22 mgd which exceeded the capacity of the 36 inch transmission line from Stayton Island. Therefore, the city was required to draw down Fairmount Reservoir during peak periods. Franzen details in his letter the projected rapid growth of the city and the corresponding projected growth of peak water supply demands. This was a crisis that needed a solution in a short period of time.

Franzen, who has been Salem's only city manager with an engineering background, was highly qualified to assess the water supply problem and to find solutions. His water department assistant head, John Geren, was equally qualified. The team of Franzen and Geren would soon create a long range plan, obtain financing, and construct excellent additions to the city water system.

However, Franzen's letter to Colonel Walsh started a long process of dealing with the Corps that was extremely frustrating for the City Council and the city staff.

This frustration could possibly have been eliminated if the city had been politically active in 1938 when the Detroit Dam system was authorized by Congress. Unfortunately, for all the cities in the Willamette Valley the Corps dams were only authorized for flood control, irrigation, navigation, power generation, and conservation and not for municipal purposes. Incidentally, the Detroit Dam system did greatly benefit the City of Salem due to the augmented flows during the low flow periods of summer and early fall. But, the lack of explicit authorization for municipal purposes eventually created a huge headache for the Corps of Engineers at their highest level in Washington D.C.

The legal problem of a lack of authorization didn't seem to bother the District Engineer in Portland, Colonel Walsh. On January 23, 1948 he responded to City Manager Franzen as follows:

J.L. Franzen
City Manager
Salem, Oregon

Reference is made to your letter of November 24, 1947, requesting that the plans for Detroit Dam consider the future domestic water requirements of 100 cfs for the City of Salem, Oregon. This requirement will be met without question.

There are, however, several possibilities as to how and where the diversion of your pipe lines can or should be made. A regulating dam is proposed at Big Cliff site, a short distance below Detroit Dam, which will also provide additional power, and it would be possible to have this serve as the head of the city supply pipe line. Then there is the possibility of your erecting a low diversion dam downstream near the mouth of little North Santiam River.

You will probably want to have your engineers consider these alternate solutions as well as diversion from the main dam direct with a view to determining the most satisfactory and economical solution. This office will be glad to discuss the problem in detail at any time with you and your engineers, in order that the most satisfactory plan can be agreed upon, and final plans for government structures made to correspond.

I will be glad to hear further from you in this regard.

Colonel O.E. Walsh
District Engineer
Corps of Engineers

Obviously when Colonel Walsh wrote his letter he believed it was entirely possible for the city to acquire water from the future Detroit Dam. Unfortunately, this letter led the city down a long, dead end road.

Nothing more was heard from the Corps until the city made contact again four years later in 1951. However, by this time the city had made major improvements to the water system as well as acquiring 60 cfs of 1856 priority water rights from Oregon Pulp and Paper Company.

In 1951 the Corps was completing its construction of Detroit and Big Cliff Dams and Colonel T.H. Lipscomb had been appointed the new District Engineer in Portland. On August 16, 1951 Colonel Lipscomb wrote the city and suggested a meeting of Corps and city officials. Colonel Lipscomb wrote:

> The conference is suggested in order that a number of technical details connected with this problem may be discussed and any difference or discrepancies reconciled. On agreement on these items, the legal aspects of the problem may then be discussed more intelligently. Ample time is available to arrive at a solution to this problem because the full conservation use of Detroit Reservoir will not be realized for some years to come until irrigation is more fully developed.

"Conservation" partially meant flow augmentation to assist the fish downstream of the reservoir. By building Detroit and Big Cliff dams and not equipping the dams with fish ladders, the system cut off huge fish habitat areas upstream. Conservation also meant to the Corps, in their authorization from Congress; irrigation, power development and navigation.

From Colonel Lipscomb's comments he obviously believed that the Corps of Engineers could sell the city stored water because the sales of water to irrigators was below expectations. What he failed to say was that no water was being sold to irrigators because the irrigators were obtaining free water with state water rights. He also must have believed this trading was legal. Later, the District Office found that it was not legal. (Unfortunately, it would not be the first or last time the Corps would make mistakes at the district level.)

The Corps completed the construction of Detroit and Big Cliff dams in 1952. Figure 5-1 is a photograph of Detroit Dam soon after construction.

Figure 5-2 is a photograph of Detroit Reservoir with Mount Jefferson in the background. The Detroit system was not authorized for recreation but it does provide boating and fishing opportunities for thousands of people in the summer.

Figure 5-3 is a map of the Detroit Dam system and the watershed upstream from the dam.

In September, 1953 the federal government started marketing stored water to the irrigators. The Bureau of Reclamation was responsible for contracting with irrigators. They issued a bulletin that stored water was available and included a sample contract. There was, however, little response from irrigators for purchasing Detroit stored water.

FIGURE 5-1: Detroit Dam after its completion in 1952.

In March, 1954, City Manager Franzen wrote to Colonel Lipscomb stating the city was making formal application for the right to use 12,000 acre feet per year of stored water in Detroit Reservoir to be drawn at a rate not to exceed 100 cfs.

In April, 1954 Colonel Lipscomb responded to Franzen and wrote:

The preliminary studies show that adequate stored water will be available to satisfy your domestic water supply demand. Some adjustments, however, will be required in the demand for conservation users in years of short supply.

Translating the Colonel's statement: municipal users will be cut back or cut off if inadequate water is available for the conservation users of irrigation, power development, and navigation.

FIGURE 5-2: Detroit Reservoir in the summer with Mount Jefferson in the background. The reservoir provides boating and fishing recreation for thousands in the summer and flood protection in the winter.

The Colonel went on to say that the Corps of Engineers will do the necessary studies on the allocation of costs for domestic water requirements. What the Colonel didn't say or hint at how long it would take to get the Corps of Engineers bureaucracy to agree on an allocated cost. In defense of the Colonel he must have had no idea it would take 20 years.

In March, 1956, Franzen again wrote the Corps and requested the feasibility of purchasing stored water. Franzen forwarded to the Corps a completed study they had previously requested regarding other alternatives the city had in supplying water and their respective costs. The study was completed by a local engineering firm, Clark and Groff, with the author being Lloyd Clark. Clark's study showed that building a treatment plant and using Willamette River water had the lowest capital costs but extremely high operational costs. He concluded using Detroit stored water had the lowest operating costs and, depending on the purchase costs of the stored water, was probably the most economical.

Hearing nothing back from the Corps, in November, 1957 John Geren repeated the Franzen message to the Corps.

On December 24, 1957 the new District Engineer, Colonel Jackson

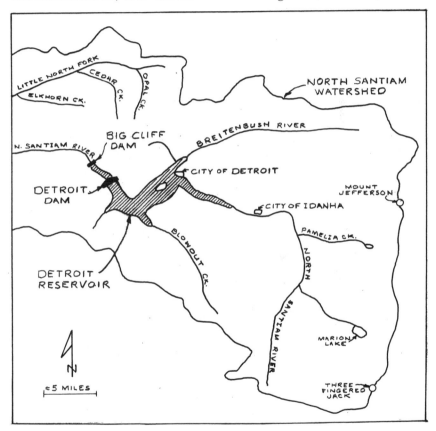

FIGURE 5-3: The Detroit Dam system, Detroit Lake and the upper North Santiam River watershed.

Graham responded to Geren as follows:

John Geren
Manager, City of Salem Water Department

Salem, Oregon

Since receipt of application by the City of Salem for 12,000 acre feet of stored water annually from Detroit Reservoir for domestic use, considerable study has been given the matter, both in this office and by higher authority. It has been determined that in the absence of specific authorization for such uses stored water in Corps of Engineers reservoirs, when surplus to project requirements for other authorized purposes, may be sold for domestic use. Although studies are continuing, it has not yet been determined what, if any, amount of stored water can be considered surplus to other project requirements.

Pending final determination as to whether surplus stored water would be available in Detroit Reservoir, this office has been authorized to further explore the problem with the city. This discussion should cover a probable agreement for the purchase of stored water, in the amount of 12,000 acre feet or such lesser amount as may be available annually. The basis for any agreement must be submitted by this office to higher authority for approval of the principles involved. When and if it is determined that surplus water is available in Detroit Reservoir, a final agreement can be drawn up on the basis of principles approved in the tentative agreement.

If it is determined that there will be no stored water surplus to needs for specifically authorized project purpose, existing laws would not permit a final agreement to be entered into by the Corps. Should that be the case, and should the city still desire to obtain stored waters Congressional action would be required to provide the necessary authority. Section 206 of the pending Omnibus Bill [S.497, 85th Congress], if enacted, apparently would provide such authority. If such a bill is not enacted, it would be the responsibility of the city to work for and obtain appropriate separate legislation.

Jackson Graham, Colonel
District Engineer
Corps of Engineers

This letter from Colonel Graham threw a definite dose of cold water on the city's ambitions to secure the right to obtain stored water at Detroit Dam. The Colonel said as a huge surprise to the city that any agreement to sell stored water will depend on new federal legislation and, if the proposed legislation in 1958 is not passed, the ball is in the city's court to propose new federal legislation. Therefore if the legislation did not pass, there was still a ray of hope for the city's proposal, however dim.

On January 28, 1958 the *Oregon Statesman* reported the Corps was refusing the city's request to buy stored water because of a lack of Congressional authority.[49]

On March 12, 1958 the city received a jointly signed letter from Senators Wayne Morse and Richard Neuberger saying the necessary legislation authorizing the city to purchase stored water would in all likelihood be passed by Congress. Their predictions were correct. Later that year the legislation became law. Exactly what behind the scenes politicking took place to get the two very influential Oregon senators to be interested in this city issue is not known, but it may have been what tipped the balance to get the legislation passed.

What happened next in 1958 is not known. We do know the city was very interested in completing an agreement with the Corps and the city had completed all the prerequisites for a completed agreement. What we do know is 10 years passed without official communications from the Corps. During those 10 years, the city was very busy pursuing additional early water rights on the North Santiam and planning for additional treatment capacity at Stayton Island. In 1962 the city acquired an additional 50 cfs of 1866 priority water rights on the North Santiam. This gave the city ample water rights for many years in the future, so the need for buying stored water from the Corps was no longer of high priority.

Believe it or not the city was still interested in acquiring stored water rights, so in 1968 a meeting was requested with the Corps staff and the Oregon State Water Resources staff. At the meeting John Geren took the following notes:

Cost to construct the Detroit system: $210 per acre foot
Cost allocation:    46% flood control, 40% power,
                    12% navigation and irrigation
Municipal costs:    $1100 per acre foot to be amortized over
                    50 years and $30,000 per year

After analyzing these costs and the probable costs of additional water rights, the city decided the costs were acceptable and a draft agreement was needed from the Corps. On July 18, 1968 Colonel Bangert of the Corps sent the city a draft agreement with the costs yet to be determined. Believing the costs would be similar to the ones presented at the meeting, the City Council upon recommendation from staff adopted a resolution requesting 15,640 acre feet of storage and a peak supply of 113 mgd. The resolution recognized the responsibility of paying all costs allocated to this request for stored water which was assumed to be in the $350,000 to $400,000 per year of amortized costs for 50 years. Why the city made this decision at this time is not understood. The yearly amortization costs were huge compared to other water department debt costs.

Meanwhile the Corps undertook a major study of all the reservoirs in the Willamette Valley attempting to determine allocated cost to municipalities for water supply. This study dragged on for years.

On October 26, 1973 John Geren wrote Colonel Clarence Gilky, the new District Engineer of the Corps. Geren reminded Gilky the city was still interested in buying stored water and also reminded the Colonel this matter has been pending for many years. Geren wrote the negotiations had covered a span of four city managers and he hoped this matter could be resolved while there was still a city official familiar with the history. Geren's haste at this point was because he was thinking of retiring and he felt a responsibility to see it through to the end.

In June, 1974 the Corps District Office completed the allocated costs to Salem as follows:

| | |
|---|---:|
| Allocated investment cost | $5,022,156 |
| Amortization per year | 225,220 |
| Operational cost per year | 9,761 |
| | |
| Total annual costs | $234,990 |

These costs did seem more reasonable than the early estimates and were acceptable to the city.

On July 10, 1974 Corps District Office requested confirmation of the allocated costs to headquarters of the Corps in Washington, D.C.

On December 16, 1974, Marvin Rees, Colonel, Executive Director of Civil Works of the Corps in Washington D.C. wrote to the District Office and said no to the confirmation. He wrote "policies and procedures acceptable to the Corps, Department of the Interior, and the Federal Power Commission have not been defined for projects in an operational status."

Uh-oh, City of Salem, back to the drawing board.

On January 8, 1975 Mayor Robert Lindsey of Salem wrote Senator Mark O. Hatfield and requested his assistance in resolving the issues with the Corps. Senator Hatfield assigned his staff member, Steve Hickok, to investigate the situation. However, after giving it a good try Hickok was unable to get additional information from the Corps.

In July, 1975 City Manager Robert Moore wrote Major General W.C. Gribble in Washington D.C. as follows:

Major General W.C. Gribble
Chief of Engineers
U.S. Army Corps of Engineers

As the head of a relatively small organization of some 1000 employees, I sometimes find that situations or problems occur within departments of the city that are of major significance and yet escape my knowledge, and hence any opportunity for me to effect a proper and timely decision. I would like to bring one of those incidents within the Army Corps of Engineers to your attention, in hopes that you wish to be informed of this type of situation; and, you are in a position to positively affect a proper and timely decision.

This situation seems impossible and unreal, but is indeed factual. For a period of more than 20 years the City of Salem has been attempting to get an answer concerning our use of stored water rights on the Santiam River, behind Detroit Dam east of Salem. As a growing urban area requiring increases in our water supply, we are faced with some very significant decisions in the immediate future, which require us to have information from your agency. It is vitally important that we have this information now in order to make both construction and financial plans for expansion of our water supply.

As I understand it, our request for a decision by the Cops on this question is now within your policy and planning section in Washington D.C. and is under active discussion. We would certainly appreciate anything that you can do to expedite a fair and reasonable decision on this question, which we have been trying to have resolved for these many long years, without success. I am not sending to you a complete file on this subject since I am sure your staff has it and will be able to review it with you. I would, however, ask you to refer to the attached list of dates and actions. which give some historical perspective on our heretofore futile attempts to attain resolution on this matter.

Thank you very much for any assistance which you can provide us.

Robert S. Moore
City Manager

Finally, on November 25, 1975 the city received a revised allocation of costs from the Corps, as follows:

| | |
|---|---|
| Investment costs | $7,700,000. |
| Annual costs including amortization | $391,800. |

Since these allocated costs were much greater than the previous estimates, the city hired Amalio Gomez of CH2M-Hill, formerly chief engineer for the Corps' in Sacramento. Mr. Gomez was critical of the Corps methodology and he computed an investment cost of $4,100,000 resulting in an annual cost of $161,000. The city and Mr. Gomez then negotiated with the Corps but were unsuccessful in convincing them to amend their allocated costs.

The city then gave up. The moral of this very long discussion and negotiation with the Corps is—if you need federal resources you had better plan on a very, very, long negotiation period, perhaps 50 years or more.

# Chapter 6
# Successes And Frustrations
# 1950-1956

The City of Salem was experiencing rapid growth in the late 1940's. Several new areas in Marion County were annexed to the city in 1947. Polk County's West Salem was annexed to the city in 1949. As a result of this growth, peak day water demands had increased from about 8.5 mgd in 1939 to 21 mgd in 1951. Since the city's 36 inch transmission line from Stayton Island had a peak capacity of about 16 mgd, the city's 10 million gallon Fairmount Reservoir was drawn down at an alarming rate during hot summer days.

The period of August 20th through the 22nd in 1951 all had water demands exceeding the capacity of the transmission line. Fairmount Reservoir was very nearly drained dry, leaving the city with no reserves and very little capacity to fight major fires.

John Geren Water Department Assistant Director at the time, studied the 1950 water supply deficit and the ever increasing water demands up to 1951. He came up with the following conclusions:[50]

1. That by virtue of growth and increased water usage Salem has reached the capacity of the existing supply and that steps must be taken to increase the available supply to avoid restricting water use and inhibiting the growth of the city.

2. That increased source facilities or storage are needed immediately to absorb peak loads of relatively short duration.

3. That plans must be laid for increase of the overall supply on a long term basis to keep ahead of the reasonably expected growth of the city.

Therefore in the summer of 1950 city staff knew additional peak day capacity must be increased as soon as possible. A $300,000 bond issue was proposed and submitted to the voters to construct a 100 million gallon reservoir on a hillside in the City of Turner between

Stayton and Salem. The hillside location allowed the city to maintain its gravity service to the reservoir and continue the service as gravity to the Fairmount Reservoir in Salem. This incredibly fortunate alignment of natural features on the transmission line route greatly benefitted the rate payers in Salem by not requiring expensive pumping of the water supply to the city.

The reservoir construction was planned to be a balanced cut and fill, thus also economizing the construction as much as possible. It has been rumored, since no engineering plans for the reservoir exist for its construction, that City Manager Franzen and John Geren designed the reservoir on the back of an envelope. However it happened the design was done and it was quite an economically creative solution to the serious lack of supply storage the city was facing.

The reservoir was constructed as an open reservoir because of its size and unusual shape. The serpentine shape was dictated by the shape of the original hill, the resulting earth and rock excavation on the uphill side, and the embankment on the downhill side.

A contract for the excavation and fill work was let in September, 1950 and completed in May, 1951. During the winter and spring of 1951-52, city forces installed the inlet and outlet connections to the city's 36 inch transmission line. They also constructed an under drain system to carry away ground water and prepared both the bottom and side slopes for lining.

Figure 6-1 shows the reservoir at near the completion of excavation and fill work.

The city used asphalt to pave the interior of the reservoir. City Manager Franzen was criticized by City Council candidates in the May, 1952 primaries for planning to line the reservoir with asphalt. Franzen defended his decision by citing several reservoirs built in California which used the same asphalt lining technique and which Franzen had observed on a trip to California. He said the linings had stood up under the stress of time. He said he had inspected the reservoirs in California himself and as an engineer conferred with the engineers of the cities to determine the economy of the asphalt linings.

Apparently the asphalt lining technique stirred up quite a controversy in the city. John Geren got into the middle of it with a quote in the *Oregon Statesman* article on June 30, 1952 as follows:[51]

> Because of the steep 31 foot high embankment most paving firms shied away from bidding on the paving job. It presented lots of problems not found in standard paving procedures. The floor presented no

great problem. It is being paved with an ordinary street paving machine. The oil in the asphalt will not taint the reservoir water.

The steep walls are being asphalted by an ingenious combination of crane, winches, pulleys and veteran construction brains. The asphalt is different from ordinary road paving asphalt. It has a higher oil content, finer gravel and more sand than road asphalt. After the asphalt is on, a thin sealer coat, which will provide a waterproof surface, will be sprayed on.

FIGURE 6-1: Turner Reservoir (later Franzen Reservoir) partially completed before the asphalt lining has been placed.

Figure 6-2 shows the technique used by the contractor to place the asphalt on the steep side slopes of the reservoir.

The entire reservoir project cost $450,000. The funds came from a $300,000 bond issue passed by the voters in 1950 with the additional $150,000 coming from water rate revenues.

The city completed all construction related to the reservoir including a control building and chlorination building by March, 1953. On March 7, 1953 the reservoir was half full and it was planned to fill the remaining half at about one foot per day.

The completion of the 100 million gallon reservoir gave the city a four day emergency supply which was critically needed. Peak day water demands were increasing rapidly. In 1953 the peak demand was 24 mgd. With the 100 million gallon reservoir on line this demand was met. However, without the new Turner Reservoir the city would have run out of water without an emergency plan for water use curtailment.

FIGURE 6-2: The side slopes of Turner Reservoir being paved with asphalt

The entire reservoir project cost $450,000. The funds came from a $300,000 bond issue passed by the voters in 1950 with the additional $150,000 coming from water rate revenues.

Apparently in the 1950's water conservation and the use of water curtailment measures just were not acceptable to the elected City Council or the residents of Salem. It was the community tradition to use large amounts of very cheap water for irrigating lawns and ornamental plants. The city was not of the mind to change that, and instead they said clearly, if we are running out of water we just need to find a way to increase the supply.

The very high peak demands of 1950 and 1951 made it obvious to City Manager Franzen that additional water treatment was needed, in addition to storage at Turner Reservoir. So, in 1951 after the maximum peak day in August of 21 mgd, Franzen authorized CH2M, consulting engineers from Corvallis, to study an auxiliary water supply from the Willamette River.[52]

Up until 1951 the city still thought they could use the decrepit Minto Island system as an auxiliary supply. However, as part of the negotiations with Oregon Pulp and Paper Company for 60 cfs of 1856 water rights on the North Santiam River, the city gave Minto Island to the paper company and agreed to sever the suction pipelines running under their plant. This meant the city's only auxiliary supply was a few wells in the city. Franzen believed a back up or auxiliary supply for emergencies was essential and that it could also be used if necessary to supplement the Stayton Island source during peak demands.

CH2M was requested to prepare a plan and provide cost estimates for a 4 mgd Willamette River source treatment plant located in West Salem. They were also asked to locate a 5 million gallon reservoir site to improve pressure conditions in West Salem. Several treatment plant and reservoir locations were studied. The engineers estimated costs at $811,000 for both the treatment plant and the reservoir.

While the city was considering the construction of the West Salem plant and reservoir, John Geren, (new Water Department Director with the retirement of Carl Guenther in 1952) discussed the pros and cons of a Willamette River auxiliary source versus construction of a second transmission line to Stayton Island. His analysis follows:[53]

Arguments in favor of early development of a source on the Willamette River:

1. An independent source would be available in case of failure of the primary source.

2. Standby pumping plans now required to be kept available for fire protection could be eliminated.

3. A source supply in West Salem would help to balance available water with centers of greatest use.

4. Quality of water would be equal to that produced by the Santiam.

5. Filter plant could be developed as the city grows in smaller increments and less capital outlay.

Arguments against use of the Willamette supply or favoring the further development of the Santiam supply are:

1. Pumping and maintenance would be added to cost of production of water from the Willamette.

2. Year around maintenance would be required even if the [Willamette] plant were used only for peak loads.

3. Unit costs per million gallons would be less for the Santiam supply.

4. Public aversion to use of Willamette River water would be diffi-

cult to overcome, even though Corvallis and Camp Adair have demonstrated a good water can be produced.

5. Early construction of a line [a new transmission line] to Turner Reservoir would enable the city to obtain maximum benefit from the investment already made there.

6. Route the proposed 48 inch line, generally along the route of the By Pass Highway [I-5] would extend into the most populous areas likely to be annexed to the city water system and would be planned to eventually extend to the Keizer area.

7. In the event fluoridation of water is adopted by the city, application could be made to the entire supply at Turner, while water produced on the Willamette would require separate treatment.

In 1952 John Geren was still working on the assumption a mechanical and chemical water treatment filtration plant could produce the same quality of water as from the North Santiam River. We now know that because of dissolved toxins in Willamette River water that this is not so. With paper mills and exotic metal processors discharging untreated wastes to the river, with pesticides being used on the many farm lands and being washed into the river, and with untreated domestic sewage being discharged, the Willamette River could hardly be considered a drinking water source in the 1950's. It was not until 1958 that the State Sanitary Authority ordered Salem, Eugene and Newberg to construct secondary sewage treatment plants which partially solved the Willamette River pollution problem. (Salem opened its Willow Lake Wastewater Treatment Plant in 1964.)

What Geren did not know in 1952 was how efficient the North Santiam River water could be treated with what Geren called a "natural treatment system." (Later it was more correctly known as slow sand filtration.)

Geren's belief that the engineering of mechanical and chemical treatment plants could solve any degree of raw water pollution problems in treating drinking water was the dominant view in the 1950's. He was a person of his time with this view but far ahead of many other professionals in the municipal water industry in looking to the future and developing excellent political and community support for the ever evolving Salem water system.

Geren in 1952 had an excellent plan for the routing of a new water transmission line from Turner to Salem, which would parallel the new Interstate 5 highway. Part of the plan was to continue the new transmission line to the unincorporated Keizer area, cross the Willamette

River and discharge to a new 10 million gallon Mountain View Reservoir in West Salem.

Geren also explored the possibility of obtaining stored water from Detroit Reservoir and extending the supply line up the North Santiam canyon to Detroit. He said the additional available head of 675 feet must be weighed against the cost of an added 35 miles of pipeline. This head, he believed, could create a large amount of power that could be marketed or used for municipal purposes. This plan of course was never realized because the city was never able to negotiate an acceptable price for stored water at Detroit from the Corps of Engineers.

Geren in 1952 was aware that water rate revenues were insufficient to support large improvements to the water supply and treatment system. His comments follow regarding the need to increase water rates:[54]

Those costs which are purely operational are increasing both with the growth of the system and with the increase in the cost of labor and materials. Cost of bond retirement and interest is now about 29 percent of the revenue coming in to the department. This cost will continue in about the same amount until about 1968, diminishing then until the bond retirement program is completed in 1976.

On an average, operation costs and bond retirement and interests, require about 60% of the yearly revenues. The remaining 40% during the past years has been put back into the system in betterment and expansion. This program has been costly due to the extension of the city limits and the many new arterials [mains] required to strengthen the old grid and serve the new areas. Much improvement has been made in this respect and although the problem is never ending one as long as the city continues to grow, most of the larger projects needed for so long have been completed at the present time. Much improvements of distribution mains are needed, however, in certain areas of the city to maintain pressures and provide adequate fire protection.

The program of arterial and distribution main improvement, plus the undertaking at Turner Reservoir, has consumed practically all the revenue available to the present time, including a $300,000 bond issue voted by the people in 1950, so that now little reserves are left, other than current income, with which to undertake other projects. Planned improvements of the existing system can likely be carried on within current income, but several years will be required to accumulate enough reserve to undertake the larger projects, such as the line to Turner, even if improvements within the city are kept to the minimum and the limits of water service are not extended.

The question, then, is how long the city can wait before undertaking further supply development. This cannot be long if water used is not to be restricted. If such project must be undertaken soon, further bonding could probably be accomplished, but, as has been already shown, debt service is already requiring about one-fourth of the department's income. Further bonding will reduce still more the amount left for normal development. The other alternative is to substantially increase water rates to the consumer. The present rates charged for water are published in an order of the Public Service Commission of Oregon dated May 15, 1916, with the special irrigation rate being established in 1928 at 7 1/2 cents per 100 cubic feet and reduced to 5 cents per 100 cubic feet after purchase [of the private water system] by the city. Although increase of water rates is always an unpopular move, continued development of a modern water supply at 1916 prices may not much longer be possible. Efficiency of municipal operation has been demonstrated by the fact that the system has been developed to its present condition within the same rate structure that prevailed 35 years ago.

Geren made it very clear in this communication that, if the city wants an adequate supply of water for continued growth, and to continue the culture of green grass in the dry summer, it is time to make major improvements and produce the revenue to pay for it. He stated explicitly that if the supply is not increased, the use of water must be restricted. This straight talk from Geren, however, apparently influenced no one because in 1957 when the City Council finally got around to reviewing a proposed 10% water rate increase, the Council actually lowered most rates. This resulted in decreasing the yearly revenues of the water department.

It is interesting to note that water rates in 1952 paid for serving newly annexed areas. This policy would continue with minor variations until 1979 when the city, under the leadership of Mayor Kent Aldrich and City Manager Ralph Hanley passed a very comprehensive Urban Growth Management ordinance (Chapter 66 of the Salem Revised Code). This ordinance required developers to extend water lines and build master plan water reservoirs and pump stations when developing land outside the currently developed area (generally the city limits in residential areas).

Geren summarized the water supply situation in 1952 as follows:[55]

During the 17 years since the city purchased the private water system, the number of water users has increased from about 7,000 to 12,000 customers. At the same time, maximum demands on the system have increased from about 8.5 to 21 mgd.

This rapid growth in demand has been met by the construction and development of the North Santiam supply, the Fairmount Reservoir and a system of arterial mains throughout the city. Higher elevation homes have been supplied by pumping stations and high level reservoirs.

Peak load demands have grown to the point where the full capacity of the available supply is being utilized and there is no margin left for future growth or other contingencies. Use of Turner Reservoir, now being completed, will provide a reserve which can be drawn upon for a somewhat increased rate of flow for short periods and will cushion peak loads for a relatively few years.

Plans must be made immediately for increased supply if the city's growth is not to be inhibited by restrictions on use of water. Additional water may be obtained from the Willamette River or from the North Santiam. A filter plant on the Willamette would require a smaller initial investment but would result in higher construction costs per million gallons, plus continuing pumping and maintenance costs.

Further development of the Santiam supply can be made in two increments by first constructing a large line as far as Turner Reservoir and later extending it to Stayton Island. Such a development would make maximum use of the Turner Reservoir and result in lower cost per million gallons. This project would create a total supply of about 60 mgd and would reasonably serve three times the present population.

Revenues from sale of water has been increasing with the growth of the city. However, rising costs and rapid expansion of the system make it questionable whether development can proceed as rapidly as required within the present rate strategies. Existing rates were established in 1916.

It is not known how widely Geren's ideas were disseminated to the City Council and the general public. The above quotes from Geren were from a draft report titled "Development of Water Supply".[56] Clipped to the top of the report is a hand written note that stated:

This report intended for publication in 1952. Never published. May be useful for historical data, signed, Geren.

We can speculate why the report was not published as maybe the City Manager thought Geren was criticizing the Council for not dealing with the crisis of an insufficient water supply and refusing to raise water rates in order to pay for the necessary improvements. I know in my tenure as public works director there were many times that, in my opinion, information that needed to go public was never sent for fear the City Council would take offense that city staff might be second guessing them. But, in Geren's case, I am sure he found a way to make public the looming crisis of an insufficient water supply that could economically hobble the city.

From 1952 to 1954 the water supply situation worsened with peak demands increasing from 21 mgd to 24.5 mgd. On peak days with a water transmission line capacity of 16 mgd the supply reservoirs were drawn down by over 8 million gallons. Obviously if the condition of hot dry weather continued for up to two weeks the reservoirs would be drained dry. Meanwhile the City Council fiddled while the city limped along with an insufficient water supply, enjoying non-irrigation water rates that had not been increased since 1916.

By 1954 the city had continued its rapid rate of growth and its annexation of new areas to the city. However, the policy of the city providing free water extensions to new areas was causing concern due to high costs to the city. On January 18, 1954, a report from a committee of city officials comprised of city manager Franzen, Robert Powell, chairman of the city planning and zoning commission, John Geren, director of the water department; and J.H. Davis, city engineer, recommended city water rates be increased. Excerpts from the committee statement reported in a *Capital Journal* article on January 18, 1954 follow:[57]

> That operating revenues of the water department, based on rates which were established in 1916, be increased. An increase of this amount is required not only to finance water distribution in new areas, but is also required to place the water department on a sound operating program and to provide for debt service for large expenditures which must soon be made to increase the supply of water in the city. Annexations to the city will naturally hasten the day when the present supply is inadequate.
>
> It is agreed that annexation of new territories at a reasonable rate is not only necessary for the normal growth of the city but at the present time is desirable from the city's standpoint as a means of providing first class residential development.

It is also felt that it is not realistic now to require new areas to provide water and sewer lines at their own expense, such a burden would
probably defeat the annexation movement to the detriment of both
the city and suburban areas.

The long term policy of providing water and sewer line extensions
of newly annexed areas and this committee's recommendation that it
be continued seemed fiscally inappropriate for this time. The water
department was spending a large percentage of their revenues and
staff time in providing this service in the face of insufficient revenues
to make necessary increases to the water supply. Just why the committee made this recommendation is not known. It is interesting to
note how drastically the city's policies have changed since 1954. As
mentioned previously, the 1979 Urban Growth Management program
required the extensions of water mains to newly annexed areas be totally paid for by the developer. Also since 2001 the City Charter requires a vote of the public for every annexation regardless of its size.
The policy in 1954 was to encourage annexations and the present policy is designed to discourage them.

On August 16, 1954 the City Council took up the issue of increasing water rates and to put two bond issues on the ballot. The first
was a water system improvement bond of $1,930,000 and the second
was a $1,750,000 bond issue to construct a civic auditorium. At this
meeting staff proposed a 25% water rate increase to pay for the water
bonds and accumulated inflation costs.

On August 17th the *Oregon Statesman* reported the City Council
was apparently opposed to submitting bond issues for either purpose
to the public. The proposed water rate increase was rejected by the
Council. However Council said they were in favor of abolishing the
extremely low irrigation rate which, in their opinion, would probably
save water on peak days.[58]

On August 23rd, the City Council made final decisions on the bond
issues. Both bond issues were rejected. The Council, however, did
make a major change in city policy regarding the furnishing of city water lines to newly annexed areas. They placed on the November ballot
a charter amendment to charge water assessments of $125 per house
in newly annexed areas where the city provided the water lines. The
Council believed that to continue to annex areas with major water
and sewer improvements paid by the city was out of the question
considering the state of present city finances.[59]

However, it can be stated unequivocally that present city finances at the start of the 21st century have not improved since 1954 with large annual deficits even though the city rate  payers now pay nothing for water and sewer extensions. These are now paid by developers and system development charges.

On October 28, 1954 the *Capital Journal* printed a map titled "Map Is City's Argument For An Annexation Policy". The map showed the existing city limits with three highlighted areas in the process of annexation (209 acres to the east of the State Fairgrounds); probable annexations in the next few years (areas in all quadrants of the city contiguous to the city limits); and, potential annexations (the Keizer area and huge areas to the south of present city limits and also east of I-5).[60] The map showed that in 1954 city staff believed Salem would in the future grow from a present population of 50,000 to a much larger city. Figure 6-3 shows a simplified map of the annexation policy.

City voters on November 2, 1954 approved the charter amendment that assessments will be charged for providing water and sewer service to newly annexed areas. So, the strategy worked in persuading voters to approve the assessment fees by forecasting large population increases and the costs of providing the infrastructure for the necessary annexations.

In August, 1955 due to hot dry weather there was an extended period of residential irrigation that coincided with peak demands from Salem's food processors. In 1955 Salem had the one of the largest concentrations of food processors in the country. They canned and froze large quantities of locally grown corn and  green beans, as well as a variety of other fruit and vegetable crops. The food processors bought very cheap water from the city and as a result conservation was not in their vocabulary. Unfortunately for the supply-short water system, the food processors usually had peak production in mid to late summer that coincided with the peak residential irrigation season. Since the cost of "irrigation water," or all the water used residentially in the summer months, that exceeded 500 cubic feet, cost only 5 cents per 100 cubic feet just about every home used large amounts of very cheap city water.

In 1955 the summer peak demand greatly exceeded the capacity of the Stayton Island facility and the 36 inch transmission line to the city. This drew down Turner Reservoir to 5 feet from a maximum depth of 28 feet. The peak day in 1955 was only about 23 mgd but the duration of the hot dry period lasted for several weeks.

During this period water department staff observed the levels of Turner Reservoir dropping every day. The city was finally ready for the first time to consider restricting water use to residential areas and shutting down the food processors and other heavy water users. However, the weather finally cooled and the production of water finally exceeded the demand. The city was spared the difficult task of shutting down the city's economic life blood and restricting residential use.

In September, 1955 city staff, with the approval of City Council, started an aggressive action to design and construct a major expansion of the city's water supply. The summer of 1955 convinced just about everyone in the city that to continue gambling with an inadequate water supply could cripple the city's industry and change the culture of the city residents who were used to unrestricted amounts of irrigation water.

In October the engineering firm Clark and Groff was retained to make a study of water requirements for the city, considering all possible supply sources and preparing an estimate of the costs. They were also to recommend a solution in sufficient detail and refined cost estimates so the city could place a bond issue before the voters in May, 1956.

The engineers reported to the City Council on January 23, 1956 with the following recommendations:[61]

1. The prolonged hot weather during August, 1955, placed a demand on the Salem water supply system which exceeded the full production capacity of the system by about 5 mgd or 25%.

2. Consumption of water is continually increasing due to the increased number of services and increased per capita use of water. Unless the present supply is enlarged soon a less severe hot season than that of last August will require water rationing. This will come at a time when Salem industries are at peak production.

3. Based on past records, it is estimated that Salem will grow to about 95,000 population within the next 30 years.

4. The suburban areas of Salem are growing at a faster rate than the city. The suburbs are expected to reach 60,000 population in 30 years.

5. Due to the unreliability of bacterial and chemical quality, and in some areas, of the quantity of water from wells, it is expected that suburban water districts will seek connections to the city supply.

6. Service to adjacent water districts is considered a proper and de-

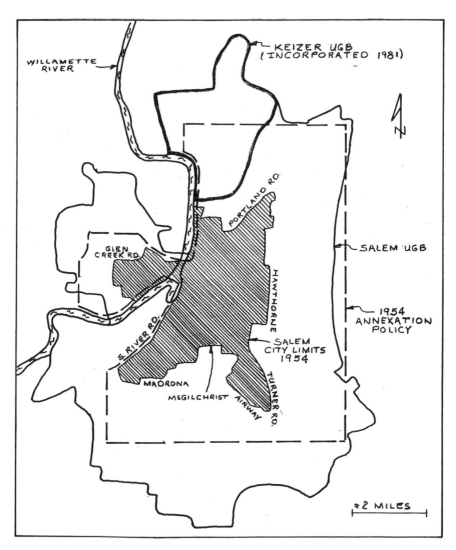

FIGURE 6-3: Map of the annexation policy of the City of Salem in 1954. The vision of a built-out city did not anticipate the incorporation of the City of Keizer or the creation of the East Salem service districts.

sirable function of a city water supply, but rates to these districts should be higher than city rates.

7. Thus, a water system for Metropolitan Salem may be expected to serve a population of about 150,000 by 1985. Average daily consumption at that time is estimated to be 30 mgd with the average day of the peak month requiring 68 mgd and the peak day 77 mgd.

8. It appears highly desirable, therefore, that Salem proceed without delay to augment the present supply. To do this, we recommend:

a. The continued use of the North Santiam River.

b An expanded intake works at Stayton Island to increase the yield to 50 mgd.

c. An additional transmission line varying in diameter from 54 to 48 inches from Stayton to Salem via Turner Reservoir.

d. A public vote to authorize the sale of up to $3,750,000 in bonds to finance these improvements.

e. A revision of the water rates in an amount sufficient to provide increased funds for the retirement of the new indebtedness and for the increased operating cost which accompany an expanding water system.

f. It is further recommended that the new water rates be placed in effect as soon as possible in order that the increase in revenue can be demonstrated to meet the new debt costs. This is of primary importance in order to obtain a favorable rate of interest for the sale of the bonds.

g. Although the city owns firm water rights on the North Santiam to meet requirements for about the next 20 years, it is highly desirable that negotiations be continued in 1956 to secure additional rights for no less than 100 cfs.

The engineers' recommendations were extremely aggressive, especially for the City of Salem where the City Council was extremely reluctant to raise water rates. The big questions then were: will the Council agree to sell bonds for the cost of this large improvement project; and also, will they raise rates to pay for the bonds?

The report recommended a 10% rate increase which was expected to cover water department operating expenses and debt payments for the bonds.

The estimated cost of the projects are shown in Table 6-1.

The Clark and Groff study also considered, as an alternative to further expanding the Stayton Island facility, a Willamette River water source and a sophisticated rapid sand filtration treatment system. They estimated a first phase plant of 25 mgd that would cost an estimated $2,500,000 to build plus an additional $350,000 for an intake and pipeline upstream from Salem. However, they concluded a Willamette River water source was not attractive because the river was polluted and would continue to be for the foreseeable future. (I wonder just how many times the City of Salem was going to come to this obvious conclusion?)

## TABLE 6-1
## COST OF WATER SUPPLY PROJECTS IN 1956

| | |
|---|---|
| Slow sand filter system | $383,000 |
| River crossing for transmission line | 30,000 |
| Right of way for transmission line | 25,000 |
| Transmission line | 2,965,860 |
| Bonds, engineering, contingency | 340,390 |
| | |
| Total | $3,744,250 |
| Recommended bond sale | $3,750,000 |

Beating the odds, the City Council approved the Clark and Groff report, and referred to the voters a $3,750,000 bond issue for a May 18, 1956 vote. Wonder of wonders!

On May 7, 1956 the *Capital Journal* published an editorial recommending the voters pass the bond issue. Excerpts from the editorial follow:[62]

> Right now Salem faces a possible water shortage during this summer season. It certainly will be up against that situation two or three years from now unless something is done about it quickly.
>
> The only way a curtailed allowance of water and an endangering of fire protection can be avoided is for the people to vote the $3,750,000 bonds in the election this month to build an additional water supply line from Stayton Island to Salem.

The editorial went on to say "this is no cry of wolf where there is no wolf," and stated in a very positive way the need for the bond funds to pay for water supply improvements. The editorial also stated "immediate action is necessary because it will take nearly two years after the bonds are authorized to design and build the new line."

What the editorial did not say was the necessity to also raise water rates to pay for the bonds. It is not known at this time their opinion on this very sensitive political issue. The editorial also did not say this bond issue would pay for a slow sand filtration system that will greatly improve the quality of drinking water treated at the island. Perhaps the folks in Salem in 1956 were more interested in quantity than quality.

The voters approved the $3.75 million bond issue on May 18th. On June 12, 1956 the *Capital Journal* reported the City Council requested the City Manager Franzen negotiate a contract with Clark and Groff for the design of the water supply system expansion.[63]

Thus, this action ended a period of extreme frustration by staff to obtain approval of the needed water supply improvements. This same period, however, had the outstanding success of obtaining 60 cfs of 1856 priority water rights from Oregon Pulp and Paper Company. So, the period from 1950 to mid 1956 set the stage for Salem to finally build an excellent water system that would produce the best of quality and sufficient quantity for a quickly growing city. It was believed by John Geren and the consultants the proposed slow sand filter treatment system would finally eliminate the musty taste of the finished water due to algae and sweet mountain water would finally be realized.

# Chapter 7
# Water System Improvements
# 1956-1971

The year 1956 was memorable for the Salem Water Department in two important ways: the voters had approved a $3.75 million bond issue for a second transmission line from Stayton Island and the construction of the first slow sand filter; and, the long time City Manager, J.L. Franzen, had announced his retirement in March, to be effective July 1st.

The retirement of Franzen was thought to be a serious blow to the Water Department. Franzen had for years taken the lead in promoting the development of the city's water system. No one knew what the priorities of a new city manager may be. Water Department staff knew that many city managers had no experience with water systems and could be reluctant to take the lead in promoting the improvements to the system because of extreme political resistance to raising necessary revenues.

Franzen was an ideal city manager for Salem during his tenure between 1947 and 1956. Salem was an extremely fast growing city during the post war years and large infrastructure improvements were primary political objectives. The City Councils of that time were dominated by business interests and a lack of infrastructure meant lean times for new industrial and business development. A typical attitude of business oriented councils was, and probably still is, the desire for growth of jobs and the general economy, but at the same time the creation of tight restrictions on increases in utility rates and taxes. These two attitudes can be contradictory and compromises must be found to get projects completed without the political risk of raising taxes, rates or fees that businesses so often despise.

Franzen was a person extremely qualified to find a way through the political quagmire to get built whatever was needed. Franzen accomplished many of his objectives as city manager. He designed and obtained funding for the city's 100 million gallon Turner Reservoir. He led the planning for greatly increasing the water supply system and gaining voter approval of the largest bond issue in the city's history. He led the effort to obtain additional extremely valuable 1856 priority water rights from Oregon Pulp and Paper Company. He led the effort to build the city's first sewage treatment plant in 1952. He also worked with the City Council in solving many growth related problems such as planning street extensions and arterials, developing a workable traffic grid, separation of the 12th Street railroad tracks, getting Bush Park into the city park system, modernization of (old) City Hall, and innumerable other projects.

The City Council, 250 local business men, and government officials met on July 18, 1956 at the Marion Hotel to honor Franzen on his retirement as the city's first city manager. The first order of the day was the official calling of the City Council into session by Mayor Robert White. The City Council then renamed Turner Reservoir the J.L. Franzen Reservoir in his honor.

The reservoir which now bears Franzen's name was built in 1952 on a hill in the City of Turner. The top of hill by lucky chance, was just the correct elevation so that gravity flow was possible for water flowing from Stayton Island in the 36 inch transmission line. This water would fill the reservoir, then  water flowing to the City of Salem would fill Fairmount Reservoir, which would establish the gravity service level for the city.

Locating the Franzen Reservoir site, designing an unbelievably economical 100 million gallon reservoir, and then finding the funds to build it from a penny pinching City Council was acknowledged by everyone in 1956 as a major achievement.

Franzen started his career as an engineer after graduating from Washington State College in 1910. He was chief engineer of an Alberta, Canada reclamation project for nine years and then spent a number of years as an engineer in Portland and 21 years as City Manager of Oregon City.

In 1946 city voters chose to drastically change the form of government in Salem and convert from a strong mayor form to a city manager form of government. This change was made as a charter amendment, which on the same amendment created a City Council of nine members: a mayor and eight councilors, one from each of the eight wards in the city. Previously, two aldermen from each ward sat on the City Council.

In 1947 the city interviewed a number of candidates and found them all lacking the management skills to deal with a new government system of a city manager type government. Salem was a rapidly growing city in 1947 and was suffering a lack of public infrastructure. Franzen, as city manager of Oregon City, was recognized as an outstanding administrator and engineer who had the skills needed in Salem. Franzen was recruited by the City Council, and to the good fortune of the city, he accepted the challenging position.

Charles Sprague, publisher of the *Oregon Statesman* was the principal speaker at the July 18th luncheon honoring Franzen. The *Statesman* article on July 19th reported the following:[64]

> J.L. Franzen has made his mark as one of the distinguished leaders in the history of Salem, Publisher Charles Sprague declared Wednesday before 250 businessmen and local government officials gathered to honor Franzen.
>
> Among the special guests of the day were former Salem mayors V.E. Kuhn, W.W. Chadwick, Robert L. Elfstrom and Alfred W. Loucks.
>
> City and County officials present included Mayor Robert White, County Judge Rex Hartley, County Health Officer Dr. Willard Stone, Salem School Superintendent Walter Snyder, County Engineer John Anderson, Kent Matthewson [new Salem City Manager], Charles McClue, John Geren, David Baker, J.H. Davis, William Lowery, Vern McMullen and John Cunningham.

Franzen said he intended to move to Long Beach, California to be near his daughter but would stay for another month to assist the new City Manager, Kent Matthewson.

After Franzen announced his retirement in early 1956, the City Council conducted a national search for a new city manager. On March 27th after interviewing several candidates from a field of 40, the Council picked Kent Mathewson, a 38 year city manager of Martinsville, Virginia. Mathewson accepted the position at $14,000 per year compared to Franzen's $11,500 per year.

The *Capital Journal* reported the following on March 28th:[65]

> Said Mayor Robert White of the selection: "We are proud that a man of Mathewson's high caliber is coming to Salem as City Manager, and we feel certain we can look forward to continued fine city government under his direction. Mathewson will bring to Salem an excellent varied and a national reputation. Only this month he turned down a $22,000 job as executive head of the International City Managers As-

sociation in Chicago. He was one of four city managers in the country selected for consideration by that outstanding association."

Mathewson had considerable experience in city government. Prior to being city manager of Martinsville, Virginia, he was city manager of Asheboro, North Carolina and assistant city manager at San Diego, California and Durham, North Carolina. He received a bachelors degree in public administration from the University of North Carolina and he had served in the military in the air transport command.

Kent Mathewson seemed on paper to be a very strong and capable city manager, however, the Water Department staff were on edge. They had no idea where his priorities were in pushing his agenda as city manager. Franzen was a passionate supporter of developing an excellent water system. Only time would tell if Mathewson would follow suit. The Water Department staff knew a very large political decision still needed to be made. With the approval of the $3.75 million bond issue for increasing the capacity of the water supply system, would the City Council raise water rates sufficient to retire the bonds and to support a strong operation and maintenance program?

The 25 year bonds were sold on March 4, 1957 to the United States National Bank of Portland at an interest rate of 3.2831%.

It is not known by the author if the bonds were rated by Standard and Poor or Moodys. In all likelihood they were not because it was pretty obvious that water rates were low and there were no assurances at the time if water rates would be increased. However, since the bonds were approved by the voters, the city was committing the full resources of the city to retire the bonds.

Losing no time in starting the construction of the new water transmission line, the city awarded a $3.093 million contract to Lord Brothers of Portland to construct the new 54 inch transmission line from Stayton Island to the city. The construction was planned to be completed in the fall of 1958.

Meanwhile back on the political scene, City Manager Mathewson proposed on May 30, 1957 a water rate increase of 10% over the rates established in 1916. The Water Department staff headed by the manager, John Geren, were very pleased with the advocacy of City Manager Kent Mathewson for improving the water supply system and most of all recommending rate increases to pay for it.

On May 30, 1957 the City Council decided not to raise water rates but instead decided to reduce them! They did decide to eliminate the special irrigation rate for residential customers but, at the same time, significantly reduced residential rates for most customers. (See Chapter 12 for the full details on water rate increases in Salem.) The rate revisions of 1957 decreased the yearly rate revenues to the water department from $555,000 per year to $519,000 per year. The City Council stated that the new rates would be sufficient to retire the new bonds but only if the water department would tighten their belts and make do. They said the citizens of Salem were paying enough for water!

So, "tighten your belts" in 1957 meant the water line replacement program and all maintenance programs were severely cut back. In water management terms this meant the City Council did not want the present generation to pay for the perpetual life of the water system. They preferred their children and grandchildren to take the responsibility. (Which is now happening with Salem's soaring water rates.)

The "Water for Salem" improvements to be funded by the new $3.75 million bond issue were built in 1957 and 1958. The improvements included a second water transmission line consisting of 50,800 feet of 54 inch concrete cylinder pipe from Stayton Island to the newly named Franzen Reservoir in the City of Turner, and 38,700 feet of 48 inch concrete cylinder pipe from Franzen Reservoir to the City of Salem.

In addition the city's first slow sand filter was built at Stayton Island. The City Council awarded the construction of the slow sand filter to Lord Brothers Construction Company on August 12, 1957 for $360,920. The next low bidder was Salem Sand and Gravel at $363,120. This project was scheduled to be completed in the summer of 1958 to coincide with the completion of the new transmission line.

The existing infiltration galleries built in 1937 were unable to produce the quantity of water now needed and they were unable to produce good low turbidity water when the Santiam River had high turbid flows. It was believed the slow sand filter had the potential to produce extremely low turbidity and produce the finest filtered water found anywhere in the world.

A third necessary improvement that was made was the construction of a control system near Franzen Reservoir. This was built where the two transmission lines come together in a common pipeline with metering and a large cone valve for flow control to the city.

Even with all of these improvements, a dark cloud still hung over the water system. In 1958 the city had only 82 cfs or 53 mgd of North Santiam River water rights. The city needed to acquire more early priority water rights, but in 1958, it was not a promising situation. The city's main hope was to buy stored water from the Corps of Engineers Detroit Dam. But as previously described in Chapter 5, "The Detroit Dam Fiasco," the city finally gave up in frustration in 1975. So, the issue of obtaining additional water rights was still looming.

In April, 1959 *The American City Magazine* published an article written by John Geren titled "Nature Provided Part of Our Water System." In the article Geren wrote:[66]

> One might say that nature and man got together to develop Salem's water system. Nature supplied the river, an island with plenty of sand and gravel, sufficient elevation to permit gravity flow. Man made a few changes to the island and added the pipelines. The system has worked so well over the past 22 years that last year it was merrily enlarged to satisfy today's increased demand for water.

Geren in this opening paragraph pretty well captured the essence of this wonderful "natural" water system the city owned. As a partnership of nature and "the few changes" that were man made, the city received the best drinking water quality imaginable at an economical price. The early vision of city leaders for a sweet mountain water source was a reality and everyone using this water benefitted greatly from its economical costs and its healthy quality of having no toxins or bacterial contamination.

Geren describes in his article the construction a new "infiltration system". Geren's description of the new infiltration system was:

> About 24,200 feet of perforated pipe laid in the gravel of the island and covered with selected sand and gravel comprise the collection system. Construction of the new addition involved excavating an area of about five acres to approximately the low water in the river. The natural sand and gravel formed the floor of the basin. Workmen then extended the 54 inch supply line into and along one edge of the basin. Three headers extended at right angles to the supply line at 180 foot intervals across the basin. Finally a series of 6 inch perforated corrugated iron laterals extend at right angles to the headers. These cover the entire basin at 10 foot spacing.
>
> The perforated laterals are bedded in a 6 inch layer of 1 3/4 to 3/4 inch gravel. Over this we placed 6 inches of 3/4 to 1/4 inch gravel; 6 inches of 1/4 inch to #10 gravel; and, 3 feet of sand having effective size of 0.35 mm and a uniformity coefficient of 1.75. The rate of infiltration of the new basin is 0.13 gallons per square foot per minute.

We will never know for sure, but it may have been Geren's and the design engineers' belief that the mechanism of removing the water borne sediments was the same as an infiltration gallery, or there was only simple physical straining of particles too large to pass through the sand layers. However, it was soon discovered this new sand filter had filtering capabilities far greater than anyone had imagined.

The city's 5 acre slow sand filter, after several days of operation, formed a gelatinous layer of river microorganisms on the top layers of sand. The microorganisms, primarily algae and diatoms but with many other river organisms, trapped the river turbidity and other impurities down to extremely small microscopic size. This phenomena of a "live river organism layer" was named by the Germans as the "schmutzdecke" or literally translated as "dirt", which it seems the Germans could possibly have misunderstood this living layer. The schmutzdecke is able to strain very small particles but also to make use of dissolved organic material and consume it as a food source, thus demonstrating again the incredible power of nature.

But, the schmutzdecke had operational disadvantages. Over time, as it consumed all the really delicious river stuff, it grew and grew and eventually plugged the top 1/4 to 1/2 inch of the top sand layer, and the filter rate eventually dropped to zero. This top sand layer then had to be removed and either wasted or stored for later reuse. To reuse the sand, it had to be washed and placed back down on the filter surface. The periodic removal of the top 1/2 inch of sand posed a severe operational problem for the Stayton Island staff, which was composed of just two employees.

How to scrape only 1/2 inch of sand from a five acre filter required a very inventive solution. There was nothing on the market that was designed to do this. So, the Water Department staff bought a used wheat combine and adapted it to scrape the 1/2 inch of sand. They then installed a conveyor powered by the combine to move the wasted sand to a dump truck following the combine. This cleaning operation, unfortunately, required the slow sand filter be taken off line. Raw river water was then routed to the newly cleaned slow sand filter and wasted until the filter "ripened" or a new layer of schmutzdecke growth was formed on the filter surface. During the ripening period the wasted water was monitored several times a day until the quality of the filtered water was again suitable to route to the transmission line and then to the city.

This entire process of cleaning and ripening took several days and during that time the city had to rely on the treated water from the infiltration gallery, which was limited to about 16 mgd maximum production, and stored water from Franzen Reservoir.

The Water Department was very pleased with the quality of water from the slow sand filter and the low tech simplicity of the operation. The slow sand filter was both highly effective and economical, which fit the needs of the city very well. It also produced for the first time that long sought after sweet mountain water that Salem had desired since the late 1880's.

But, it was obvious that two slow sand filters were needed for flexibility and capacity during the high water demand periods of summer and early fall.

On March 12, 1957, the City Council awarded the construction of the new transmission line to Lord Brothers. Their successful bid was $3,093,190.53. This new line would start at Stayton Island, cross the north channel of the North Santiam River, traverse the City of Stayton, and follow a parallel route of the existing 30 inch pipeline, through farm land to the City of Turner, traverse the City of Turner and end at "D" Street in Salem after paralleling the Interstate 5 route. Obviously the easement procurement for the new line was very controversial outside the City of Salem.

Cliff hanger negotiations with the City of Stayton for an easement through the city for the new 54 inch transmission line were finally concluded the week of June 2, 1957 as reported by the *Oregon Statesman* on June 9th.[67] It is not known why the contract with Lord Brothers was awarded prior to completing this agreement. Crossing through the City of Stayton was essential for a gravity line operation. Because of hilly topography the route through Stayton was the only route where gravity operation would be possible. All other routes would require expensive pumping, so this agreement with Stayton was crucial for minimizing the construction costs and later operational costs.

I assume using the philosophy of completing essential elements just in time, the agreement with the City of Stayton was completed prior to the scheduled start of construction. The agreement with the City of Stayton included the following provisions:

1. Salem agreed to install two valved outlets in Stayton and furnish Stayton surplus water when requested for 75% of the lowest rate charged any other municipality.

2. Salem agreed to indemnify Stayton up to $10,000 for any future extra expense Stayton may incur while maintaining their water and sewer system.

The *Oregon Statesman* reported on May 26, 1957 the contract with Lord Brothers for construction of the new transmission line was one of the largest in Mid Willamette Valley history. The projects they listed are shown in Table 7-1.[68]

With completion of construction in 1958, Stayton Island increased its peak capacity from 16 mgd to 66 mgd when the slow sand filter and the infiltration galleries were in simultaneous use. However, when the slow sand filter was being cleaned, Stayton Island could only supply 16 mgd (million gallons per day) which was the firm capacity. So, drawdown of reservoirs were required during peak demand periods.

TABLE 7-1
LARGE MID-WILLAMETTE VALLEY PROJECTS

| Detroit Dam | $58,899,000. in early 1950's |
| Big Cliff Dam | 6,478,000. in early 1950's |
| Salem-Portland I-5 | 6,962,000. in 1953 |
| *Stayton to Salem Pipeline* | *3,093,190. in 1957* |
| South Salem High School | 3,067,000. in 1953 |
| Meier and Frank Dept. Store | 2,400,000. in 1955 |
| Oregon Capitol Building | 2,750,000. in 1938 |
| Oregon Public Service Building | 1,700,000. in 1948 |
| Oregon Highway Building | 1,999,931. in 1950 |
| Marion County Courthouse | 1,672,156. in 1952 |

The dual transmission line to the city also had a maximum capacity of 66 mgd. In 1958 the water supply system served a population of 50,000. The new improvements were, at that time thought to be, designed to serve a population of 150,000. Salem now had a water supply system that would serve robust growth and be extremely attractive to industry wanting excellent quality water at very cheap rates. But a large need of improving the firm capacity at Stayton Island still existed. The firm capacity was the capacity with a treatment unit out of service.

Anticipating the huge increase in water supply the new transmission line will furnish, the city contracted with the Four Corners Water District (later the East Salem Water District) in 1957 and the Keizer Water District (later the City of Keizer) in 1958 to furnish them water at 125% of city water rates.

In 1964 the North Santiam flooded with persistent turbidities lasting several weeks. In those days city officials just piped the turbid waters to city customers because there was little the city could do to clarify the water. The slow sand filter was incapable of filtering water with high turbidities so the water had to bypass the treatment plant. It was chlorinated at Franzen Reservoir but received no other treatment.

The 1964 flood destroyed the wooden crib type upper Bennett Dam. The dam's function was to force the main channel of the North Santiam partially into the north channel where the city's water inlet was located, as well as the inlet of Salem Ditch and Santiam Water Control District's power canal. The city and its co-owners, Boise Cascade and Santiam Water Control District, replaced the control dam in 1966 with a concrete dam and fish ladder. During the two years the dam was out of service the city and its co-owners were forced to continue the diversion to the north channel. They accomplished this by creating a temporary gravel dam during low flow periods.

The addition of the water districts to the city system and the fast growth of Salem in the 1960's made it obvious that seat of the pants planning would no longer do, and the city needed a formal water master plan. So, in March, 1967 the city contracted with CH2M, Consulting Engineers of Corvallis, to prepare a comprehensive water master plan. The plans title *Water Distribution System Master Plan, Salem Metropolitan Area* (*1968 Plan*) projected water demands and distribution and supply requirements to the year 2000.[69]

The *1968 Plan* prepared by Fred Harem and Joe Worth was very detailed. Unfortunately, the *1968 Plan* became dated very quickly because of statewide planning requirements (Oregon Senate Bill 100 passed by the legislature in the 1970's). The *1968 Plan* assumed the future water service area for the City of Salem to be the Salem Planning Area which was proposed by the Mid-Willamette Valley Planning Council in 1965. The Salem Planning Area consisted of a 136 square mile area (where the present Urban Growth Area of Salem/Keizer is now only a little more than half of that). Population projections prepared in 1965 were also extremely high when compared to later actual populations. Therefore, with existing state planning laws the *1968 Plan* greatly over projected the future population and future water demands.

The *1968 Plan* projected the maximum day water demands as shown in Table 7-2:

The actual maximum day demands for the mid 1990's prior to strict water conservation approached 60 mgd, and approximately 55 mgd after water conservation programs were initiated in 1996. So, these projections in 1968 were extremely high.

The *1968 Plan* acknowledged that per capita water usage had greatly increased since 1938 and it would probably continue to increase. Thus the 1968 Plan had no water conservation element and assumed water would continue to be available to the city from the North Santiam River at ever increasing amounts. This type of assumption was not unusual or non professional in the 1960's, because it was the belief that water resources would not restrict the size of a city in the Willamette Valley.

TABLE 7-2
PROJECTED MAXIMUM DAY WATER DEMANDS

|                | mgd  | cfs |
| -------------- | ---- | --- |
| Existing 1967  | 46.2 | 72  |
| Projected 1982 | 78.0 | 121 |
| Projected 2001 | 64.0 | 254 |

The *1968 Plan* recommended the city acquire additional water rights on the North Santiam River and continue to use and expand Stayton Island as its primary water source. The 1968 Plan also evaluated the option of a Willamette River Treatment Plant. The consultants felt the option was technically feasible but did not recommend it because of the superior water quality in the North Santiam River.

Lastly, the *1968 Plan* recommended an additional slow sand filter was needed prior to 1976 because of population growth and peak projected water demands exceeding 66 mgd. This recommendation was based solely on the capacity of the existing Stayton Island at full production of 66 mgd, assuming the slow sand filter and the infiltration gallery are operating in parallel. However, the *1968 Plan* did not take into account the problem of greatly decreased production when the slow sand filter was off line being cleaned, and the peak supply from Stayton Island drops to 16 mgd. Therefore, it was prudent for the *1968 Plan* to recommend an immediate program of adding an additional slow sand filter to increase the firm capacity to 66 mgd.

The time schedule for a second slow sand filter recommended by CH2M posed a significant risk in supplying filtered water because of the time it took to clean the only slow sand filter. During the cleaning period the city had to rely on Franzen Reservoir and the infiltration galleries on Stayton Island. This was considered by John Geren to be an unacceptable risk to continue taking. In 1968 the Salem engineering firm of Clark and Groff was hired to investigate the current operation of the slow sand filter and to study a capacity addition to the slow sand filtration system.

In May, 1968, the City of Salem hosted the 41st Annual Conference of the Pacific Northwest Section of the American Water Works Association. John Geren was anxious to tout his "natural treatment system" of slow sand filtration. Geren produced a brochure "Water For Salem"[70] that described the Salem system for the conference attendees.

In March, 1969, Clark and Groff submitted a report "Stayton Island Filtration System — Preliminary Study Report on 50 mgd Addition." The report's main findings were:

> The study design for this report has carefully analyzed several alternatives as to site and materials in order to obtain the greatest product of high quality water at the least cost.
>
> It is our conclusion that a 50 mgd unit [a 50 mgd slow sand filter] is justified and the estimated cost of construction prior to detailed design and bidding will be approximately $400,000.
>
> In order that the addition may fit into an orderly expansion of an overall system, we have taken the liberty of suggesting a long range plan of filtration development. The long range plan visualizes an eventual production of 300 mgd from Stayton Island using a system of eight 50 mgd units constructed as the water needs for the city develops.

Clark and Groff did not include population projections in their report but roughly 300 mgd of water supply would support a population of approximately 650,000 assuming there was not a significant water conservation program. CH2M projected the Salem Planning Area population in 2002 to be about 470,000, so the Clark and Groff projection of 300 mgd would be a sufficient water supply for at least 100 years in the future. An extremely long planning horizon!

Additionally, the planned 300 mgd supply would equal 460 cfs or approximately the natural low flow of the North Santiam River. Clark and Groff assumed this quantity of water would be obtained by Salem by purchasing additional early priority water rights and purchasing stored water from the Corps of Engineers.

These early attempts at forecasting future water supply requirements by CH2M and Clark and Groff were possibly realistic with the

1960's vision of virtually unlimited water resources, the eventual growth of Salem to a large city, and that water conservation was not wanted or needed. Later, several decades later, we found these assumptions were all wrong.

The 1969 Clark and Groff report concentrated on evaluating the technical performance of the slow sand filter constructed in 1957 and to provide a design basis for the second slow sand filter. This evaluation was performed by Bill Light, an engineer with Clark and Groff and later supervisor of water production for the city. City staff always had the highest regard for Bill Light's expertise in designing and operating a slow sand filter, so the technical analysis was considered state of the art slow sand filter design.

The Clark and Groff report concluded that the city's slow sand filter had been operating satisfactorily but increased water demand required more continuous and ever increasing higher rates of filtration. The problem with the single filter was that it had to be taken out of service periodically when the top layers of the filter became clogged. (As already discussed the top layers of approximately 1/2 inch must be removed and wasted. The filter, when water is put back on top, must develop a fresh community of water organisms before the highest degree of river turbidity and other pollutants can be removed.)

The entire process of cleaning and ripening took several days and involved a degree of risk for the city if Franzen Reservoir was not able to supply the city's water demands. It was recommended a second filter be constructed to be available when a filter must be cleaned.

Clark and Groff further justified the need for a second slow sand filter as follows:

> Peak daily flows in the Salem system have nearly doubled in the 11 year period since the Stayton Island expansion was completed in 1957. In 1955 the peak daily flow was 23 mgd. In 1967 it was 43 mgd. This was an average increase of 2 mgd each year.
>
> Of equal importance, however, is the rate of increase in the 3 year period between 1964 and 1967. In this short span the 3 year increase averaged more than 3.24 mgd each year. Between 1966 and 1967 industrial consumption in the month of August increased by 44%.
>
> Thus it appears that Salem has an immediate need for increased water production, not only from the standpoint of a continuing supply during peak consumption but also to be prepared for rapidly increasing demands in the near future.

Clark and Groff presented data in their report that indicated the slow sand filters removed all coliform bacteria from the finished water. In 1968, the only day that tested for coliform in the filtered water was after a long filter run. Once the filter was cleaned, it continued to remove all coliform. However, the infiltration galleries when used were not as efficient. On some days the infiltration galleries removed all coliform bacteria but on about 60% of the days coliform bacteria passed through the infiltration galleries. Even so, on 100% of days all coliform were killed by the chlorination system. This further justified the construction of the second slow sand filter with less reliance on the infiltration gallery.

In 1971 the construction of the second slow sand filter was completed. This gave the city a much needed redundancy in filter capacity and created a "firm" capacity of 50 mgd from slow sand filtration with one filter off line with an additional 16 mgd from the infiltration galleries available during emergencies.

Figure 7-1 shows the supply system and reservoirs existing in 1971. Figure 7-2 shows the Stayton Island system existing in 1971 after construction of the second slow sand filter.

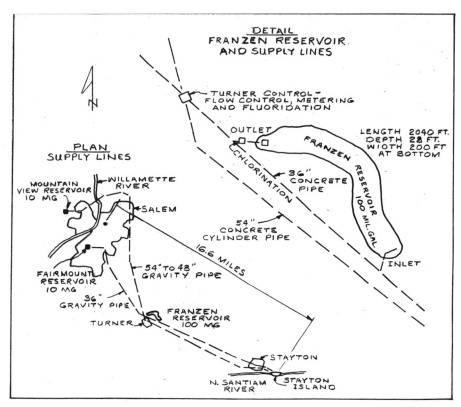

FIGURE 7-1: Transmission supply pipelines from Stayton Island to the City of Salem (on the left), and Franzen Reservoir with its supply pipelines and control structures (at upper right).

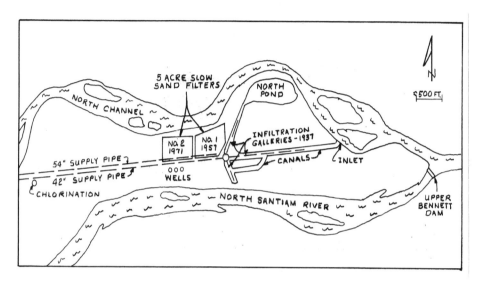

FIGURE 7-2: Stayton Island after major improvements were completed in 1971 with the construction of the second slow sand filter.

# Chapter 8
## Water Rights Purchases
## 1960's and 1970's

In 1962 the city owned 82 cfs or 53 mgd of water rights on the North Santiam River. The 22 cfs water right had a priority date of 1923 and the 60 cfs water right acquired from Oregon Pulp and Paper Company had a priority date of 1856.

CH2M in their *1968 Water Distribution System Master Plan* forecast a maximum day demand of 121 cfs (78 mgd) by 1982, just 20 years away. This forecast greatly exceeded the owned water rights. In 1962 the city was still actively negotiating an agreement with the Corps of Engineers to purchase about 175 cfs (113 mgd) of stored water at Detroit Dam. This would have satisfied the city's demand for North Santiam River water for many years in the future. This purchase would have been the city's ace in the hole, because the purchase of early water rights seemed very remote. However, as discussed previously the city found with extreme disappointment that stored water purchases were far too expensive for municipal purposes and concluded their negotiations with the Corps.

In 1962 the city approached the Marion County Investment Company with the possibility that the city purchase some of their 812 cfs, 1866 rights. Marion County Investment Company acquired the water right when they purchased the holdings of the A.D. Gardner estate. The possible availability of these rights came in an around about way. The North Santiam water adjudication proceedings of 1945 awarded to A.D. Gardner the right to 812 cfs of diverted North Santiam River water for power and manufacturing use with a priority date of 1866. Later, Marion County Investment Company acquired the 812 cfs right.

In 1962 the city negotiated the purchase of 50 cfs from Marion County Investment Company for $30,000 with the contingency the state engineer would approve a change of use to a municipal consumptive right.[71]

On October 8, 1962, State Engineer Chris Webber, agreed to a change in use of the 50 cfs 1866 water right to municipal purposes, including place of use and point of diversion. The place of use was the water customers of the City of Salem and the point of diversion was Stayton Island. This acquisition was of great importance to the City of Salem. It increased the city's North Santiam water rights to 132 cfs or 85 mgd, which with CH2M's projections would be sufficient to last for at least 20 years assuming a rapid growth rate.

In 1966 Marion County Investment Company sold the remaining 762 cfs of the original A.D. Gardner power and manufacturing rights to the Santiam Water Control District, a farming cooperative in the Stayton area.

On January 27, 1976, John Geren proposed by letter to the Santiam Water Control District the possibility of the city purchasing 100 cfs of their 1909 priority water rights.[72] Santiam Water Control District acquired the 1909 rights from their predecessor, the Willamette Valley Water Company, around 1955. Willamette Valley Water Company acquired the rights as a result of the 1945 North Santiam adjudication proceedings. They were awarded 300 cfs of inchoate rights which means the water company had no rights to the water until they had put it to beneficial use. There was some doubt when Geren made his offer of just how much of the original 300 cfs inchoate right had been perfected and therefore could be sold.

Geren also proposed to the Santiam Water Control District that they could replace the 100 cfs right at a very economical price by purchasing stored water from the Corps of Engineers at Detroit Reservoir. Geren wrote:

> Such an arrangement would place cash in the hands of the District in exchange for a future obligation to purchase water at a very low price. If this proposition has any interest to you, we would welcome an opportunity to discuss it further with you.

On February 18, 1976 David Drews, Secretary-Treasurer of the District wrote back to Geren. Mr. Drews wrote the District Board is receptive to enter into negotiations on selling 50 cfs with the option open for additional amounts later. He wrote:[73]

> The Board recognizes the city's need to secure additional water for

future growth in the area and are willing to work with the city to achieve the greatest overall benefits for the region.

This statement of the Santiam Water Control Board showed that a high degree of cooperation existed in 1976 between farming interests and the urban interests of the City of Salem.

In July, 1976, John Geren in a memorandum to City Manager Robert Moore, indicated his disappointment of being able to purchase only 50 cfs instead of the preferred 100 cfs. Geren was as always planning and thinking about the next required improvement of the water supply system. He told Moore in his memorandum:[74]

> While I am disappointed that we can not complete the purchase as planned, I feel we should proceed immediately to purchase the first 50 cfs at the $4,000 per cfs price offered.
>
> Purchase of only 50 cfs carries some risk to the city. Our present rights are almost exactly equal to our present pipeline capacities. It would not be economic to construct another supply line of only 50 cfs capacity. To construct a new line, which must be started within next few years of 100 cfs capacity will carry the gamble of being able, by some means, to acquire the remaining 50 cfs by the time it is needed.

Geren's math at this point seems a little faulty. The city in 1976 had water rights of 134 cfs (86 mgd) and pipeline capacity to the City of Salem of 102 cfs (66 mgd). He was correct that in 1976, at present city growth rates, the pipeline capacity will soon be exhausted because of high peak days during hot summer days and the lack of a well communicated water conservation program.

The proposed agreement with the Santiam Water Control District with Salem paying $200,000 for 50 cfs of water rights disturbed many Salem residents. These residents still believed wells in the city would be more economical than continuing with the North Santiam River as Salem's water source. On August 24, 1976 the *Oregon Statesman* defended the North Santiam water source. They reiterated that North Santiam water with its gravity supply was less expensive than drilling wells and the high operational costs for the pumps.[75]

By September, 1976 a tentative agreement had been negotiated between the city and the district. The city would purchase 50 cfs at a price of $200,000. The city would also have the first right of refusal to purchase an additional 50 cfs at the highest offer received by the district.

However, the tentative agreement was put into doubt by B.T. Van Wormer, Director of the combined Utilities/Public Works Department. Van Wormer had been the long time Director of the Public Works Department. When John Geren retired as Utilities Department Director, the city decided to create a "super" department by combining the two departments. Geren was then acting as a contract advisor to Van Wormer on utilities' matters.

Van Wormer requested the following provision be added to the tentative agreement, because he felt the district may not have a perfected water right for the 50 cfs:

> That the water right herein conveyed has been perfected by the District through beneficial use and is valid, available and transferrable to and useable by the City of Salem for its domestic and municipal needs.

This action of Van Wormer to protect the city's interests led to information from the Oregon Water Resources Department that stopped further negotiations. Further research showed that the full 300 cfs inchoate 1909 water right was never fully perfected by the district. The perfected part of this right was attached to the land that was irrigated and the landowner would need to be a party to the agreement of sale.

The land owner approval killed the deal. The individual land owners were unwilling to sell and the district had nothing to sell without the landowners approval. So, this ended the negotiation that seemed very promising at first but ended in failure due to both parties not understanding the nature of the district's rights.

In concluding the failed acquisition of the 1909 water rights, Herb Arnold, sanitary engineer, with the Utilities-Public Works Department and a past assistant to John Geren in the Utilities Department, wrote to B.T. Van Wormer as follows:[76]

> Both Mr. Karver and Mr. Jones of the State Water Resources Department think the city could more realistically negotiate with Boise Cascade who is the remaining claimant to some 240 cfs of old rights for power and manufacturing which antedate the 1909 rights being 1856 rights. They survive from Woolen Mills power, Ice Plant power and Oregon Pulp Manufacturing. If they could be acquired and the use changed to municipal, we could divert at the Island, treat and bring down in a pipe. We could bring down in Mill Creek and treat here if

we want to undertake defending Mill Creek from poachers during irrigation season. This would eliminate pipeline costs of $8 to 10 million.

There are some 1000 to 1200 cfs flow available in the Willamette and I have obtained application forms for appropriating. We should apply and establish a claim just to cover what may develop into the most feasible route to Salem with its future peak water supply.

Herb Arnold with this memorandum was passing on to the director, Van Wormer, a great idea offered by the State Water Resources Department staff—go after the 1856 water rights owned by Boise Cascade Corporation!

Commenting on Herb Arnold's memorandum: staff had still not bought into a policy that the best water quality should dictate the future water supply improvements for the City of Salem. Mr. Arnold was still considering a conventional water treatment plant that would be very expensive to build and operate which would treat either Willamette River water or, worse yet, treat North Santiam River water polluted by farm runoff, routed down Mill Creek to a treatment plant in Salem.

Boise Cascade's 1856 power and manufacturing water rights were inherited from their predecessor, Oregon Pulp and Paper Company. The 254 cfs water rights came about with the 1945 North Santiam River adjudication decisions. This decision granted 254 cfs with an 1856 priority date to south power (Mill Race) and north power (Mill Creek). The 60 cfs obtained by the city from Oregon Pulp and Paper Company was north power rights that were owned exclusively by Oregon Pulp and Paper who inherited these rights from Willamette Woolen Manufacturing Company. However, South Power was much more complex. In proportioning the 254 cfs, a total of 172 cfs right was assigned to south power. This 172 cfs right was owned as undivided equal interest by Oregon Pulp and Paper, Thomas Kay Woolen Mills, and the City of Salem.

Therefore what Boise Cascade now owned was the right to use the 172 cfs to produce power and to use for manufacturing purposes after Thomas Kay Woolen Mills and the City of Salem had previously used the same water to produce power.

That said, lets go back to Herb Arnold's memorandum to Van Wormer and see how Van Wormer responded. In January, 1977 Van Wormer asked staff to take action on the following:

1. Investigate Boise Cascade's water rights and future needs.

2. Open negotiations with Boise Cascade.
3. Set a meeting with the State Water Resources Department.
4. Find out what became of the city's 1/3 undivided interest in the 172 cfs south power.

The above questions prompted the City Attorney, Bill Juza, to hire a law student, Paul Silver, to research and report on current water rights on the North Santiam River and the status of South Power water rights. On June 9, 1977 Silver submitted his final report. His findings for South Power rights follow: [77]

In 1959 the Thomas Kay Woolen Mill forfeited all rights to the waters of South Power due to nonuse. Several years later, the City of Salem abandoned its power plant alongside South Power.

Oregon law expressly provides that a municipality cannot forfeit water rights simply by nonuse. The law further provides, however, that the non-forfeiture provision applies only to water used by a municipality for "all reasonable and usual municipal uses", and thus it is the position of the Water Resources Department that (1) the city's former use of the waters of South Power to operate its power plant is not a "reasonable and usual municipal use", and therefore (2) the city forfeited its rights in South Power when it abandoned its power plant during the 1960's.

The issue however, has little practical significance. Boise Cascade today holds the right to 162 second feet in the water flowing through South Power, and thus any application filed by the City for a change of use from power and manufacturing to consumption would first have to meet with Boise Cascade's approval regardless whether or not the City still holds an interest in the water. Moreover, in the event the City decided at some future date to reestablish a power plant on South Power, it seems rather unlikely that the City's action would be disputed by either Boise Cascade or the Water Resources Department, since this would not in the least affect the free flow of the water in South Power.

One final change in the nature of the rights in South Power should be noted. In 1971, pursuant to its efforts to beautify the new Salem Civic Center, the City entered into an agreement with Boise Cascade by which 10 of the 172 second feet of water held by Boise Cascade in South Power were transferred to the City. The transfer was subsequently approved by the Water Resources Department. This 10 second feet of water is diverted from South Power into the ponds around the

Civic Center and thereafter into Pringle Creek, eventually to be deposited in the Willamette River.

Silver also discussed the possibility of Salem acquiring part of Boise Cascade's South Power rights as follows:

> Boise Cascade currently holds a power and manufacturing right to 162 second feet of water in South Power. This could be an important new source of water for the City, assuming that Boise Cascade is willing to sell all or part of it. The right carries an extremely favorable priority date of 1856. Moreover officials of the Water Resources Department have orally given their assurance that, on the basis of facts now within their knowledge, they would not object if the City sought to acquire and change the use of the right from power and manufacturing to consumption. Naturally the flow of water in South Power will be reduced to the extent that water is withdrawn from it for purposes of consumption.

In July, 1977 Van Wormer met to discuss strategies for the purchase of a portion of Boise Cascade's 1856 water right with City Attorney, Bill Juza, Herb Arnold, and Paul Silver. At first city staff believed only 125 cfs would be available because Boise Cascade was unable, using the Mill Race flume, to transport more than that amount to their plant. However, after much discussion and negotiations with Jim Fahlstrom, manager of the Salem Boise Cascade Plant, 62 cfs or 40 mgd was offered to the city at $2,000 per cfs. Boise Cascade chose to retain the remaining water rights which could be as much as 100 cfs (but probably less due to nonuse).

The city accepted the Boise Cascade offer on July 24, 1978 contingent on the Water Resources Department approving a change in the diversion to Stayton Island and a change in use to municipal consumption. On July 27, 1978 an article in the *Oregon Statesman* by Lance Dickie had a positive tone. The article follows:[78]

> City of Salem's growing thirst has been quenched well into the next century. City officials Wednesday purchased North Santiam River water rights from Boise Cascade Corporation that will add 40 million gallons a day to the city water supply.
>
> Mayor Kent Aldrich, who signed the agreement on behalf of the city, estimated the purchase will satisfy Salem's water needs to the year 2020. "It's not the most sexy thing, but it means a great deal to

the community," Aldrich said. The deal, which concluded seven months of negotiations, gives the city rights to 62 cfs of North Santiam River water.

Boise Cascade will be paid $124,000 for the water rights. "It's just a super deal," Aldrich said of the sale price.

Boise Cascade has water rights previously held by the Thomas Kay Woolen Mills and Oregon Pulp and Paper Company that date back to 1856. Water is fed into the Boise Cascade plant by way of a flume that runs along Pringle Creek north of the Civic Center. The company sold 62 of the 162 cfs of North Santiam River water it owns.

Salem's 30 year effort to buy North Santiam water rights from the U.S. Corps of Engineers has been unsuccessful.

The sale still must be approved by the State Water Resources Board which reviews changes in water use and in points of water diversion.

During hot summers, peak water use has pushed the 55 million gallon per day mark for the past several years. Officials feared the city's population growth, combined with water sales to two suburban water districts would outstrip water supply in the next few years. Wednesday's agreement solves most of those worries.

"It's good" Herb Arnold said of the water rights purchase. "We can plan better."

And, Herb Arnold, the Utilities/Public Works Department key staff person for water planning and utilities engineering, was correct. This purchase brought the total water rights the city owned on the North Santiam River to 194 cfs or 125 mgd which assured the city with sufficient water rights to serve more than double the present population of Salem. Salem was now very rich in the earliest priority water rights on the North Santiam.

As expected, on October 6, 1978, the Water Resources Department Director James Sexton approved the change of ownership, the point of diversion, and the change in use to municipal consumption for the entire 62 cfs.

In 1976 the city contracted with Stevens, Thompson and Runyon, Engineers and Planners, from Portland to update the *1968 Water Distribution System Master Plan*. Their report "Future Water Source, Supply and Distribution"[79] was submitted to the city in April, 1977.

For what reason the city authorized this update of the water master plan at this time is very much a mystery. With the 1971 improvements at Stayton Island, the city had a firm treatment capacity (one filter assumed out of service) of 66 mgd which was matched with 66 mgd of transmission pipeline capacity to Salem. In 1976 the peak day demand was in the lower 50 mgd range without any water conservation program and with very economical water rates.

It appeared in 1976 the supply system had a capacity that would not be exceeded for many years. However, Stevens, Thompson and Runyon correlated peak month demands with housing values and population. They then forecast the peak day demand with this model for the year 2000 to be 109 mgd.

The consultants recommended that the city consider one of two options as follows:

> 1. Continued reliance on the North Santiam River and Stayton Island treatment as Salem's only source of water.
> 2. Continued utilization of the present facilities on the North Santiam River with additional future supplies coming first from wells along the Willamette River and second, from further expansion of the North Santiam River facilities.

The consultants then recommended: the first major improvement should be a $4,800,000 transmission line (a 54 inch line from Turner control to the Four Corners area in East Salem) will be needed almost immediately if wells are not developed along the Willamette River. The city should proceed with the test drilling program and use the results of this program in the evaluation of the two options for a future water supply.

In my opinion, the bottom line is the city should not have accepted this report. First, an additional water transmission line was clearly not needed for many years in the future. Second, the use of the specialized wells recommended by the consultants with perforated collectors running out from a large well casing was certainly a water quality disaster. The Willamette River was still very polluted and the only treatment the water would receive would be the filtering action of the bottom sediments and sand of the Willamette River. The Salem Water Company tried this back in the 1930's on Minto Island only to find the water quality was horrible, to say the least.

This brings us back to why the city applied for Willamette River water rights. Since the water entering the proposed wells and collectors was considered a surface water, the city needed a surface water right on the Willamette. In December, 1976 the city applied for a 200 cfs or 129 mgd water right. In 1981 the State Water Resources Department granted the permit with a priority date of 1976. As of 2003 this water right has never been used and the city probably will never be able to perfect it. (Unless the Community Services Department uses it to irrigate the very thirsty Riverfront Park turf. This park is now being irrigated with city drinking water at no cost to the parks system.)

Other than the acquisition of the Willamette River water rights, the Stevens, Thompson and Runyon report was never used by the public works department.

# Chapter 9
## Water Wars
### Along Salem Ditch

The City of Salem with little controversy or competition was able in 1978 to purchase 62 cfs of 1856 high priority water rights from Boise Cascade. However, who will be able to acquire Boise Cascade's remaining 100 cfs of early water rights produced several contenders.

In the mid-1980's the City of Salem, the City of Stayton, and the Santiam Water Control District went to war over two issues: first, who will own and maintain Salem Ditch; and, second, why was Salem trying to purchase and hog all of the remaining 1856 water rights owned by Boise Cascade?

There is an old saying in the western United States: "whiskey is for drinkin' and water is for fightin'." The stage was set for fightin' when in the early 1980's Boise Cascade decided to close their pulp and paper operation in Salem. Boise Cascade still owned 100 cfs of prime 1856 priority water rights for power and manufacturing use. They also owned Salem Ditch.

Salem Ditch was dug in 1856 with plows, shovels and wagons primarily by Chinese labor. It followed a natural swale created when the North Santiam River overflowed during floods, so the 1856 work created a constant gravity flowing diversion from the North Santiam River to Mill Creek. The work was funded by the Willamette Woolen Manufacturing Company so Mill Creek would maintain high flows year round for power purposes.

The Oregon Territorial Government then proceeded to grant Willamette Woolen Manufacturing Company the right for the full flow of the North Santiam River. Lucky for the downstream pioneers and the wildlife on the North Santiam that the new Salem Ditch would only divert a fraction of the full North Santiam flow! Boise Cascade, the eventual successor of Willamette Woolen Manufacturing Company, inherited these water rights.

The City of Salem had purchased 60 cfs from Boise's predecessor,

Oregon Pulp and Paper Company in 1951, and 62 cfs from Boise Cascade in 1978. When the decision was made to close the Boise pulp and paper operation, Salem naturally felt they had the inside track in purchasing these remaining valuable 1856 water rights and Salem Ditch.

Figure 9-1 shows the location of Salem Ditch as it diverts water from the north channel of the North Santiam River, winds its way through the City of Stayton and progresses northward to intersect with Mill Creek.

Figure 9-2 is a photograph of Salem Ditch within the City of Stayton.

Now enter the City of Stayton. They desperately needed more North Santiam River early priority water rights and, just as important, wanted to preserve the flows in Salem Ditch which was a highly aesthetic, valued creek flowing through the center of the city.

To complicate this even more, now enter the Santiam Water Control District. Over the years the district built a complex system of interconnected irrigation ditches serving customers from Salem Ditch (which was owned by Boise Cascade). The district at this time was unhappy that Boise Cascade was not maintaining the ditch and they were having to do the necessary maintenance.

So, all the players were present and all desired to remedy their own shortcomings by getting a piece of this highly prized early water right. In late 1982 the author participated in negotiations with Jim Falstrom, the manager of Boise Cascade in Salem, to purchase for the City of Salem both the 100 cfs water right and Salem Ditch.

In December, 1982, to make this competition even more interesting, Stayton Canning Company requested Boise Cascade include them in a bidding process for the water rights. They desired to purchase 20 cfs of the 100 cfs water right. In a letter from Gary Inbrie of Stayton Canning to Jim Falstrom, Mr. Inbrie stated he had met with Frank Mauldin of the City of Salem and that Mr. Mauldin informed him the City of Salem desired to purchase the entire 100 cfs water right, and that Jim Falstrom had verbally agreed to sell the entire right to the City of Salem. He further added that Mr. Mauldin told him the City of Salem would be agreeable to allow Stayton Canning the right to use the water for non-consumptive uses.

Stayton Canning, a large food processing cooperative, operated large canning and frozen food processing plants in both Stayton and Salem. At their Stayton plant, they had been using water from Salem Ditch to cool refrigeration equipment. So, the author's offer for non-

consumptive use of the water right was the start of a long process of
negotiation and conflict over the future ownership of these valuable,
early priority water rights.

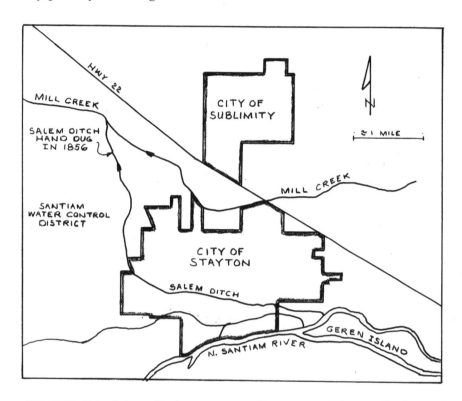

FIGURE 9-1: Salem ditch starts as a diversion of the north channel
of the North Santiam River, then travels across the City of Stayton as
an urban creek, crosses farm land and then empties into Mill Creek.

On December 20, 1982 the Salem City Council received a staff report through Ralph Hanley, City Manager and from Ronald J. Merry,
Public Works Director.[80] The reports advised the City Council on ongoing staff work regarding the intended purchase of the 100 cfs water
right. Staff reported negotiations would begin at $2,000 per cfs. The
City Council approved the staff recommendation.

The City of Salem had now made it clear with a public staff report
its intention to purchase the entire 100 cfs and to offer Boise Cascade
$2,000 per cfs. This left the door open for the competing interests to

contact Boise Cascade and make a bidding war out of the process, if that was what Boise Cascade desired. However, it was the opinion of City of Salem staff that Boise did not want to enter into a bidding process, but, being a Salem industry would allow Salem the first right of refusal on the price set by Boise.

FIGURE 9-2: Salem Ditch as an urban creek inside the City of Stayton.

In the meantime Salem staff investigated the ownership and maintenance costs of Salem Ditch and other facilities owned by Boise Cascade related to diversion dams on the North Santiam and Mill Creek. James Sexton, Oregon Water Resources Department Director, was consulted regarding verification of the size of the existing water right. Was it still 100 cfs or had Boise lost some of the right due to nonuse? In the meantime a draft agreement for purchase of the water right was sent to Boise Cascade for their review.

On May 26, 1983 an article appeared in the *Stayton Mail* reporting the City of Stayton also wanted to negotiate for the Boise Cascade water right. George Hall, city engineer for Stayton and formerly an engineer for the City of Salem, proposed a provocative theory to the City of Stayton City Council. The *Stayton Mail's* article on Hall's theory follows:[81]

> STAYTON - City officials here have been authorized to proceed
> with negotiations to acquire Boise Cascade's rights to water in the
> Salem Ditch. Authorization came in the form of a Council directive
> Monday night after the city council discussed the possible ramifica-
> tions of the purchase of those water rights by the City of Salem.
>
> George Hall, city engineer, told the council Boise Cascade wants to
> dispose of water rights to 100 cubic feet per second. "We would be
> looking for about 20 cfs," Hall said. The city has looked at other
> ways of increasing the municipal water supply and "none of them
> look too optimistic," Hall said.
>
> The City of Salem, Hall said, also is negotiating with Boise Cas-
> cade for water rights. Salem, he said, "apparently wants all or
> nothing." Hall suggested that buying 100 percent of the water rights
> would "probably guarantee a deed to the ditch, pretty much right
> through the center of the city." Boise Cascade owns the ditch bed
> through Stayton except for a portion owned by Wilco Farmers and
> Cocky Dozler.
>
> Hall advanced a theory that Salem plans to extend a pipeline
> from Four Corners through Turner and Aumsville. If Salem owned the
> ditch he said, it would extend its pipeline up the ditch to the river
> and dry up the flow of the ditch.
>
> Salem has told Stayton Canning "they want control over what
> goes into the ditch," Hall reported. An estimated 60 to 70 percent of
> Stayton's storm sewers drain into the ditch. "What you're telling us
> is, they could tell us to take our storm drainage?" Mayor Porter
> asked. "That's right," Hall said.
>
> To substantiate his theory, Hall said Salem has awarded an engi-
> neering contract for a pipeline from Four Corners to Turner. "They
> need the water rights to justify the cost of buying the ditch."
>
> "Is there any reason for us not to start negotiations?" asked council-
> man Dick Morle. "No," Hall said. "Then we've already spent too
> much time talking about it," Morle responded.
>
> The council agreed city staff should begin negotiating for the wa-
> ter rights.

Hall's testimony to the Stayton City Council certainly was startling
and if it were correct would mean Salem's intentions were indeed not
designed to foster good intercity relations. Even worse it would indicate Salem had no interest at all in preserving both a valuable aes-

thetic amenity, and a necessary part of the Stayton drainage infrastructure, as well as preserving an invaluable part of the irrigation system for the Santiam Water Control District. It would also mean that Salem would cut off early water right diversions to Mill Creek via Salem Ditch and therefore virtually dry up Mill Creek through Salem in the summer time.

Was Hall correct in his assertions? Only on one point. Salem did desire to own the entire 100 cfs water right. However, Salem did not want to dry up Salem Ditch. The water right diversion to Mill Creek via Salem Ditch was an equally valuable aesthetic amenity in Salem as well as providing sufficient flows in Mill Creek to continue to support abundant fish life. The City of Salem as well as Willamette University had spent large amounts of funds to beautify the Mill Race and the Mirror Pond at the Civic Center. Obviously the City of Salem had an intense interest in maintaining and even increasing the flow in Salem Ditch, and certainly had no motivation in drying up the ditch. Enough said.

In June, 1983 Stayton Canning Company's Jerry Butler wrote to Sue Miller, Mayor of Salem, requesting a non-consumptive use of 20 cfs of the 100 cfs future Salem water right diverted to Salem Ditch. Mayor Harris Miller answered and said it was the intention of the City of Salem to grant this non-consumptive use after the City had obtained the water rights from Boise Cascade. This apparently satisfied Stayton Canning Company and they dropped their pursuit of the Boise Cascade water rights. Stayton Canning Company's negotiations with the city was conducted by Jerry Butler, a very colorful man of language and dress. He frequently wore a green bean colored suit and was very popular with the Salem City Council because of his wit and engaging personality.

On August 1, 1983 the Salem City Council approved an agreement with Boise Cascade for purchasing the 100 cfs 1856 water right for $2,000 per cfs which included the purchase of Salem Ditch, the Mill Race, and all the control structures in the system. After several weeks of clarifying the agreement with Boise Cascade, the two parties signed the agreement. Russ Abolt, City Manager, then wrote to Jim Sexton and requested a transfer of Boise Cascade's power and manufacturing right to municipal consumptive use and a change of diversion to Stayton Island (which was now named Geren Island to honor John Geren's long term contributions to the water system).

On January 3, 1984 the city received a letter from Samuel Allison that the Oregon Water Resources Department needed proof that

Boise Cascade still had 100 cfs of water rights. Mr. Allison wrote:

> The water used for power generation and the water used for non-con-
> sumptive uses within the mill cannot be transferred to a consumptive
> use. So that the consumptive use can be calculated. Records should be
> submitted showing the amounts of water withdrawn and returned to
> the stream at the mill.

Uh-oh, this was a surprise for the city and Boise Cascade! The
rules must have changed, because in 1978 and 1951 when the City
purchased Boise Cascade water rights, this condition was not brought
up. Could it have been that the water resources staff knew this purchase by the City of Salem would be contested and a very strict interpretation of rules would be necessary?

Meanwhile the City of Salem staff headed by Dave Prock ran into
delay after delay in getting the required data from Boise Cascade. Finally after a year and a half Boise Cascade supplied the needed information which was not good. On June 3, 1985 Salem staff informed
the City Council that only 55 cfs had been of consumptive use by
Boise Cascade and this was the maximum water right that could be
transferred to the city. The City Council then approved a revised
agreement for purchase of 55 cfs for $110,000.

In August, 1985 after receiving the city's revised application for
transfer of 55 cfs, the water resources department notified the city
that prior to approving the transfer the proposal needed to be published in a newspaper. They stated that if a protest was filed, then a
hearing would be held and the water resources director would make a
decision within 60 days.

On October 25, 1985 the City of Stayton filed a formal protest for
transferring the water right. The protest was signed by Wayne Lieberman, Mayor of Stayton. His letter follows:

> The City of Stayton has shown great interest in acquiring a portion
> of the water right that is subject of the above referenced application.
> After unsuccessfully trying to talk to both parties, Stayton filed a let-
> ter in 1983 requesting notice of any applications regarding these water
> rights. Unfortunately, notice of the current proceedings came just prior
> to finalization of the transaction between Boise Cascade and the City
> of Salem. Stayton wanted very much to be a part of these proceedings
> and is now compelled to file a protest under the circumstances. Were
> these water rights part of the land purchase and exchange between

the two parties?

Stayton's goal is to acquire 10 cfs of the total amount of water right that is being transferred to the City of Salem. Stayton has demonstrated need to acquire the additional 10 cfs in order to serve their urban growth boundary during their planning period to the year 2005. Does the City of Salem have a demonstrated need for the extra water and should they be allowed to acquire all the available surplus from Boise Cascade?

Beyond the basic goal of acquiring 10 cfs , the City of Stayton has some serious concerns that need to be addressed before any transaction is finalized.

1. NEW POINTS OF DIVERSION

The City of Salem is proposing to divert the subject water from the Salem Ditch to Stayton Island. If the proposed 55 cfs is diverted, this would decrease Salem Ditch's flow through the City of Stayton by approximately 50%. Stayton is very concerned about what impact this action would have on Mill Creek and the vicinity.

The decreased flow would have a negative impact on Stayton's recreational use of the Salem Ditch that Stayton has enjoyed since the 1880's. There would also be an adverse affect on fish habitat as well as the aesthetic value of the Ditch.

Also, what effect would this have on the Santiam Water Control District if 55 cfs they now use for irrigation on the easterly end of the Salem Ditch and replacing downstream, if diverted at the Stayton Island and not available at the existing point of diversion?

2. OWNERSHIP OF THE RELEVANT WATER RIGHTS

It is the City of Stayton's understanding that the water right is an undivided 1/3 interest between Boise Cascade, the City of Salem and Thomas Kay Woolen Mills. We can not see that Thomas Kay Woolen Mills' interest has been represented in the proceedings. The City of Stayton also wants a stay of the proceedings pending a determination of exactly how many cfs have been abandoned by Boise Cascade and how many are available for transfer.

3. OWNERSHIP OF THE STREAM BED

The City of Stayton understands that the City of Salem is trying to acquire the stream bed property of the Salem Ditch. We feel there is a substantial question regarding the underlying ownership of the stream bed that needs to be cleared up before any transaction takes place. And if Salem does acquire the Salem Ditch stream bed and bank, Stayton wants to know what Salem intends to do with the property. The City of Stayton will strongly oppose any attempts to restrict access to the Ditch.

4. CONSUMPTIVE vs POWER AND MANUFACTURING RIGHTS

Boise Cascade's Certificate of Water Right indicates that the subject right is the purpose of power and manufacturing. It appears that Salem is trying to acquire these rights as consumptive rights. It is our understanding that these classifications can not be converted from one to another.

These are the City of Stayton's concerns which need to be addressed before any transaction is finalized.

Mayor Lieberman's letter was intended to be a formal protest of the transfer of water rights to the City of Salem. In the author's opinion it was an excellent comprehensive stating of legitimate City of Stayton's needs and concerns. But, the letter of protest amounted to a declaration of war that appeared at this time to have no compromises on the horizon.

The City of Stayton, however, did have a powerful ally in the Santiam Water Control District.

The district weighed in on October 29, 1985. Dan Wilson, manager of the district, consistent with his communication style, lobbed a written grenade with a letter to the State Water Resources Department. Wilson's letter expressed concern about who will own and maintain Salem Ditch. He said in the past the district has done minor maintenance on the ditch and the owner, Boise Cascade, had reimbursed the district for their costs.

However, his real concern was obviously that the new owner would be the City of Salem, and his relationship with Salem had been rather rocky of late. In a letter to the Water Resources Department he wrote:

> The Santiam Water Control District has been using the Ditch since 1968 to deliver water to 1500 plus acres. We would like to continue this operation without the fear that the City of Salem will use the stream bed for some other use.

Wilson was of course appealing to the Water Resources Department to help him because the district was very dependent on Salem Ditch to supply irrigation water to a large part of the district for which they had no legal right to use. They did not own, have easements nor had they made agreements to use the ditch. It was little wonder that Wilson was concerned.

On December 12th James Carver of the Water Resources Department wrote to Ellis Vandehey, City Administrator of Stayton, and informed him Stayton's protest did not provide statutory grounds for a protest, because Stayton's water rights would not be jeopardized by the transfer. He did leave Stayton some hope by writing that the Water Resources Department had no objection to delaying action on the transfer if the parties would like some time to work out issues.

Salem staff were at this point taken back by the accusations and tone of the protests by Stayton and the Santiam Water Control District. Staff were disturbed that both parties believed Salem would attempt to change the present and historical uses of the ditch. But Salem staff did agree the protests brought up one excellent point—that in the far distant future all the early water rights that once flowed down Salem Ditch and then to Mill Creek for use by Salem industry for power and manufacturing would eventually be diverted at Geren Island and piped to Salem.

This meant that only a total of 32 cfs were permanently dedicated for diversion to Salem Ditch and then Mill Creek. The 32 cfs came about because Boise Cascade donated 10 cfs in 1971 of its South Power rights for the use of supplying the mirror pond at the new Civic Center. The remaining 22 cfs was donated by the Methodist Home in 1971 for recreational use. This 22 cfs was part of the 82 cfs allocated to North Power. The Methodist Home inherited this right from Salem Ice Works, a previous power user on the North Power (Mill Creek).

So, with this astounding revelation that in some distant future Mill Creek would only have 32 cfs of diverted water from the North Santiam, the lights finally went on with the smart guys at Salem City Hall. They finally understood the issues that Stayton and the Santiam Water Control District had because Salem would face the same problem of insufficient future flows in Salem Ditch and Mill Creek. (This certainly proves that to have empathy for someone's else's problem, you probably have to experience it yourself. These empathetic experiences can broaden understanding between organizations, even governments.)

On November 6, 1985 the City of Salem applied for a 70 cfs water right to divert North Santiam River water to Salem Ditch and then to Mill Creek. The intended use of the water right was for maintaining minimum stream flows for aesthetic and wildlife purposes.

This noble action, however, awakened a sleeping giant. Well, maybe it was a mini-giant, the Oregon Department of Fish and Wildlife (ODFW). On December 24, 1985 ODFW weighed in on the water right application. They recommended the city maintain a minimum flow of 50 cfs in both Mill Creek and a parallel Salem waterway, Shelton Ditch, for salmon spawning purposes.

The application for the 70 cfs water right languished for one and a half years while the city and ODFW sparred on how to manage flows in Mill Creek and Shelton Ditch. The origin of Shelton Ditch is a little murky as to who created it and when it was created. It serves as an overflow for Mill Creek and to prevent flooding from lower intensity storms in downstream Mill Creek. After construction it started acting as a natural creek year round and became an excellent spawning area for salmon, thus the interest of ODFW in maintaining adequate flows. However, the City of Salem was reluctant to take on the responsibility of managing flows in both systems because of liability during flood events.

The city finally agreed to a flow control structure where flow would be split between Mill Creek and Shelton Ditch during low flows but not managing the flows further during flood events. The city also agreed to take responsibility of Waller Dam, the flow control structure for Mill Creek waters entering the Mill Race. The city also agreed to maintain the fish ladders at Waller Dam.

ODFW was also concerned about the lack of a full fish screen at the entrance of the Mill Race. Boise Cascade had installed a fish screen at this location at some point in the past but had removed it because of the maintenance problems it created. ODFW was requesting the city install another fish screen because fish that entered the Mill Race became trapped and had no downstream outlet.

Pete Meuleveld, the current Boise Cascade manager, responded as to why Boise had removed the fish screen. He wrote the following to Dave Siegel of public works staff:

> As we have discussed, it is our recollection that the fish screen at the 19th Street diversion point [to the Mill Race] was discontinued and taken out of service about 1977. The reason we took the screen out was the Fish and Game Commission [ODFW] was no longer propagating salmon at Cascade Gateway Park. Thus there was no longer a need for any screen.

Dave Siegel also had a telephone conversation with Carson Poe, a past employee of Boise Cascade. Siegel's notes quoting Mr. Poe follow:

When the fish propagation was discontinued, Boise Cascade contacted Fish and Wildlife and asked if the screen could be removed. They were told it would be fine to remove it. Boise Cascade viewed it as a hazard to small children who like to swim and play in that location.

On May 11, 1987 City of Salem staff and ODFW staff met and discussed fisheries requirements for Mill Creek as special conditions to the proposed 70 cfs water right. The meeting did not produce a final agreement because of ODFW's insistence on a fish screen at the entrance of the Mill Race. The city did not object to the requirement that a fish screen be installed but it did object to ODFW attempting to make the screen a requirement for the water right diversion which was a pure benefit by itself for the fish.

On May 12th City Manager Russ Abolt wrote the Water Resources Department as follows:

It is the position of the City of Salem that there is adequate statutory authority in the Oregon Revised Statutes to require the city to construct, operate and maintain necessary fish passage facilities. It is unnecessary to complicate this permit application [city's application for 70 cfs water rights] procedure with redundant conditions and requirements.

The city recognizes its responsibilities to operate and maintain those fish passage facilities located on the Mill Creek system within its municipal limits.

Abolt also made some specific commitments of the City related to the repairs of Waller and Shelton dams and the city's willingness to work with ODFW to improve all fish facilities, but cautioned the fish agency that these projects must be accomplished within budgetary restrictions and the water right be issued without conditions. (The city finally installed a fish screen at the entrance of the Mill Race in 2003.)

On May 15th ODFW commented to the Water Resources Department as follows:

The Department recommends approval of the appropriation by the City of Salem for 70 cfs from the North Santiam River to the Mill Creek system, provided the following conditions are included in the water right:

1. The City of Salem shall provide, operate and maintain to the

Department's satisfaction, upstream and downstream fish passage fa-cilities in any watercourse under the City's operational control af-fected by this diversion.

2. The City of Salem will work with the Department to determine and implement, insofar as practical, the most beneficial distribution of flows within the Mill Creek system for optimum reproduction and growth of fish.

The water right permit was approved by the Water Resources De-partment on July 17, 1987 and included the conditions requested by ODFW.

Now lets return to the concerns of the City of Stayton and the San-tiam Water Control District for the City of Salem purchasing Boise Cascade's 55 cfs water right with a priority date of 1856.

In January, 1986 City of Salem staff were internally discussing how Dan Wilson's concerns of who owns and maintains Salem Ditch could be accommodated, and at the same time, ensuring the perpetual de-livery of diverted North Santiam River water to Mill Creek. City of Salem staff verbally proposed to Mr. Wilson that an agreement be-tween Salem and the Santiam Water Control District may be possible where the district would own the ditch and, in return, they would de-liver Salem's water rights to Mill Creek. (At this same time Salem had 32 cfs of 1856 rights dedicated to aesthetic and fish purposes and had applied in 1985 for an additional 70 cfs.)

Dan Wilson was enthusiastic about the district owning the ditch but he clearly stated the delivery of Salem's water with such an agree-ment would not be free. He estimated the charge to the City of Salem would be between $5,000 and $7,000 per year to deliver 102 cfs.

Salem staff was of course opposed to this charge. They believed it was a fair trade to transfer ownership of the ditch to the district for the perpetual delivery of 102 cfs to Mill Creek. Salem staff reminded Wilson that such an agreement would most likely alleviate the City of Stayton's concerns.

On March 5, 1986 the *Stayton Mail* newspaper published an article by Ed Merriman titled: "Stayton Battling for Rights to Water." On March 7, 1986 the same Ed Merriman authored an article in Salem's *Statesman-Journal* newspaper titled: "Stayton Charges Salem with Conflict of Interest." The *Statesman Journal* article follows:[82]

STAYTON - A pending deal between the City of Salem and Boise Cascade for the purchase of North Santiam River water rights has come under fire from a Stayton official. Stayton City Manager Ellis Vandehey said the deal not only is unfair to Stayton, but may by tainted by the involvement of Salem City Councilman Ralph Jackson, who works for the State Water Resources Department, the agency that must approve water rights transfers.

In a telephone interview Thursday, Jackson said he is handling the City of Salem's latest application dealing with ownership of the Salem Ditch, a seven mile long manmade stream bed that carries diverted North Santiam water through Stayton and into Mill Creek below Santiam Golf Course. He said Stayton had expressed concerns that if Salem obtains the Boise Cascade water rights, water would be diverted upstream from the ditch to the city's filtering ponds at Geren Island and from there into pipes that carry drinking water to Salem.

If that were to happen, Vandehey said both the ditch and Mill Creek would dry up and become a veritable sewer during the summer. In addition, he said if Salem acquires all the water rights in question, Salem would have the power to cut flow to another canal through Stayton that carries irrigation water to 15,000 acres of farmland. He said any involvement by Jackson on behalf of the Water Resources Department on the issue raises a conflict of interest question.

Jackson said his involvement does not represent a conflict of interest because he personally has nothing to gain or lose from the department's actions. "If I thought there were a conflict of interest I would bow out, probably on the Council end," Jackson said.

Meanwhile, the story told by Vandehey of Stayton's efforts to a piece of the Boise Cascade water rights dates back to 1982, when Stayton first contacted Boise Cascade about acquiring 20,000 cubic feet per minute [units not correct - should be about 20 cfs] of the 55,000 cubic feet per minute [ should be 55 cfs] water rights granted to Boise Cascade in the 1800's. In addition to numerous telephone conversations about the water rights, Vandehey wrote a letter to officials at Boise Cascade dated May 31, 1983.

An excerpt from that letter reads:

"If your firm is still contemplating the transfer of these rights, the City of Stayton is interested in purchasing some or all of your available North Santiam rights. The City Council is concerned not only in the acquisition of these rights, but also in the ownership and protection of the stream bed flowing through town, which is an important community resource."

Vandehey also wrote a letter the same day to water resources officials reiterating Stayton's interest in the water rights. In that letter he asked that the city be notified in writing prior to any hearings or actions concerning the transfer of those rights.

A written response from the department dated June 6, 1983 stated: "The records have been marked so that you will be notified of any transfer application filed on these rights." Despite these communications Vandehey said, Stayton was not notified of the transfer application later filed by Salem. On October 25, 1985 after Vandehey inadvertently learned that the transfer of the water rights was in process, he filed a protest with the water resources department.

But Vandehey said that letter of protest was rejected because he failed to include a $25 filing fee. After he mailed the $25, water resources officials told Vandehey that the protest was not necessary and that they would place a hold on the transfer application until the dispute could be settled. Sam Allison, head of the water resources transferring division, said a decision on Salem's transfer application could be made within a month.

"Our position is that Stayton has an immediate need for the water—Salem doesn't."

Since 1935 Salem has been taking water rights on the North Santiam—now Salem's primary water source. Vandehey said that over the years Salem has acquired more North Santiam water rights than it needs, and Stayton officials feel so strongly about the issue they are ready to take their grievances to court. He said while Salem has been negotiating for Santiam water behind the scenes, the Stayton City Council has been struggling to find a solution to the city's water shortage. However, without additional water rights their options are limited.

Stayton now draws its water from wells tapping the North Santiam water table, and from the canal. Jackson said Stayton has no grounds for a protest of the water rights transfers. "There is a formal process set up to allow protest of transfers," he said. "The law is specific on who is allowed to be party to that. Stayton would not be party because Stayton's water is not coming from the river."

Vandehey responded by saying, "We don't have any trouble at all proving our case. We don't want to play hardball on this, but we are prepared to take this to the courts and let them decide the issue, if they're going to try to steamroll this thing through."

But there is more at stake than drinking water. If Salem acquires the Boise Çascade water rights, Vandehey said city officials there could, under drought conditions, cut off the flow of water through

Stayton, stopping the flow of irrigation water to farmland.

In an effort to avoid those sticky issues, Stayton has sided with a Santiam Water Control District request to be put in charge of regulating the canal. In a letter to both cities in October 1985, Santiam Water Control District Manager Dan Wilson wrote: "The Santiam Water Control District has been using the canal since 1968 to deliver water to 15,000 plus acres. We would like to continue this operation without fear that the City of Salem will use the stream bed for some other purpose."

Jackson said Salem has submitted a new application proposing to guarantee a minimum flow of water to the Salem Ditch to protect fish in Mill creek during the summer. However, he said the application did not address concerns about water supply to the irrigation canal.

The newspaper interviews with Ellis Vandehey and Dan Wilson were very surprising to City of Salem staff because by March, 1986 Salem staff had already discussed ownership of Salem Ditch by the Santiam Water Control District. Also Salem had applied in 1985 for additional water rights to flow down Salem Ditch to Mill Creek. This should have alleviated many of Dan Wilson's concerns and the concerns of Ellis Vandehey that Salem would dry up Salem Ditch in the future. But, neither bothered to mention these intentions of Salem nor was Salem staff interviewed for this article.

Regardless of the slanted newspaper article, discussions continued between Dan Wilson and Dave Siegel of Salem's public works staff regarding an agreement on owning and maintaining Salem Ditch. On May 9, 1986 Salem City Manager Russ Abolt wrote Dan Wilson with the City of Salem offer. The letter's summary and proposal follow:[83]

> By way of summary, the City of Salem views Salem Ditch as a valuable commodity, for which you desire a long term commitment. We feel the responsibility for maintenance goes along with ownership. As a result, we feel that we have proposed an even trade: deeded ownership of Salem Ditch in return for guaranteed delivery of our 32 cfs and 70 cfs water rights through whatever facilities you deem necessary. We are not willing to pay an annual maintenance fee for a facility we would not own.
>
> However, given the fact that the ditch is presently in need of substantial initial maintenance in order to get it into free flowing condition with adequate capacity, we are willing to share the cost of this initial cleanup.

The city then offered the district $13,000 as an initial fee for cleaning the ditch.

On May 13th Dan Wilson called Dave Siegel and informed him of the following:

1. The Santiam Water Control District Board of Directors rejected the city's offer.

2. The district wants compensation for annual maintenance.

3. The district will protest Salem's purchase of Boise Cascade's 55 cfs water right.

In a telephone conversation the same day Dave Siegel spoke to Sam Allison of the Water Resources Department. Allison indicated that if a protest is filed before May 19, 1986 a hearing will be set and it will be up to the plaintiffs (the Santiam Water Control District) to prove that they have a water right which will be injured by the transfer of the 55 cfs water right. Allison further added that the district would like the Water Resources Department to rule on ownership of Salem Ditch and Water Resources will do no such thing.

On May 19th the district, the City of Stayton, and Stayton Canning Company filed an official protest to the Water Resources Department over transfer of Boise Cascade's 55 cfs water right to the City of Salem.

On May 27th Boise Cascade managers met with the staff of the district, City of Stayton, and Stayton Canning Company. At the meeting the participants agreed to propose to the City of Salem the following compromise:

1. The district will receive an initial one time fee for maintaining Salem Ditch of $37,000.

2. The City of Salem would pay their initial offer of $13,000 plus an addition amount of $6,000 for a total amount of $19,000.

3. The City of Stayton, Stayton Canning, and Boise Cascade would pay $6,000 each to the district.

4. There would be no yearly maintenance fees paid to the district.

5. The district would receive a deed of ownership to Salem Ditch.

The Salem City Council on June 9, 1986 agreed to this compromise provided that the parties withdraw their protests for transfer of the Boise Cascade water rights to the City of Salem.

The next week all parties met to finalize an agreement. The district contended there was a "misunderstanding" and the district would not accept $37,000 as a one time payment but would require $41,000. The district staff proposed each of the four parties pay an additional

$1,000. The City of Salem staff refused, noting the City Council action that approved the original compromise. Boise Cascade, the City of Stayton and Stayton Canning Company all agreed to the additional $1,000 each. The District then reluctantly agreed to a total one time payment of $40,000.

Over the following two weeks, all water right transfer protests were withdrawn.

On June 2, 1986 the *Statesman Journal* published an article describing the agreement process and Salem's costs for acquiring the water right.[84]

On July 8th the Water Resources Department approved the transfer of the 55 cfs water right to the City of Salem with a change in use to municipal and a change in diversion to Geren Island.

The author delivered a check for $105,000 to Boise Cascade in August for payment of the water right. Thus ended the water wars along Salem Ditch.

The author was involved in the negotiations for this water right from start to finish. During these extremely stressful meetings and negotiations with the Oregon Water Resources Department, the Oregon Department of Fish and Wildlife, the City of Stayton, Stayton Canning, the Santiam Water Control District, and Boise Cascade, it was obvious all the parties with the exception of Boise Cascade became very competitive and protective of their own interests. The competing parties owe a lot of thanks to Boise Cascade for mediating a final agreement.

In hindsight, the author believes the City of Salem was unfair to the City of Stayton and overly generous and accommodating to the Santiam Water Control District. Certainly the City of Stayton needed the 10 cfs of water rights it wanted to purchase, and certainly, the City of Salem was over banking its own water rights.

The City of Stayton has been very cooperative with the City of Salem for many years and the respective staffs have worked together closely on issues of mutual interest. In 2001 the City of Stayton agreed to allow the City of Salem to build a third water transmission line of approximately 70 inches in diameter through Stayton. As part of these negotiations Salem agreed to give Stayton 10 cfs of certificated water rights on the North Santiam along with other considerations. Hopefully the old wounds of 1986 have been healed.

In addition the City of Salem and the Santiam Water Control District with Larry Trossi as their manager are working closely together on many North Santiam River and Salem Ditch issues.

Table 9-1 shows the North Santiam surface water rights and perfected water right certificates:

TABLE 9-1
NORTH SANTIAM RIVER
WATER RIGHTS OWNED BY THE CITY OF SALEM[85]

| AMOUNT IN CFS | PRIORITY DATE | STATUS |
|---|---|---|
| 12 | 1923 | Certificate |
| 60 | 1856 | Certificate |
| 50 | 1866 | Certificate |
| 62 | 1856 | Water Right |
| 55 | 1856 | Water Right |

TOTAL   239 cfs or 154 million gallons per day

# Chapter 10
# Watershed Protection

The City of Salem took huge risks when it acquired Stayton Island in 1936 and constructed its first treatment works and transmission line to Salem. Construction of both the 13 mile transmission line and the treatment works was a tremendous cost and could only be justified by acquiring a pristine water supply from a pristine watershed. City of Salem residents were ready for the very best water quality and there would be "hell to pay" if that didn't come true.

In the 1930's the North Santiam River above Stayton Island was predominately an ancient forest producing crystal clear water. During the dry summers, the river ran clear but during winter storms the turbidity and sand carried by the river could rise to high levels. During this time very few people lived or traversed through the watershed but some logging was occurring and a railroad had been built to the City of Idanha. Also, over the years many wild fires had devastated some of the high forest areas. So, the watershed may not have been as pristine as Salem residents thought when they approved funding of this mountain water system in 1931.

Prior to the European settlers inhabiting the Willamette Valley, the North Santiam watershed was very sparsely inhabited by Kalapuya Indians in the lower Santiam watershed and the Santiam Indians in the upper watershed. It was the custom of the Kalapuya Indians to annually burn away brush and small trees in order to promote the growth of edible natural plants, primarily the camas lily, acorns, and berries. The Kalapuya apparently ignored the plentiful anadromous fish in the North Santiam River except during times of shortages of wild plants.

The annual burning produced a landscape dominated by oak savanna in the lower portions of the North Santiam watershed. The higher elevations were dominated by an ancient coniferous forest.

Prior to European settlement periodic fire and floods were the catastrophic events affecting this ancient forest. Fires were frequent and quite widespread. And of course floods occurred on schedule frequencies of 500 years, 100 years, 50 years etc. However, impact of water quality because of the natural disturbances was poorly understood because of the lack of data when the natural forest was still intact.

We know of at least six major events that have shaped the physical land forms, hydrology, and the harvesting of the abundant natural resources of the watershed. The first event was from seven to 50 million years ago and the last five events were all in the twentieth century. So, as we know, events that affect the natural world are accelerating very quickly at the present time. But, the good news is that the latest events have all been to conserve the watershed and to start a long process of repairing the damages created in the twentieth century by both natural disasters and unwise abuse of the natural resources in this once ancient forest.

## FIRST MAJOR EVENT: CREATION OF THE HIGH CASCADES

The first major event was the geological formation of the watershed. What else could it have been? But what may be surprising to some, and disturbing to many, is that the geologic activity which created the North Santiam River and the entire Willamette Valley is still very active. Who knows what the future holds for the lands west of the volcanic Cascade mountains?

We can speculate all we want about the future, but what we do know is that the geologic history of the North Santiam watershed is also the history of the southern portion of the Cascade mountains from the Columbia Gorge to Klamath Lake.[86] The formation of the old Cascades started about 40 million years ago. At about 17 million years ago the old Cascades were fully formed due to a subduction zone created by the Juan de Fuca tectonic plate plunging beneath the North American tectonic plate.[87]

The old Cascades were formed due to many volcanic eruptions. The volcanoes were created from the generation of magma deep in the subduction zone of the Juan de Fuca plate merging into the North American plate. Magma is generated by the melting of the basalts in the plunging ocean crust. The melting of the colliding plates produces andesites. Because of their lower density, the andesites migrate upward through the crust and can accumulate as andesitic batholiths or be pushed to the surface as ash or andesitic lava.

Approximately 12 to 13 million years ago the present high Cascade mountain range began to rise due to extensive volcanic activity.[88] The conical volcanic mountains including Mount Hood and Mount Jefferson were all formed as part of the high Cascades.

The Juan de Fuca plate plunges beneath the North American plate and creates the magma formed volcanoes and the arc trench gap which includes the Willamette Valley and the Coast Mountain Range.[89] The Willamette Valley was the result of convergent plates.

Figure 10-1 shows a representation of the Juan de Fuca plate

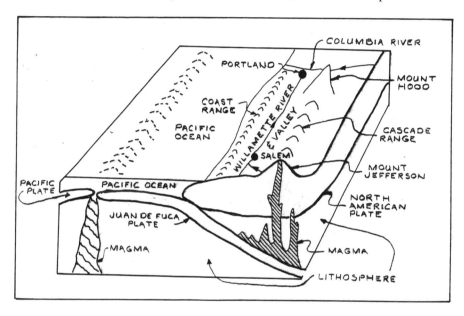

FIGURE 10-1: The Juan de Fuca plate and its impact on creating the high Cascade Mountains and the Willamette Valley.

and its effect on the creation of the Willamette Valley.

The plunging Juan de Fuca plate created the Cascade Mountains. Fortunately the location of the Cascades created the healthy weather conditions in the North Santiam watershed. As moist westerly Pacific Ocean air approaches the Cascade Mountains this large mass of air experiences a drop in temperature due to a decrease in air pressure at higher altitudes. The dew point is the critical temperature at which air becomes saturated during cooling. Below the dew point condensation sets in which results in precipitation.

So, due to the geologic event of the Juan de Fuca plate moving eastward plunging below the North American plate, the mountains were formed by the resulting volcanic action. And due to the mountains being formed in this location it created the ideal conditions for snow to accumulate on the western side of the Cascades. The snow gradually melts in the spring and summer and we have pure mountain runoff water in the North Santiam River.

We Willamette Valley residents, lucky enough to get water from the Cascades, should give many thanks to the Juan de Fuca plate. We love the water your young mountains produce. (But, please don't get real active again and mess up such a good thing.)

## SECOND MAJOR EVENT: RAILROADS IN THE WATERSHED

The second major event was the construction of the railroad up the North Santiam River in the early 1900's that allowed for massive cutting of the ancient forest.

The Oregon Pacific Railroad was the brainchild of Thomas Hogg, a civil war veteran of the Confederacy. Hogg migrated to Oregon in the early 1870's when he was miraculously released from San Quentin prison after being sentenced to life for war crimes. Exactly how he was able to be released after serving only two years is not known. However, it is known that Hogg was a convincing salesman and he had the passion of starting a railroad in Oregon that would run from the Oregon Coast, across the Coast Range, the Willamette Valley and then cross the Cascade Mountains ending in Idaho. His ambition was huge, but unfortunately his financial resources were nil.

In 1877 Hogg met with Wallis Nash, a banker in Nash's offices in London. Hogg made a very positive impression on Nash and he decided to take the plunge at being Hogg's partner in starting the Oregon Pacific Railroad.

The first phase of the railroad apparently went well. Finances were obtained and the railroad was completed through the Coast Range from Yaquina Bay on the coast to Corvallis in the Willamette Valley. The partners apparently made this section of the railroad financially successful. This line linked other railroad lines in the Willamette Valley serving Portland, Salem, and Eugene. However, the partners were determined to continue the rail construction up the North Santiam River canyon and then over the Cascades to eastern Oregon and beyond. This ambition may have been their undoing.

With many trials and uncountable disputes with contractors and unpaid laborers, the rails were finally laid as far as the City of Idanha in about 1890. At this point the Oregon Pacific Railroad was bankrupt and was sold for a mere $100,000 in 1895 to A.B. Hammond, an enterprising businessman who knew a good value when he saw it.

Hammond said that when he purchased the railroad it was worth $400,000 as scrap. Hammond reincorporated the Oregon Pacific Railroad as the Corvallis and Eastern Railroad.

Hammond used financial resources made in Montana enterprises. During a very lucrative situation in the early 1890's, while there was a depression which were known as "the hard times of the 90's," he was able to purchase railroads and lumber mills at bargain prices. In 1899 Hammond purchased a large lumber mill in what is now Mill City. Hammond purchased the mill from W.W. Curtis.

Now, for the first time massive cutting of the ancient forest was possible as a business enterprise. Hammond Lumber Company and Hammond's railroad made it possible to log, cut, and transport 400 year old Douglas firs to markets. By 1926 over 200,000 linear feet of logs up to six feet in diameter were being cut and transported every day.

Figure 10-2 is a photograph taken in the late 1800's that shows the large old growth logs and a typical steam powered tractor of a type probably used by Hammond for moving the logs.

FIGURE 10-2: An early steam powered tractor moving the large logs from the forest to the mill.

But this was only the beginning of even more massive cutting of the

ancient forest, because in the early years only the relatively low elevation trees were easy to get access to and cut. The next phase would
require an extensive forest road system for the cutting of trees in the
higher elevations of the watershed.[90]

## THIRD MAJOR EVENT: THE NATIONAL FORESTS

The third major event was the creation of the federally protected
Cascade Forest Reserve which eventually became the Willamette National Forest and other national forests in Oregon.

The federal government claimed much of the forested areas of the
North Santiam watershed. Initially under the management of the
United States Forest Service (USFS) and the Bureau of Land Management (BLM), the ancient forest, or as more commonly used the "old
growth forests", were cut with little regard for protecting wildlife
habitat and water resources. Later the federal agencies decreased
their harvests of timber and started to manage all of the resources of
the watershed. This change of management priorities was a dramatic
about face that happened in the early 1990's, but only after most of
the old growth forest had been cut.

Before continuing with the history of the federal forest programs in
Oregon lets take a look at the definition and benefits of an old growth
forest.

On federally owned land in the North Santiam watershed less than
5% of the old growth forest is still intact. Even worse on private lands
and State of Oregon forest lands the remaining old growth is essen-
tially zero. So, what exists today are vast lands of tree plantations
containing predominately one species, normally Douglas Fir. Land
that once was forested is now bare because of shallow soils or very
steep slopes

Chris Maser, a zealot for the preservation of old growth, states:[91]

> Old growth coniferous forests differ significantly from young for-
> ests in species composition, structure and function. Most of the obvious
> differences can be related to four structural components of the old
> growth forests; large live trees, large snags, large fallen trees and
> large fallen trees in streams.
>
> On land this large dead woody material is a critical carryover
> component from old growth forests into young growth forests. When
> snags are removed from short rotation stands following liquidation of
> the preceding old growth, 10 percent of the wildlife species (excluding
> birds) will be eliminated; 29 percent of the wildlife species will be

eliminated when both snags and fallen trees are removed from inten-
sively "managed" young growth forests. As pieces are continually removed from the forest with the notion of the simplistic uniformity
that is termed "intensive timber management" the ultimate simplistic view of modern forestry - the plantation or "Christmas tree farm"
comes closer to reality.

How important at the present time is preservation of the remaining
old growth forest for supplying excellent drinking water? Maser an-
swers this question.[92]

> Water is a physical necessity of life. The worlds supply of quality
> water is therefore precious beyond compare. Water is the most impor-
> tant commodity from the worlds forests.

Why is it important to concentrate on forestry management of water resources for the North Santiam watershed? The answer is that
forestry is the dominate use of the land in the watershed encompass-
ing 95% of the total land area of 676 square miles. The forested area
therefore has a huge impact on the river water quality at the City of
Salem's water intake at Geren Island.

The USFS has nearly three-quarters of all timber producing land
and virtually all the high elevation forests where most first order watersheds begin. What is the importance of first order streams to drinking water quality? Again Maser supplies his opinion.[93]

> The problem with watersheds begins with the headwaters; the
> first order stream and its watershed. Unfortunately we do not see that
> the first order watersheds are the initial controllers of water quality
> for our supplies of domestic water. We therefore cut timber down into
> the stream bottoms of both first and second order streams because the
> timber is thought to have greater immediate economic value than the
> water.

More about protecting headwaters will be discussed later. Now lets
return to the early history of the federal government taking control of
forests in Oregon.

Federal protection ot the Cascade forests was created by proclamation of President Grover Cleveland in September, 1893. The USFS
within the Department of Agriculture was created in 1905.

An unknown was the early cutting of the ancient forest when the railroad was built in the watershed in the early 1900's. Was this cutting done under the supervision of the USFS or not? It appears it was not. Exactly when the USFS exerted its ownership of the national forests and set standards and fees for the cutting is not clearly known.

It is clearly known that the USFS from its inception through the 1980's actively promoted and assisted in the clearcutting of the old growth forest. The USFS employees did not do this as a personal unthinking act but acted to carry out the dictates of Congress and the President's Secretary of Agriculture. So, to change this culture of chain sawing the forests for the sake of the economy it took the intervention of the President of the United States. More about the Bill Clinton Forest Plan will be described later, but lets continue with the history of the Willamette National Forest in Oregon. [94]

The Cascade Forest Reserve was created in September, of 1893 by proclamation of President Grover Cleveland. This proclamation was in response to numerous petitions from local citizens requesting protection of the Cascade mountain range. The Cascade Forest Reserve stretched from the Columbia River almost to the California border. From 1893 to 1897 the Cascade Forest Reserve was largely managed as a reserve.

The Sundry Civil Appropriations Act of June 1897 (Organic Act) appropriated funds for management of the national forest reserves and mandated management goals. Those management goals included: "securing favorable conditions of water flows, and to furnish a continuous supply of timber for the use and necessities of the citizens of the United States"; protection of the forests from destruction by fire and depredations; and development of mineral resources; among other provisions. The Organic Act led to establishment of forest reserve boundaries, forest supervisors, and forest ranger patrol districts. Addie Morris and Cy Bingham were noteworthy early rangers in areas that would become the Willamette National Forest.

In February of 1905, management of the forest reserves was transferred from the Department of Interior to the Department of Agriculture. Gifford Pinchot was appointed as the first chief of the Forest Service. The result was an increase in professional management of the forests. The philosophy was sustained utilitarian use of the forest resources. In 1908, the Cascade National Forest was divided into the Oregon National Forest, the Cascade National Forest, the Umpqua National Forest and the Crater National Forest. In 1911, the Santiam National forest was created from the portions that drain into the

Willamette River. In 1933, the Santiam NF and Cascade NF were combined to form the Willamette National Forest.

1905 to 1933 was a period of decentralized administration for the forests of the Western Cascades. Forest and district administrative boundaries were further refined. The Forest Service made efforts to establish relationships with local communities and with the forest users. This was a time of extensive recreation planning in the western Cascades. A fire control organization was built. Mining claims were established and the first large timber sales were sold near Detroit and Oakridge.

During the Depression and World War II (1933-1945) the Willamette National Forest became a representative of the Federal government in the communities of the Western Cascades. Efforts were made to improve employment and economic conditions through the Civilian Conservation Corps and through the use of sustained yield forestry. During World War II, the Willamette stepped up timber sales to provide resources for the war effort. Between 1942 and 1945, the Willamette sold 559 million board feet (MMBF) of timber.

The years 1945 to 1970 mark an era of intensive forestry and forest management. This era included dramatic increases in recreation use, timber sales, dam construction, campground construction and wildlife management. Mining claims were looked at much more critically. Grazing on the Willamette NF was reduced and then virtually discontinued during this era. In 1962, the Columbus Day storm downed an estimated 140 MMBF of timber and created many log jams on the rivers. In 1964, the Christmas week flood hit the Willamette hard. Six campgrounds were totally destroyed, seven more were damaged. Roads, bridges and culverts were also lost. The passage of the Wilderness Act of 1964 created new wilderness areas and controversy over the management for the new areas. This era also marked the establishment and growth of an activist environmental movement. The movement is best known for the controversy surrounding the French Pete addition to the Three Sisters Wilderness Area.

The history of the Forest Service, and the Willamette NF, in the period of 1970 to present is one of dramatic change and heated controversies. The Willamette's timber sales continued at about 750 MMBF per year through the 70's, however, the price bid per thousand increased dramatically. This price speculation led to timber sale defaults. and sale buybacks in the early 1980's. The volume not cut in the early 80's was resold in the latter half of the decade. The "section 318" bill passed by Congress increased the volume sold on the Willamette in 1990 to nearly 1 billion board feet of timber. After that, timber sale volumes declined rapidly. The Willamette NF Land Management Plan was approved in 1990, two and one-half years after the release of the draft plan. The Forest Plan was amended in 1993 by the Northwest Forest Plan (also called the President's Plan). In 1997 the Willamette's planned sale volume is 132 MMBF.

As very briefly described in the above official USFS history, the "President's Plan" was an earthquake that shook the USFS to its core and demanded a totally new ethic of sustainable forestry, the preservation of the endangered species such as the northern spotted owl, and recognition at last that the quality of water running off the forest was of the highest importance.

On April 2, 1993 President Clinton chaired the Forest Conference in Portland, Oregon. This conference was initiated by the President because lawsuits had caused the federal courts to issue injunctions blocking timber sales. The injunctions were based on the USFS and BLM not protecting the habitat of the endangered Northern Spotted Owl. President Bill Clinton, Vice President Al Gore, the Department of Agriculture Secretary Mike Espy, and Department of the Interior Secretary Bruce Babbitt spent a long day listening to testimony and collecting information.

The President directed the secretaries to develop a balanced, comprehensive and long term policy for management of over 24 million acres of public lands in the Northwest. The President stated five principles to guide the federal interagency team to develop a management strategy to protect the old growth related species and produce a sustainable level of timber as follows:[95]

> First, we must never forget the human and the economic dimensions of these problems. Where sound management policies can preserve the health of forest lands, sales should go forward. Where this requirement can not be met, we need to do our best to offer new economic opportunities for year-around, high-wage, high-skill jobs.
>
> Second, as we craft a plan, we need to protect the long term health of our forests, our wildlife, and our waterways. They are a gift from God, and we hold them in trust for future generations.
>
> Third, our efforts must be, insofar as we are wise enough to know it, scientifically sound, ecologically credible, and legally responsible.
>
> Fourth, the plan should produce a predictable and sustainable level of timber sales and non timber resources that will not degrade or

destroy the environment.

Fifth, to achieve these goals, we will do our best, as I said, to make the federal government work together and work for you. We may make mistakes but we will try to end the gridlock within the federal government and we will insist on collaboration not confrontation.

We're here to begin a process that will ensure that you will be able to work together in your communities for the good of your businesses, your jobs, and your natural environment. The process we have begun will not be easy. Its outcome cannot possibly make everyone happy. Perhaps it won't make anyone completely happy. But the worst thing we can do is nothing.

In the authors opinion this message of President Clinton was exactly what was needed as a conclusion to this unprecedented conference where all the top decision makers were present. The odds for getting the President and his secretaries at a conference of this type seemed impossibly long, but the impossible happened. As a decision maker for the city's mountain water system his message made me very happy, and we at the City of Salem looked very positively at the plan that would be developed.

After three intensive months the Forest Ecosystem Management Assessment Team led by Jack Ward Thomas and composed of an expert interdisciplinary team completed a report assessing in detail 10 options for management of federal forests within the range of the northern spotted owl.

The report was sent out for public review as an Environmental Impact Statement (EIS) with 10 options studied and analyzed. 102,000 comments were received. The Final EIS responded to thousands of these comments.

In April, 1994, the Assessment Team published a *Record of Decision for Amendments to Forest Service and Bureau of Land Management Planning Documents Within the Range of the Northern Spotted Owl and Standards and Guidelines.*

So, why should the City of Salem be interested in spotted owl habitat protection when the city is trying to protect its drinking watershed? Because the *Record of Decision and the Standards and Guidelines* went way beyond protecting spotted owls. The new plan also provided for greater protection for water quality discharged from the federal forest lands.

Generally in the National Forest what's good for the northern spotted owl is good for water quality also. Stranger partners may have never existed before.

How did the *Record of Decision and Standards and Guidelines* benefit the watershed for enhanced water quality? Because it contained an aquatic conservation strategy that included four components, including: 600 foot buffers on riparian reserves for fish bearing streams and 300 foot buffers on non fish bearing streams; the designation of key watersheds where water quality is protected; watershed analysis where restoration is identified; and, watershed restoration to restore degraded watersheds.

The Detroit Ranger District, as part of the Willamette National Forest, manages the USFS lands in the North Santiam watershed. This ranger district prior to the Clinton Plan had the reputation of cutting more trees than any of the other ranger districts. During the 1980's this district cut up to 150 MMBF per year which was supposed to be a sustainable yield. After the Clinton Plan and the *Record of Decision* was completed, the district with the new standards and guidelines, computed the sustainable yield at about 22 MMBF, which appeared to be much closer to reality.

How much damage was done to the watershed because of the huge unsustainable yearly cuts and the construction of hundreds of miles of high elevation logging roads? The answer is not clear as it relates to water quality in the North Santiam River during non-flood events, but it appears little degradation of water quality has occurred during these times. Possibly Detroit Reservoir buffers the water quality downstream by settling out sediment from open clear cut areas.

However, it is a different story for major winter storm events. The city has recently contracted with the United States Geological Survey to measure the impact of clear cuts and logging roads on the sediment reaching the river during major storms. The data so far clearly shows that increased erosion, primarily from the logging roads, creates large amounts of sediment in the North Santiam River. This has required the city to build expensive new facilities at the Geren Island Treatment Plant which will be described in more detail later.

The watershed also has large acreage (about 32,000 acres) of State of Oregon forestry lands primarily in the Rock Creek area. In addition there are large acreage (about 44,000 acres) of private timber lands in the watershed. Theoretically state forestry lands and private forest lands are regulated by the State Forest Practices Act, which the State of Oregon takes much pride in. However, even though the regulation of the Act affords some protection to water quality, the standards are far below the new standards in the Clinton Plan.

See Table 10-1 for land use acreage in the watershed above Geren Island.

TABLE 10-1
LAND OWNERSHIP IN SALEM'S WATERSHED

| OWNERSHIP | ACRES | PERCENT |
|---|---|---|
| Miscellaneous local public lands | 791 | 0.2 |
| BLM | 20,860 | 4.8 |
| Private farms and urban | 30,163 | 7.0 |
| State of Oregon forest lands | 31,198 | 7.2 |
| Private timber | 43,751 | 13.0 |
| US Forest Service | 294,902 | 68.0 |
| TOTAL | 421,665 | 100.0 |

In 2001 the Oregon State Forestry Department went through a thorough review of their standards which apply to state forests. The revised standards are marginally better but still extremely deficient in protecting riparian areas for intermittent and non-fish bearing streams which means very little protection for the headwaters! (The State Forestry Department needs to read Chris Maser's opinions about the value of protecting the headwaters and then apply this unquestionable wisdom.)

Tina Schweickert, water resources coordinator for the Public Works Department, summarized the City of Salem's involvement with forest practices in the watershed with a presentation at the Sixth Annual Water Conference at Lewis and Clark College in Portland in May, 2001. The presentation included: the Salem City Council's interest and involvement in the watershed; an EPA study conducted by Michael Rylko; the General Accounting Office study of the 1996 flood; the Memorandum of Understanding with the USFS, BLM, and the Corps of Engineers; the large scale turbidity and sediment studies by the U.S. Geological Survey and the City of Salem; and, the Opal Creek mediation group.[96]

In conclusion, federal standards for managing the federal forests have been greatly modified in the 1990's to now offer significant protection of wildlife habitat and water quality. State standards in the State Forest Practices Act need to be strengthened for protecting riparian areas, headwaters, and especially municipal watersheds.

## FOURTH MAJOR EVENT: THE DETROIT DAM AND RESERVOIR

The fourth major event that shaped the watershed was completing construction of Detroit and Big Cliff Dams in 1953. Previously on June 28, 1938 Congress approved the Flood Control Act that authorized the building of dams for flood control. On December 22, 1944, less than three weeks after the Normandy invasion of World War II, Congress passed the Federal Reclamation Laws. These laws authorized and funded the construction and operation of a system of multipurpose reservoirs in the Willamette Valley, called the Willamette Basin Project.

Detroit Dam was originally constructed for flood control, irrigation, power, navigation and conservation purposes such as low flow augmentation. The original construction costs were $41,400,000.

In 1958 the Water Supply Act amended the previous federal laws and allowed the addition of water supply for municipal or industrial use as an authorized use of stored water. However, the purchasers of this stored water would not be subsidized like the irrigation users. They would be obligated to pay the full costs of allocated dam construction and operational costs. As the City of Salem found out in 1974, the allocated costs to municipal water systems were prohibitively high.

The costs to buy stored water was included in an "Evaluation Report, Proposed Storage Reallocation for the Detroit Project." This report seemingly over pricing stored water for the City of Salem to purchase, does provide excellent background information on the original authorized purposes and how the storage releases are managed. As previously discussed recreation or municipal water supplies were not authorized uses but flow augmentation as a conservation use was authorized. Nothing was stated about maintaining Detroit Reservoir water levels in the summer for recreation purposes.[97]

The City of Salem and all the water right holders on the North Santiam River benefit tremendously from flow augmentation releases from the Detroit Dam system. The Corps of Engineers releases from storage 1000 cfs from February 1st through June 30th and 750 cfs from July 1st through November 30th.

Since minimum natural stream flows on the North Santiam are as low as 450 cfs, the lack of flow augmentation would seriously jeopardize the exercising of Salem's full water rights during a drought year.

As will be shown in Chapter 13, "Fish Exert Their Rights", the construction of the dams  produced a very negative impact on wild salmon and steelhead runs. The creeks and rivers above Detroit Reservoir used to be a major and valuable habitat for anadromous fish, and since there are no fish ladders on Detroit Dam, this habitat has been lost.

Losing this habitat may have played an important role in greatly decreasing fish runs which resulted in the National Marine Fisheries Service listing in 1999  Spring chinook and winter steelhead as threatened under the Endangered Species Act. And because the Endangered Species Act trumps virtually all other environmental laws and state water rights legislation, all water rights on the river could be in jeopardy. We'll examine this extremely important subject in much more detail in Chapter 13.

The construction of the Detroit Reservoir system has had both positive and negative impacts on the North Santiam. A major positive impact is that, with flow augmentation, the minimum stream flows have been greatly increased which benefits all the downstream wildlife and the water right holders. When natural minimum flows are 450 cfs and Detroit Reservoir storage releases are 750 cfs, the new minimum flow is about 1200 cfs. During major winter time droughts which don't allow for complete filling of Detroit Reservoir, conflicts between recreation in the lake and flow augmentation can occur similar to what occurred in the year 2001.

The low reservoir levels in the summer of 2001 had a devastating affect on tourism and the local economies of the City of Detroit and other Santiam Canyon communities. Also, the Corps was unable to maintain their normal flow augmentation level and during the summer of 2001 the total flow dropped to about 900 cfs. The same weather patterns occurred in 1977/78 so drought conditions of this severity may be on about a 25 year cycle. A much more severe drought cycle of 100 years has not been defined.

## FIFTH MAJOR EVENT: THE FLOOD OF 1996

The flood of 1996 and its aftershocks was the fifth major event in the watershed. The flood of 1996 was much more significant for the future management of the watershed than previous major floods. In 1964 a flood approximately equal in magnitude to the 1996 flood occurred and there were virtually no aftershocks for forest management agencies. At that time the City of Salem did not thoroughly investigate the negative impacts to the water system partly because Federal Safe

Drinking Water Act standards were not in place and delivery of turbid water was not a regulatory issue.

However, in 1996 the delivery of turbid drinking water was regulated by both the state and federal governments. So, after the flood of 1996 there was a very intensive effort by the USFS and the City of Salem to understand the reasons for very high turbidities being persistent in the North Santiam River for several months after the flood.

The flood of 1996 began on February 6, 1996 and was the result of quick warming with intensive rain on snow and ice. This resulted in a flood water runoff that reached a 90+ year frequency flood in Mill Creek and a 50+ year frequency flood on the North Santiam and Willamette rivers.

The persistent turbidity in the North Santiam lasted for several months and created havoc with the Geren Island filtration system. It was later found the persistent turbidity was from colloidal smectite clays that were virtually unsettleable and tended to plug the slow sand filters. These clays because of their microscopic size, contaminated the entire depth of sand in the filters.

The persistent fine turbidity continued for months because a huge amount was trapped in Detroit Reservoir and was slowly released for several months. The Little North Fork and the Rock Creek tributary watersheds downstream from Detroit cleared within a couple of weeks which helped to dilute the smectite rich waters being released from Detroit Reservoir.

During the early stages of high turbidity the city came very close to running out of water because of the inability of using the slow sand filters. An intensive stage three water curtailment program was initiated in the city that restricted irrigation, car washing and all nonessential uses of water. Water was purchased from the City of Stayton, the City of Keizer, and emergency wells were developed in the East Salem Water District. Also a crude but effective pretreatment system was constructed at Geren Island by mixing coagulants in the canals entering Geren Island allowing a limited use of the slow sand filters. It wasn't until June that conditions in the North Santiam River were back to normal turbidity's and the long four month crisis ended.

To the credit of the Detroit Ranger District and the Willamette Forest staff, a study was initiated immediately to investigate the sources of the turbidity and to find out whether possible corrective measures could be employed. The results of the turbidity study during 1996 and 1997 were published in the *Watershed Management Council Networker*, Fall 1998.[98] The authors of the study were; Deigh Bates, Fred Swanson, Ph.D., J. Reed Glassmann, Ph.D., and David Halemeier of the USFS; and, Katherine Willis and Hank Wujcik of the City of Salem.

The main findings of the study were as follows:

> Smectite clay is the major component of persistent turbidity in reservoirs on the North Santiam River and in the Salem City intake water, and as shown by this study, has multiple sources in broadly identifiable locations within the North Santiam watershed.
>
> Levels of turbidity in streams flowing into the reservoir dropped to 12-21 ntu in the days immediately following the February flood. However, reservoir levels of turbidity stayed high well into the summer months (Ruffing,1996). The temporary storage and release of turbid waters from the reservoir contributed to the persistent turbidity experienced at the Salem intake.
>
> The mineralogy of lake sediment reflects the regional importance of deep-seated slope failures (earth flows) and river incision into deeply weathered, smectite deposits of the ancestral Western Cascades (Glassmann, 1997). The removal of the toes of these deep-seated failures during high flow events may be the primary source of smectite clays contributing to persistent turbidity.
>
> February, 1996 flooding was associated with major reworking of sediments stored in stream valleys and dumped a tremendous amount of material into Detroit Reservoir. Smectite clays remained in suspension in the reservoir through the summer and continued to affect downstream water quality for many months after the major flood event. (Glassmann, 1997)[99][100]

The findings of the study indicated in large storms, smectite clays, which are widely dispersed in areas of the old Cascades will continue to be released to the river.

The February, 1996 flood taught the city some very valuable lessons. First, a more sophisticated pretreatment system was needed. Second, the city needed to rebuild the slow sand filters for more operational flexibility and construct them using the latest state of the art technology that has been developed by the London water system in England.

On August 12, 1996 the Salem City Council, being very concerned because of the long-term impact of logging practices on the water system, passed a resolution with three sections as follows.

Section 1: The City of Salem urges our Congressional delegation to support legislation to repeal the timber salvage rider, and further requests that our Congressional delegation support a General Accounting Office (GAO) study of the watershed in order to provide an independent assessment of the relationship between impacts from the 1996 flood on the city's drinking water source and forest management practices;

Section 2: The City of Salem opposes further sales in the North Santiam Canyon until such time as a GAO Study has been completed on the watershed or at least until such time as an Environmental Impact Statement has been completed for said sales, and;

Section 3: The City of Salem requests that the Forest Service work with the City in developing a Memorandum of Understanding to guide further cooperative efforts in the North Santiam Watershed to protect water quality for municipal use.

The Timber Salvage Rider was a bill recently passed by Congress that allowed additional timber cuts in excess of the new Clinton Forest Management Plan. The City of Salem was in agreement with the sustainable yield that came from the Clinton Plan. However, the Timber Salvage Rider allowed additional logging in the watershed and the city was opposed to it.

Previously in 1996, but after the flood, the Detroit Ranger District had proposed selling timber in two areas of the watershed. These two sales were not timber rider sales of salvage timber but clearcutting of green trees. Both sales consisted of major timber sales of several thousand board feet and both contained both clear cuts and thinning operations. The two proposed sales, the Sphynx and French Marten sales were opposed by the city because of the flood damage in the Straight Creek part of the Sphynx sale and the steep rocky slopes in the French Marten sale. It was agreed after much discussion with Bill Funk, Chief Ranger with the Detroit Ranger District, and the staff of the Willamette National Forest that an outside independent party perform an environmental study of the two proposed sales. It was agreed that a technical peer review would be performed by Federal Environmental Protection Agency (EPA) staff in Region 10.

The technical peer review performed by Michael Rylko of EPA was completed in August, 1996 with several technical recommendations regarding watershed management and specific assessments of the Sphynx and French Marten sales. Rylko's assessment of the two sales were somewhat positive by agreeing to forest service alternatives that reduced the clear-cuts to an absolute minimum. For Sphynx he recommended that the clear-cut area be reduced to two acres on a flat hill-top along with areas of thinning and with the log road mileage being reduced it resulted in a positive environmental gain.

For French Marten he recommended an alternative proposed by Detroit Ranger District that still contained some clear cuts and logging on steep rocky slopes. He believed that because the steep unstable slopes were above the timber harvest areas the timber sale would not be a problem for water quality.

City staff critically reviewed Rylko's report and agreed with his recommendations for the Sphynx sale but disagreed with the French Marten sale. The city staff's opinion was closer to Rylko's opinion than the opinion of the Oregon Natural Resources Council (ONRC) who advocated a very conservative no cut policy in Salem's watershed. The City Council in a split vote decided to recommend city staff's position. The Detroit Ranger District decided to complete the sale as recommended by Rylko and city staff for the Sphynx sale and to delay the sale of French Marten.

ONRC staff, Regna Merritt, and city staff were usually in full agreement on forest service proposals. ONRC assisted the city tremendously in analyzing timber sales and recommending prudent positions. The Sphynx sale was one of the few instances where there was a different opinion. This difference resulted in ONRC's position that no clear cuts and no old growth should ever be cut in the watershed, but alternatively city staff recognized the USFS expertise in watershed analysis and was more willing to go along with some timber sales that seemed to have a very low probability of creating sediment in the waterways.

The federal government agreed to investigate the problems to Salem's watershed due to the flood of 1996 with a General Accounting Office (GAO) Report to Congress. Senator Ron Wyden made the request to the Committee on Energy and Natural Resources. GAO accepted the assignment and assigned staff to complete the study. The study was conducted between July, 1997 and June, 1998.

The official name of the GAO Study was *Oregon Watersheds: Many Activities Contribute to Increased Turbidity During Large Storms.*[101] The least said about this study the better because it was hastily written and poorly researched by the GAO staff. The report's principal findings were as follows:

> All five of the cities included in GAO's review have experienced timber harvesting and related road construction in their municipal

watersheds. GAO's review of scientific studies and other documents showed that the activities can contribute to elevated sediment levels in rivers and streams during large storms. Past timber harvesting practices, including removing all of the trees from a stream side timber harvesting site at one time and using heavy equipment such as tractors to haul logs along trails, were often not designed to protect water quality. These practices resulted in cleared and compacted areas that exposed soil to the erosive impact of rain and contributed sediment to streams, especially during large storms. In addition, forest roads constructed prior to the early 1970's along streams and on hillsides used designs that were subject to erosion and failure. These roads have been found to be a major contributor of sediment to streams.

Two of the municipal watersheds - those serving Eugene and Salem - also have agricultural, industrial, urban, and residential development that can contribute sediment to streams during large storms. Agricultural operations can compact soil and frequently clear the land of most vegetation. A 1997 study commissioned by the Governor of Oregon found that agriculture in the Willamette River basin contributes more sediment to the river than any other activity.

The 1997 study also found that urban sites in the Willamette River basin contribute the greatest amount of suspended sediment to the river on a per acre basis. Residential and industrial development have increased the percentage of the basin covered by roofs, paved roads and parking lots, and other surfaces that prevent rain from penetrating into the soil and can increase runoff and erosion during storms. In addition, stream bank stabilization projects, which were constructed to protect property from flooding (1) prevent flood plains, wetlands, and riparian areas from filtering suspended sediment from surface runoff before it reaches streams and (2) increase a river's velocity and erosive power.

The accelerated erosion that naturally occurs during large storms, combined with the sediment from human activities in a municipal watershed, can shut down a city's water treatment system, as occurred in Salem in February, 1996.

The above "Principal Findings" shows the bias, or maybe the total lack of understanding, of the Salem situation that the GAO staff exhibited. Salem's major problem in the flood of 1996 came from sediment created above Detroit Reservoir which has only two very small villages with virtually all the land being federal or private forest lands. There is no agricultural land which makes GAO's statement invalid that agriculture is a major contributor of sediment. Maybe in the Willamette River this is true, but definitely not in the North Santiam River above Detroit Reservoir.

Conclusion: the GAO Study was an academic study that had very little relationship to Salem's problem. GAO was correct in one finding that Salem's water treatment system was inadequate to deal with a deteriorating watershed. Later we will see the huge investment Salem had to make to the Geren Island water treatment system and the soaring water rates that were necessary to pay for it.

One more point about the GAO Study. The peak turbidity measured in the North Santiam River at Geren Island during the flood was about 150 ntu, (the normal turbidity of the North Santiam River in the summer is about 1 to 2 ntu and increases to 8 to 12 ntu during winter storms). Yet the peak turbidity measured in the McKenzie River during the flood was 2200 units. Both watersheds have dominant land uses of timber, yet the GAO never speculated what caused this huge spike in the McKenzie turbidity. Was it from the federal timber lands and if it was, why didn't GAO question this incredibly deteriorating situation?

In conclusion the 1996 flood was a devastating event for the City of Salem that required a new look at the city's backup water supply capabilities that would eventually cost the city's rate payers a huge increase to pay for improvement bonds.

## SIXTH MAJOR EVENT: CREATION OF RESTRICTED AREAS

The sixth major event that impacted the long term viability of the watershed was the creation of congressionally restricted areas. These restricted areas have been mostly positive for Salem's watershed. Presently there are three reserved areas in the North Santiam watershed: the Detroit Reservoir system; the Mount Jefferson and Bull of the Woods Wilderness areas; and the Opal Creek Wilderness.

The Detroit and Big Cliff Dams and reservoir areas were established by Congress as part of the Flood Control Act of 1938 and the 1944 Federal Reclamation Laws. This system has had a huge impact on the watershed, both positively and negatively.

Because of the controversy of the Corps of Engineers emptying the reservoir to augment flows downstream for the benefit of threatened fish, and the resulting economic impact to the marina on Detroit Reservoir due to the drought in 2001, the political jury is still out for determining the highest priorities for use of the stored water. Maybe Congress will end up forcing the Corps of Engineers during a drought to keep the reservoir full and keep the owners of the marina and the boaters happy instead of increasing flows downstream for the benefit of threatened fish, irrigators, and cities. During the next drought we may find out.

The Mount Jefferson Wilderness was created by Congress in 1964 with the enactment of the Wilderness Act. The Bull of the Woods Wilderness was authorized by Congress in 1984 as part of the Oregon Wilderness Act. The wilderness areas are totally protected from development, logging, and road building. Since the wilderness areas contain the headwaters of many streams flowing to the North Santiam and Little North Fork Santiam Rivers they have had a huge positive and stabilizing affect on the hydrology of the watershed.

The protection of the Opal Creek Wilderness Area was created in October, 1996 by Congress in a bill initiated by Senator Mark Hatfield. The protected areas include a 20,330 acre Opal Creek Wilderness, the 13,640 acre Opal Creek Scenic Recreation Area and the 1920 acre Wild and Scenic River designation for Elkhorn Creek.

A 151 acre area around Jawbone Flats is privately owned by the Friends of Opal Creek which was established in 1989. The land was given to the Friends by the Shiny Rock Mining Company in 1992. The Shiny Rock Mining Company had obtained title to the land from the USFS because they had developed an economically viable mine on the property in accordance with federal law.

The Friends of Opal Creek was established to aid the efforts to secure permanent protection of the Opal Creek area. The establishment of Friends was motivated by the proposal of the USFS in 1989 to clear cut several areas of old growth forest. To save Opal Creek from extensive clearcutting the Friends marshaled some powerful allies, such as Ted Turner, Paul Newman and the National Audubon Society.

In 1989 prior to the Opal Creek timber sales a video was sponsored by the Audubon Society and produced by Turner Broadcasting titled "Rage Over Trees." [102] It was narrated by Paul Newman and was broadcast over Turner's TBS cable network.

The video "Rage Over Trees" was a classic debate between adversaries that refused to listen or understand each others viewpoint. The advocates for cutting the old growth were Rob Freres of Freres Lumber Company; Bill Swindell, Chief Executive officer of Willamette Industries; and, Dave Alexander, Chief Ranger for Detroit Ranger District. On the "save the old growth" side were: Dr. Jerry Franklin of the University of Washington; Jim Montiff, Executive Director of the Oregon Natural Resources Council; George Atiyeh, a local resident and one of the founders of the Friends of Opal Creek; and, Chris Maser, author and forest consultant.

Some notable quotes from the video were as follows (not in context):

Dr. Jerry Franklin: "The rate of timber cutting in Oregon exceeds the rate in tropical forests. Its all you have to do is fly over the northwest and see the rate of cutting. Brazil has nothing over Oregon."

Rob Freres: "Old growth will be here forever and it will be a supply we will have forever. We are cutting 1% per year. It will be here forever."

Jim Montiff: "We're running out."

Rob Freres: "No we're not."

Chris Maser: "We're cutting old growth for the dollars. Nothing else is considered."

Rob Freres: "If we can't cut Opal, mills will close."

George Atiyeh: "When Opal is cut, what will you cut then?"

Dave Alexander: "Willamette [Forest] is the largest timber producer of the national forests. Congress in 1984 decided Opal would not be a wilderness. We can not have it all. The way we resolve Opal Creek will be indicative of how we solve the whole issue."

George Atiyeh: "If the chain saws start cutting in Opal they will have to lock me up."

Paul Newman in commentary: "We ought to save ancient forests. They belong to the American people."

This debate in "Rage Over Trees" showed the passionate and very wide differences of opinion between the preservationists and the timber industry officials. Who were the eventual winners? The preservationists. Opal Creek old growth was not cut because of lawsuits to protect the endangered Northern spotted owl's habitat. The future Mayor of Salem, Attorney Mike Swaim participated in these law suits

Today, Opal Creek produces clear water even during major storm events and is the largest low elevation old growth forest in the United States. It is truly a jewel that belongs to the American people and it made Paul Newman's wish come true.

Figure 10-3 shows the new Opal Creek Wilderness area and the Opal Creek Scenic Recreation Area as part of the Little North Fork watershed.

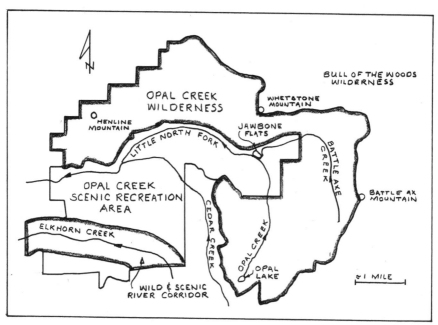

FIGURE 10-3: Opal Creek Wilderness and Scenic Recreation Area created in 1996 through federal legislation sponsored by Senator Mark O. Hatfield.

## OTHER EVENTS OF SIGNIFICANCE

### 1. Creation of the North Santiam Watershed Council

In 1995 the watershed council was created by local interests including City of Salem representatives in accordance with the Governor's Watershed Enhancement Board program to create stake holder driven watershed councils throughout the State of Oregon. The City of Salem became a charter member. The Mayor of Salem, Roger Gertenrich, attended the organizational meetings along with Tina Schweickert, public works water resources coordinator, and the author. The watershed council continues to work on watershed enhancement projects and completion of a watershed assessment.

### 2. Intergovernmental Agreements

A Memorandum of Understanding (MOU) was negotiated and

signed in August, 1999 between the City of Salem, the USFS, BLM and the Corps of Engineers. The purpose of the MOU was to provide an agreement to coordinate efforts to maintain high quality water in the North Santiam River for municipal use. The MOU was intended to clarify the responsibilities and activities to be performed by each federal agency in the North Santiam watershed.

The MOU was a major breakthrough for City of Salem and federal agency cooperation. However, a disappointment was the refusal of the Oregon Department of Forestry to also to become a partner in the MOU. Dan Christensen and Mike Schnee of the Department of Forestry staff actively participated in the MOU discussions but for some unknown reason were unable to commit the Department of Forestry to signing the MOU. Probably their superiors vetoed the commitment.

### 3. The Three Basin Rule and the Kinross Copper Mine

In 1977 the Oregon Department of Environmental Quality (DEQ) adopted the Three Basin Rule as part of the department's administrative rules. This rule eliminated any further direct point source discharges of municipal or industrial wastes to three municipal supply watersheds; the McKenzie, the North Santiam and the Clackamas.

In the early 1990's the DEQ's governor-appointed policy board, the Environmental Quality Commission (EQC), reconsidered the rule because of development interests in the watershed. The EQC appointed a large committee representing all stake holders including economic interests in the North Santiam River canyon. The City of Salem was represented by Floyd Collins, Public Works Assistant Director. The EQC held a public hearing after concluding the committee meetings and reconfirmed the rule. This was a huge positive decision for Salem and the other cities on the North Santiam who use this water supply.

The Three Basin Rule regulates the discharge of municipal and industrial wastes to a zero discharge standard in the North Santiam River above Salem's water intake at Geren Island.

In the mid 1990's a copper mining company, Kinross Copper (a Canadian corporation), attempted to construct a large copper mine along Cedar Creek in the Opal Creek area. However, the DEQ would not issue a discharge permit for the mine wastes. After a very lengthy legal battle led by Al White of Oregon Watersheds, a nonprofit environmental advocacy organization and Susan Smith, law professor at Willamette University the courts upheld the three basin rule and DEQ's right to deny a waste discharge permit. Another legal issue was Kinross's claim that this was an illegal taking of their federal right to mine. Kinross also lost this case in the courts. Kinross then chose to lobby the Oregon Legislature to create a statute to exempt them from the Three Basin Rule. A Salem legislator, Bryan Johnston, led a close but successful fight to defeat this bill.

The Kinross Copper Corporation has not been heard from since.

### 4. Amalgamated Mill Site

Along Battle Ax Creek, tributary to Opal Creek, and just upstream from Jawbone Flats, a huge pile of mining wastes with significant amounts of toxic heavy metals were piled for future disposal by the USFS. The leaching of the toxic metals to Battle Ax Creek was a threat to water quality and wildlife in downstream Opal Creek, the Little North Fork Santiam River and the mainstream North Santiam River.

The owner of the mining waste, the Persis Corporation, along with the USFS and Friends of Opal Creek agreed in 1996 to move the wastes to a supposedly water proofed site on Friends of Opal Creek property adjacent to Opal Creek. The City of Salem objected to this lousy so called solution where the buried mine wastes would remain in the watershed in perpetuity. Roger Gertenrich, Mayor of Salem, and Tina Schweickert, the public works department water resources coordinator, appealed to Senator Mark Hatfield for funds to move the mining wastes out of the watershed and to an appropriate hazardous waste site. Senator Hatfield included funds in a federal appropriation bill to make this happen. The funds included $10,000 of City of Salem funds and $600,000 of federal funds.

Good bye Amalgamated Mill toxic wastes and good riddance. You were not wanted in the North Santiam watershed.

### 5. Eugene Water and Electric Board (EWEB) Dam

In 1983, EWEB made a proposal to the Federal Energy Resources Commission (FERC) to construct a large hydroelectric dam on the North Santiam River several miles downstream from Detroit and Big Cliff dams. However, this aggressive move by EWEB to develop water power outside the Mckenzie basin was stopped by State Representative Chuck Bennett who introduced a bill to ban construction of new hydroelectric plants on the North Santiam between Big Cliff dam and the community of Mehama. The bill was passed by the House and Senate with an overwhelmingly positive vote.

A *Stayton Mail* article on May 26, 1983 [103] quotes Representative

Bennett as follows:

> This bill will preserve the unique beauty of the North Santiam River for current residents and future generations of rafters, kayakers and others. The people of the North Santiam don't want a hydro project in their backyard, with a resulting two or three year disruption of business and highway 22 and irreversible destruction of the pure water we now enjoy.

Representative Bennett may have been only looking after his own constituents in the North Santiam canyon, but also did a huge service for all the cities whose water source is from the North Santiam River.

In conclusion, it is unfortunate that water quality and wildlife preservation in the watershed has had to compete against a local canyon economy of cutting and processing timber. It has been the City of Salem's opinion that timber harvest practices which consider the long term health and economic viability of the watershed is the best way to manage. The author believes the Clinton Forest Plan of 1993 created the compromise of preservation versus harvesting that should be continued. Hopefully politicians in the future will not upset this well crafted balance.

# Chapter 11
## Modernization
## 1996 To 2003

By the mid-1990's Salem's water supply system was showing its age and in need of modernization. The original mountain water system was built at Stayton (now Geren) Island in 1937 with only an infiltration gallery treatment system and a single 36 inch transmission line to Salem. The two slow sand filters were built in 1957 and 1971 respectively. A second 54 inch transmission line was built in 1957 to 1958 which gave a transmission capacity of 66 mgd. The most recent Water Master Plan was adopted way back in 1968, so it was time to plan for the next 20 years and start financing and building a modernized system.

The need for the modernized system was made even more obvious during the flood of 1996 when the Geren Island water treatment system was incapable of treating the river water because of a long term persistent turbidity problem that resulted from the flood.

## WATER MASTER PLAN OF 1994

In 1993 the Public Works Department contracted with CH2M-Hill to complete a new *Water System Master Plan*.[104] Floyd Collins, Assistant Public Works Director, Paul Eckley, Chief Utilities Engineer and project manager, along with the author actively participated with CH2M-Hill to complete the new master plan in June, 1994. The CH2M-Hill project manager was Bob Fuller and the project engineer was Paul Berg.

A new water master plan was long overdue. The existing master plan was completed in 1968. Since then the city had grown considerably and peak water demands were nearing the ultimate capacity of Geren Island and the water transmission lines.

The general objectives of the new *Water System Master Plan* were to answer the following four questions:

1. What and when is additional treatment needed?
2. What source or sources of water should be used?

3. What is the water conservation policy of the city?

4. How can the water best be delivered to customers?

The first question "what and when is additional treatment needed?" required first an evaluation of the infiltration galleries to determine if they met the Oregon Health Division's and the EPA's filtration requirements.

The infiltration galleries (IGs) were modernized in 1982 with the anticipation they would be an integral part of Geren Island and would operate parallel and independently of the slow sand filters. The IGs were always needed after the slow sand filters were built during periods of river turbidity above about 8 NTU, because high turbidity could plug the slow sand filters. They were also needed when one filter was being cleaned and high water demands in the summer exceeded the capacity of one slow sand filter. However, surface water rules as part of the federal Safe Drinking Water Act, require efficient filtration of the raw water.

A series of experiments to test the efficiency of the IGs were performed by CH2M-Hill and city staff. At the completion of the master planning process the tests were still ongoing but it was not encouraging that they could meet the strict new standards. Therefore it was assumed in the master planning process that the IGs would not meet the new standards and they could not treat raw water parallel and independently of the slow sand filters. Instead it was the master plan recommendation that they be used as a pretreatment system when river turbidities were high.

With the assumption that the IGs could no longer treat in parallel with the slow sand filters meant that additional slow sand filters would be needed in the near future to meet peak system demands.

CH2M-Hill projected water demands to the year 2013 with two options: first, meeting a city water conservation objective of reducing peak projected demands by 10% and reducing total projected yearly demands by 5%; and second, projected demands without water conservation. With water conservation objectives accomplished the maximum day projection in 2013 dropped to 94 mgd.

CH2M-Hill evaluated the production capacity of the slow sand filters and the IGs. During high demand periods in the summer the slow sand filters were operated to produce about 22 mgd each and the IGs were operated to produce about 16 mgd for a total production of 60 mgd. When maximum demands exceeded 60 mgd, water stored in Franzen Reservoir made up the difference.

If a slow sand filter needed to be cleaned and taken off line, then the production of Geren Island dropped to 48 mgd using conservative filtration rates. With higher filtration rates and lower treatment efficiencies the maximum production was about 58 mgd.

Because of the projected increasing demand for water on peak days it was recommended in the *Water System Master Plan* that a third slow sand filter be constructed as soon as possible and fourth filter be constructed in about the year 2010.

The *Water System Master Plan* recognized an emergency water system was needed if the Geren Island treatment system became inoperable and it was recommended the development of an innovative "aquifer storage and recovery system" (ASR system) be developed in the Salem Heights area of Salem which had a well defined aquifer. The ASR system was planned to be a sophisticated aquifer recharge system where a large quantity of water could be stored in a suitable underground aquifer during periods of low water demands and high North Santiam River flows, then pumped out when the water was needed, either during an emergency or during high summer peak flows.

Assuming ASR could supply about 10 mgd of peak demand meant a fourth slow sand filter could be delayed for several years.

The *Water System Master Plan* did a thorough evaluation of the second general objective question of "what source or sources of water should be used?" Five water source alternatives were evaluated for primary and backup supplies, as follows:

1. The North Santiam River and Geren Island;
2. Main channel of the Santiam River;
3. Willamette River;
4. Mission Bottom aquifer; and,
5. Aquifer storage and recovery (ASR).

The alternatives were evaluated against the following criteria:

1. Availability—is supply adequate to meet future demands?
2. Water rights—can they be obtained?
3. Water quality—is the raw water treatable to meet current and assumed future regulations?

The evaluation found the Mission Bottom aquifer and the ASR system both had insufficient water capacities for a primary system but were adequate for a backup system.

CH2M-Hill rated all the alternative water sources the same for treatable water quality. This meant they rated the North Santiam and the Willamette Rivers as both being treatable to meet existing and assumed water quality regulations. However, the Willamette River was not seriously considered as a City of Salem water source because of health related contaminants. The Willamette River has significant biological, heavy metal, pesticide, and synthetic organic chemical contamination. Only the most sophisticated, and of course, non-economical treatment systems could hope to make acceptable drinking water out of the Willamette River soup.

We can only hope that in the future the Willamette River can be adequately cleaned up, but it is not a risk the City of Salem should take in using it for a drinking water source. Salem citizens voted in the 1930's at considerable cost to not use Willamette River water as their drinking source. It was, and remains, an excellent decision.

CH2M-Hill's recommendation was the continued use of the North Santiam River and Geren Island as the City's water source. This meant, as previously described, that considerable dollars would need to be spent to modernize the Geren Island facility.

ASR was recommended as the city's backup water system by CH2M-Hill for the following reasons:

    1. ASR is a backup system that can be relied upon during a failure of the Geren Island or transmission pipeline facilities or a chemical spill into the North Santiam River;

    2. ASR is a secondary source that can be used during high turbidity events that limit the use of the slow sand filters; and,

    3. High summer demands mean that treatment and transmission facilities need to be designed for capacities more than twice the average use levels. ASR can reduce peak use of the Geren Island facilities and may result in delaying or downsizing planned transmission pipeline improvements, as well as future treatment expansions.

The third general objective question of the *Water System Master Plan* was "what is the water conservation policy of the city?" This question was a critical determination in completing the master plan because of several reasons:

    1. The State Water Resources Department requires by administrative rule a water conservation program and a water curtailment plan when emergencies occur. However, there is a lot of flexibility in the state required program. A minimal program would probably meet their requirements.

    2. It makes good economic sense to conserve water both for the city as a whole and for each individual water customer. Individual customers can reduce their water bills with a prudent water saving philosophy, and for the city, water conservation, if successful, will delay future capacity improvements by several years.

3. Supply management by the city makes excellent economic sense by reducing the leakage of water lines, the recycling of fountain water, and better management of public irrigation systems.

4. Reducing the water demands of all users of the water system requires an excellent public outreach program with plenty of salesmanship and persistence over a long period of time. The appeal here is to "keep the water in the river for the fish" instead of wasting it, even if you can afford to waste it.

The *Water System Master Plan* recommendations were to create three levels in a comprehensive conservation program:

Level 1 - This level is directed at supply management. Its focus is on operation of the water supply system to reduce leaks and set a positive example to ensure the water system is being operated in the most efficient manner possible before asking customers to reduce their wastes.

Level 2- The second level is on demand management activities. It emphasizes customer outreach for educating the public on attainable water saving methods.

Level 3 - This level is a conservation based rate structure. It would offer lower water bills for successful conserving customers.

The *Water System Master Plan* also recommended a water curtailment ordinance to enforce the water curtailment measures already adopted by the city and approved by the State Water Resources Department in 1992.

The *Water System Master Plan* addressed the fourth question "how can the water best be delivered to customers?" as follows:

1. Transmission Pipelines

The *Water System Master Plan* recognized the limiting section of transmission piping from Geren Island to the city was in the segment from Geren Island to Franzen Reservoir. The existing 36 inch line built in 1936 was wearing out and needed to be replaced with a larger line. The existing 54 inch line built in 1957 was in good condition and was projected to give good service for many years in the future. Both lines have a peak capacity of 66 mgd. The master plan recommended the 36 inch line be replaced as soon as possible with a 75 mgd line, and into the future when needed, the 54 inch line be replaced also with a 75 mgd line. The two 75 mgd lines would have the capacity to use the entire senior water rights on the North Santiam River. The *Water System Master Plan* also recommended the segment of 36 inch transmission line from Franzen Reservoir to the city be replaced in about 10 years with a new line that starts as a

54 inch line then is reduced to a 48 inch line in the city.

2. Supply Storage

The *Water System Master Plan* recommended the open 100 million gallon (mg) Franzen Reservoir be replaced with a closed 40 mg reservoir and a new 20 mg reservoir be added. The Franzen Reservoir was recommended to be abandoned because the open reservoir was open to pollution and vandalism. It was also recognized that keeping Franzen in the system would require extensive seismic improvements as well as providing a cover. It was believed this level of restoration would cost as much as a new structural reservoir.

3. Distribution System

As a result of modeling the piping system the *Water System Master Plan* recognized the existing distribution system was adequate to meet the city's peak flow needs. The future distribution system improvements would be growth driven and would be needed as new areas develop.

The author believes the master planning process with key public works staff working closely with CH2M-Hill produced a plan that was as good as this team could produce in 1993 and 1994.

However, as we all know plans are made to be broken, and broken it became because of three unforeseen events.

First, capital costs would far exceed the estimates in the *Water System Master Plan* and this would raise havoc with the financial planning that was being reviewed by a City Council appointed Water/Sewer Task Force that also included four City Councilors and representatives of the food processing industry, the Chamber of Commerce, and neighborhood groups. As will be discussed in the next chapter, the capital costs produced a need for soaring water rates for several years to pay for bonded projects.

Second, the flood of 1996 pointed out in a direct way the limitations of the Geren Island water treatment system when the North Santiam River was upset for very long periods of time.

Third, the U.S. Fish and Wildlife Service (USFWS) listed as endangered the Oregon chub and National Marine Fisheries Service (NMFS) listed as threatened spring Chinook and winter steelhead. These three events required some basic rethinking of the 1994 *Water System Master Plan*.

## GEREN ISLAND MODERNIZATION

In January, 1996 one month preceding the flood of 1996, the city retained Black & Veatch Consulting Engineers to design and manage the construction of modernizing the Geren Island treatment system in accordance with the adopted 1994 *Water System Master Plan*. However, little did the city or Black and Veatch know that three unrelated events would drastically modify the planned scope of the work.

The first event had already occurred but no one understood its significance when the design work was contracted. This event was the listing of the Oregon chub by USFWS  as endangered. Because wetlands and ponds on Geren Island were ideal habitat for this small minnow-like fish, and before the Corps of Engineers could issue a permit to build a new screen in the waterway, the Corps was required by the federal Endangered Species Act (ESA)  to consult with the USFWS. The USFWS  then required under the authority of the ESA an environmental assessment and a habitat conservation plan be prepared to protect essential habitat for the Oregon chub. These requirements greatly increased the scope and cost of the construction and the engineering and environmental assessment work.

The second event was the flood of 1996. The flood was a disastrous situation for the city for two weeks and a severe operational problem for months due to persistent high turbidity in the river caused by non settleable smectite clays. In hindsight, the flood came at very opportune time. It clearly pointed out the major weaknesses of the Geren Island treatment system. A slow sand filter can not accept high turbidity waters and a pretreatment system is essential for long term high turbidity river conditions.

The third event occurred in 1999. It was the listing of spring Chinook and winter steelhead as threatened by NMFS. The only impact this listing had on Geren Island was the design of the screens for incoming river water. However, it appears it will have a significant effect on further diversions of water from the river. That means the city's earliest water rights may be compromised!

Chapter 13, "Fish Exert Their Rights", will discuss the possible long term impacts of both the Oregon chub and the salmon/steelhead listings on diverting more water from the North Santiam River, perfecting additional early water rights, and the construction of a new water transmission line.

Prior to modernization improvements, the Geren Island treatment facilities consisted of the following physical features and operational practices:

1. The facility was very low technologically and required only two operators. Each operator worked an 8 hour day shift for 5 days of which 3 days were worked alone and two days were with the second

operator. When both operators were present two person jobs were undertaken such as cleaning a filter. The facility was all gravity flow with no chemical pretreatment facilities.

2. The two raw water intakes were not screened but did have trash racks. The main upper intake was located on a side channel of the north channel of the river. The north channel had diverted flows from the main North Santiam River created by the Upper Bennett Dam diversion. However, the side channel had very low natural flows. To increase flows in this side channel the operators had to berm with river gravels the north channel to divert flows to the intake.

3. Two slow sand filters had a maximum capacity of 42 mgd each. However, the filters produced optimum water quality at about 22 mgd each. The first was constructed in 1957 and the second in 1971. Neither of the filters were lined and a considerable amount of filtered water seeped back to the river through very porous soils. This required the operators to direct even more water to the filters and increase the overflow rates. However, even with this early design filter, the filtered water was excellent because of the generally pristine quality of the raw river water and the incredible efficiency of the schmutzdecke layer to remove river impurities. It was low tech and, because the filters used the natural biota of the river to do the filtering, they performed excellently.

4. An infiltration gallery system of perforated pipes laid in the sands below the intake canals provided 16 mgd of near zero turbidity water year around. This was the original treatment system built in 1937 and was the champion of a low tech and easy to operate system. The galleries were replaced in 1982 with modern stainless steel perforated pipe. However, this system of treatment was too good to last because the surface water treatment rules, as part of the Safe Drinking Water Act, doomed the galleries as a final treatment process. It was found when completing the 1994 *Water System Master Plan* that the filtered water from the infiltration galleries was very slightly influenced by the raw river water thereby eliminating the galleries as a final process.

5. Three shallow wells with a total capacity of 2 mgd had for years supplied near zero turbidity finished water. They were used when the slow sand filters were off line due to high river turbidity. They were also found to be slightly influenced by raw river water and therefore could no longer be used to supply finished water.

6. All filtered water was disinfected on Geren Island with chlorine gas with a 66 mgd capacity.

Even though the Geren Island treatment system had low technology prior to 1997, the filtered water was of excellent quality year around. A typical finished water quality compared to Safe Drinking Water requirements is shown in Table 11-1:

TABLE 11-1*
TYPICAL WATER QUALITY ANALYSIS PRIOR TO 1996

| PARAMETER | SALEM QUALITY | EPA |
|---|---|---|
| turbidity | 0.28 | 1.0 |
| alkalinity | 16.0 | none |
| hardness | 24.0 | none |
| manganese | 0.95 | none |
| trihalomethanes | 0.007 | 0.1 |
| nitrates | 0.11 | 10.0 |

*all concentrations in mg/l except turbidity in NTU

Prior to design of the new slow sand filters a thorough pilot plant study was conducted to determine design and operational criteria.

An excellent consultant team managed, advised and performed this basic research work. The consultants were: Black and Veatch; Economic and Engineering Services, Inc.; Thames Water Utilities (operators of the greater London's largest slow sand filtration system in the world); Oregon State University and University of New Hampshire.

Randy Krueger of Black and Veatch was the project manager. Economic and Engineering Services and Thames Water Utilities performed a crucial microbiologic test of the slow sand filter for the removal of cryptospiridium. Dr. Robin Collins of the University of New Hampshire, who had performed considerable research on slow sand filters, was a key advisor. Oregon State University, under Dr. Peter Nelson, established sampling protocols for all tests. The Thames Water Utility laboratories analyzed samples for the very difficult cryptospiridium tests.

When the 12 month pilot testing program was completed, the consultants evaluated anticipated filtration performance if filter sand met very rigorous requirements of effective size and uniformity coefficient. Their evaluation concluded that slow sand filtration with the new rigorous specifications could produce an extremely high quality drinking water that greatly exceeds all existing and proposed safe drinking water requirements.

That was very good news. So, design of the new slow sand filters proceeded in early 1997 with confidence that the full scale filters would perform excellently.

Construction of modernization facilities at Geren Island was initiated in 1997 and was concluded in 2003. The Geren Island modernization program was as follows:

First, the construction of a new 42 mgd slow sand filter #3 was bid in April, 1997 and completed the summer of 1998. Filter #3 was designed with two independent cells of 21 mgd each to improve the flexibility of operations. Each cell was fully lined to prevent surface water seepage and intrusion. In combination with existing slow sand filters #1 and #2, this new filter gave the facility a firm capacity (with one filter being cleaned) of approximately 66 mgd assuming 42 mgd from filter #3 and a conservative 24 mgd from the existing filters #1 or #2. For the first time a firm capacity equal to the transmission line capacity was achieved without the use of the infiltration galleries.

Because the new filter #3 was partially constructed on wetlands, an Oregon Division of State Lands permit was issued February 26, 1997 and with minor amendments reissued on March 6th. The permit required compliance with the Federal ESA to ensure protection of the Oregon chub. The permit required also an environmental assessment and a habitat conservation plan (EA/HCP) be prepared for the USFWS to protect the Oregon chub and the federal "species of concern," the northern red-legged frog. The EA/HCP was also required to address the federal "candidate species" winter steelhead and spring Chinook salmon. (Both of the salmon species were later listed by NMFS as threatened in March, 1999.)

To facilitate construction of filter #3, the fish agencies agreed to a memorandum of understanding as an interim understanding of the city obligation prior to the completion of the EA/HCP. (In Chapter 13 the incredibly long process of completing the EA/HCP is described.)

Next, a new 147 mgd raw water intake with fish screens meeting the design requirements of NMFS was bid in August, 1997 with construction completed in the summer of 1998. Federal Corps of Engineers and State Division of State Lands permits were obtained for material removal and fill in a waterway in June, 1997 prior to award of construction. The screen was designed with openings that precluded the entry of salmon or steelhead fry. It also had an automated air burst cleaning system and sluice gates for cleaning the intake.

Next a new 50 mgd chemical pretreatment system was bid in August, 1997 with construction completed in the fall of 1997. The facility used aluminum sulfate as a coagulant and soda ash to adjust pH for more effective flocculation and settling of raw water turbidity.

A new 42 mgd slow sand filter #4 was bid in June, 1999 with the construction completed in the summer of 2000. This new filter was designed with the same specifications as the new filter #3. With completion of this filter, the existing filter #2 built in 1971 was retired because of damage it incurred in the flood of 1996. With filter #4 on line the combination of filters #3 and #1 increased the firm capacity to 84 mgd with filters #3 and #4 on line and filter #1 being cleaned. With filters #3 or #4 being cleaned the firm capacity became 66 mgd.

The reconstruction of slow sand filter #1, first built in 1957, created a short time concern with firm capacity. Reconstruction started in June, 2001 and was completed in the summer of 2002. Again the same design was used in this reconstruction as filters #3 and #4. With completion of this reconstruction the firm capacity at all times was 84 mgd with one filter being cleaned. Finally the city has redundant filter capacity that may be needed during emergencies.

Next during the summer of 2001 and 2002 the existing infiltration gallery and existing filter #2 were converted to roughing filters in series with filters #1, #3 and #4. To create the series roughing filter process a new 50 mgd process pump station was completed the summers of 2001 and 2002. The new process pump station gave the filtration system much greater flexibility than possible with the existing gravity system. The process pump station provided the following flexible operations:

1. Pumps water from the roughing filters to any of the slow sand filters;

2. Allows dual pass filtering through the slow sand filters;

3. Allows recycling of water previously wasted to the river during filter ripening (creation of the top layer schmutzdecke after cleaning); and,

4. Provides lower ground water adjacent to the slow sand filters during maintenance activities.

The last project was a new 125 mgd hypochlorite disinfection system and fluoridation system built in the summer of 2002. The hypochlorite system used salt and electrolysis to produce chlorine. This new disinfection system eliminated the very hazardous chlorine gas system previously used.

With completion of construction in the summer of 2002 the Geren Island treatment facility was completely modernized with state of the art slow sand filters, addition of a pump station that allowed flexibility to produce the very best finished water quality, the elimination of gaseous chlorine as a disinfectant, and the construction of a pre-treatment system to be used when the North Santiam River has a tur-bidity greater than 8 turbidity units.

Figure 11-1 is a plan of the modernized Geren Island treatment fa-cility.

The modernization projects accomplished the *Water System Master Plan* objectives but at great expense to the rate payers. The completed system cost was more than twice the cost estimated in the 1994 *Water System Master Plan*. The cost of the modernization projects are shown in Table 11-2:

### TABLE 11-2
### COST OF MODERNIZATION PROJECTS

| | |
|---|---:|
| New raw water intake with fish screens | $1,400,000 |
| Chemical pretreatment | 1,100,000 |
| Slow sand filter #3 with Oregon chub mitigation | 7,900,000 |
| Slow sand filter #4 with wetland mitigation | 8,400,000 |
| Slow sand filter #1 with IGs and slow sand filter #2 as roughing filters | 7,400,000 |
| Process pump station | 1,100,000 |
| Disinfection/fluoridation | 2,500.000 |
| Consultant and staff costs | 4,000,000 |
| Total | $33,800,000 |

In comparison, the 1994 *Water System Master Plan* estimated these costs at $18 million but with modernization assumed to take place approximately five years sooner. Adjusting the costs by 4% per year gives a comparable *Water System Master Plan* cost of approximately $22 million. This created a funding shortfall approaching $12 million and obviously created a huge problem of meeting the financial plan in 1999 and the political problem of explaining ever increasing soaring water rates. Staff decided at this point that future water projects would need to be reconsidered to save as much capital costs as pos-sible.

To partially accomplish needed cost savings it was decided to analyze the feasibility of restoring Franzen Reservoir instead of build-ing two new supply reservoirs which the master plan had estimated to cost $26 million.

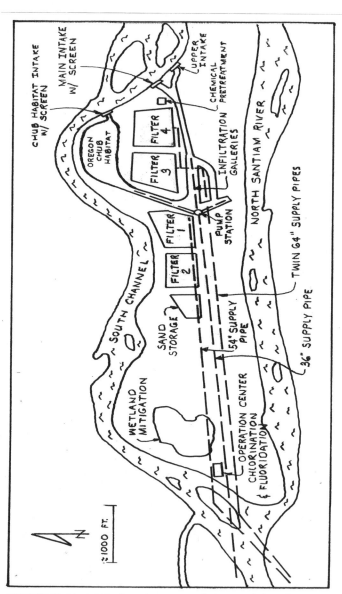

FIGURE 11-1 Modernization of Geren Island at a
cost of $33,800,000.

Figure 11-2 is a photo of the modernized sand filter #1 showing dual two and one half acre cells and the outlet control system between the two cells.

FIGURE 11-2: Modernized slow sand filter #1. The first cell is in the foreground and the raw water intake is in the background and to the right. The second cell is in the far background. The water shown over the first cell is the raw water from the river. Filtered water exits from the bottom of cell and flows to a transmission pipeline to the right of the filters.

Figure 11-3 is a photo of the fish screens at the treatment system inlet where Tim Sherman, the supervisor of operations and maintenance at Geren Island is cleaning one of the screen segments with compressed air.

Figure 11-4 is a photo of the dedicated habitat at Geren Island for the endangered Oregon chub.

The modernized slow sand filters have performed excellently and produce high quality finished water as shown in Table 11-3.

FIGURE 11-3: Fish screens on the
main inlet at Geren Island being
cleaned by compressed air.

## WATER TRANSMISSION LINE

Salem's existing upper transmission lines of 36 inches and 54
inches from Geren Island to Franzen Reservoir have a capacity of 66
mgd. Both lines are gravity with a fall of 142 feet from Geren Island to
the overflow of Fairmount Reservoir which floats on the gravity service level in the City of Salem.

The 1994 *Water System Master Plan* projected the need for additional transmission capacity in the year 2000. The master plan sized
the future transmission lines at 147 mgd or the amount of senior water
rights the city held on the North Santiam River. The master plan recommended two new pipelines with each sized for a nominal 75 mgd.
This would require two pipes of approximately 69 inches in diameter
each.

FIGURE 11-4: The north pond at Geren Island dedicated for endangered Oregon chub habitat.

TABLE 11-3
FINISHED WATER QUALITY AFTER MODERNIZATION

| PARAMETER | RANGE LOW | HIGH | EPA LIMIT |
|---|---|---|---|
| Fluoride | 0.05 | 1.4 | 4.0 |
| Nitrate | 0 | 0.1 | 10 |
| Turbidity | 0.07 | 0.65 | 1.0 |
| Total coliform | 0 | 0 | 0 |
| Halo acetic acid | 13 | 30 | 60 |
| Trihalomethanes | 3 | 49 | 80 |

The first 75 mgd pipeline was to replace an aging, leaky 36 inch concrete pipe built in 1937. The estimated master plan cost of the first 75 mgd line was $20 million. Additional lower transmission line capacity from Franzen Reservoir to the city was forecast as needed in the year 2006.

The city awarded an engineering contract to Black and Veatch to design and manage the construction of the 75 mgd upper transmission line that replaced the original 36 inch line. At some time in the future the existing 54 inch line would also need to be replaced because of capacity needs or because of aging and excessive maintenance costs. Therefore, a right of way accommodating twin 75 mgd lines needed to be obtained from Geren Island to Franzen Reservoir. The project team knew this would be no easy task because it would need to cross the City of Stayton and several miles of prime farm land.

The consultant team prepared a detailed map showing the proposed right of way for the twin 75 mgd lines through the City of Stayton, and across farmland that closely paralleled the existing 54 inch line to Franzen Reservoir.

The consultant and city staff then presented the map to the City of Stayton staff who recommended a presentation to the Stayton City Council. After reviewing the proposed right of way the Stayton City Council requested public input. The public input produced concerns from several Stayton citizens about such a major facility crossing their city.

City staff at this point took the lead in meeting with the Stayton City Council. The project was under the general supervision of Karl Goertzen, City Engineer, who assigned Jim Bonnet his Assistant City Engineer, along with Gary Myzak, Senior Project Engineer, to shepherd this critical city project. Jim Bonnet took the lead in presenting the transmission line information to the Stayton City Council.

After several meetings and lengthy discussions the Stayton City Council agreed to the new transmission lines. An intergovernmental agreement signed by Stayton and Salem City Councils allowed Salem to build the lines. In return the City of Stayton received some cash for anticipated damages to city properties and the transfer of a City of Salem 10 cfs water right certificate for the North Santiam River.

The consultants estimated the costs for the new 75 mgd line from Geren Island to Franzen Reservoir to be $45 million compared to the master plan and financial plan's estimate of $20 million. This difference created an additional problem for the city's financial plan to cover the inflated cost.

This 75 mgd line was originally projected to be needed in the year 2000 but because of unprecedented water conservation by water customers in Salem the peak demands in 2000 and 2001 were far below the 66 mgd capacity of the exiting two transmission lines. The city has decided to hold off on the construction until demands start to approach the peak capacity. It is now projected the need will be sometime between the years 2005 and 2010.

## AQUIFER STORAGE AND RECOVERY (ASR)

The 1994 master plan recommended that an ASR system be built to be used for emergencies and as a peaking supply during the hot summer months.

The ASR goal in the master plan was to develop a backup water source with a capacity of 20 mgd and a storage volume of 440 million gallons. The plan was to develop ASR in three phases. Phase 1 was a siting study and pilot program to locate and test the ASR concept. Phase 2 was to develop 10 mgd capacity and phase 3 was to develop the remaining 10 mgd of capacity. The city retained Montgomery Watson, Consultants to design build the ASR system.

For phase 1 temporary permits were obtained from the Oregon Department of Environmental Quality (DEQ) and the State Water Resources Department. Montgomery Watson then developed and tested well #1. The output of this pilot well was 1000 gpm. That first year 38 million gallons were injected and 37 million gallons were recovered. The city and the contractor both felt the pilot plant was successful and phase 2 should be started with a permanent license from the DEQ.

An extensive permitting process was required from DEQ to allow the recharge of the aquifer from treated North Santiam River Water. The recharge water was the drinking water quality from Geren Island and met all safe drinking water requirements but still DEQ was uncertain if this water would negatively impact the Salem Heights aquifer. Finally a limited license was received from DEQ in 1997 that required monitoring and testing of any impacts on the aquifer. The limited license allowed the city to develop ASR to a 20 mgd capacity and store up to one billion gallons of water.

In phase 2 Montgomery Watson developed five ASR wells with a major Salem well development contractor, Ed Butts of Stettler Supply Company. All the wells were in the ASR identified aquifer in South Salem known as the Salem Heights aquifer believed to be confined in a known area. The aquifer was of fractured basalt with considerable ability to receive a large amount of recharge water.

The operation of the ASR system has turned out to be less than ideal because of the complexity of the system. It has taken the water division of public works much more time and effort to manage and operate this system than was intended. In addition the water quality recovered from the aquifer has been below that of Geren Island water. In the first year of operation there were many complaints from the public about the musty taste and smell of the water. Even with the musty taste and odor, the water met all drinking water regulations.

The taste and odor problem was of considerable concern to Salem staff because the city residents had not had problems of this kind from the Geren Island source. The city did extensive testing of the water with chemical and biological tests as well as using taste and odor panels, but the exact cause was never found. To the relief of everyone the taste and odor problem subsided to non-detect for most people after three years of operation. However, there remain some customers with world class taste buds that can still detect ASR water when it was being withdrawn.

Because of the operational complexity and public relations problems that ASR created, the city decided not to develop phase 3, the second 10 mgd capacity. Instead it was decided to develop better intergovernmental agreements with neighboring cities to share water during emergencies. Such agreements were made with the Cities of Keizer and Stayton to the economic benefit of all.

## FRANZEN RESERVOIR ANALYSIS

The 1994 water master plan recommended Salem abandon the existing open 100 million gallon Franzen Reservoir in the City of Turner. However, because of a critical need to reduce capital costs, it was decided to retain Black and Veatch to assess the feasibility of rehabilitating Franzen to meet earthquake, dam safety, and safe drinking water regulations.

The Black and Veatch analysis determined it was feasible to rehabilitate the reservoir and save considerable capital expenses. In early 2000 a design contract was let to Black and Veatch. The design largely completed in the year 2000 produced a project that had the following features:

1. The dikes would be rebuilt to earthquake and dam safety requirements of the the State Water Resources Department;

2. The design maintained 92 million gallons of storage;

3. The reservoir would be divided into two separate operating cells (the existing reservoir was built with one 100 million gallon cell);

4. There would be new inlet/outlet piping to each cell;

5. A new lining of PVC would replace the existing asphalt lining;
6. A floating cover would be provided as required by the drinking water regulations;
7. A new under drain system would be installed; and
8. A system required by DEQ of dechlorinating the water discharged to Mill Creek when a cell needs to be cleaned would be constructed (cleaning should be very infrequent with a floating cover).

The construction of the rehabilitated reservoir was bid in 2003 and construction was scheduled to be completed in fall, 2004. Therefore, the reservoir would be off line for two summers and the system would lose the ability to provide peak demands greater than the capacity of the transmission lines and the filtration system.

City staff hope this loss of the reservoir will not create extreme water curtailment measures during these two summers because the filtration system has a firm capacity of 84 mgd and the transmission lines have a peak capacity of 66 mgd, which both are far greater than the peak demands during the past several years. City staff believe with water conservation outreach programs the peak demands should be less that 60 mgd. The only fly in the ointment would be an extremely hot dry summer with huge irrigation demands. (But, with Earth warming weather conditions, there is no telling what the weather will be.)

The estimated construction cost of the Franzen Reservoir project was originally $18 million compared to the master plan estimated $26 million for the two new reservoirs. The anticipated savings of $8 million will partially offset the extreme cost inflation of the Geren Island modernization projects and the construction costs of the first 75 mgd upper transmission line. Salem's public works director, Tim Gerling (my highly qualified assistant director later promoted to public works director) desired to hold down the capital costs of the Franzen project to $16.6 million.

In Table 11-3 is a summary of actual and latest cost estimates for the master plan modernization and improvement projects compared to the original 1994 *Water System Master Plan* estimates. The latest estimates show a $27,400,000 estimated overrun for all the projects. This overrun has created considerable problems for financing the projects.

The next chapter, "Soaring Water Rates" describes the financial plan and the fancy footwork it took to finance the improvements.

In conclusion, the modernization of Geren Island gave the city a treatment system with the capacity and the treatment ability to operate at high efficiency, even during flood events, and to produce finished water meeting EPA Safe Drinking Water Act standards for several decades into the future.

TABLE 11-3
MODERNIZATION COST COMPARISONS

|  | Actual Costs and Latest Estimates | Master Plan Estimates |
|---|---|---|
| Geren Island Modernization | $33,800,000 | $22,000,000 |
| Transmission Line | 45,000,000 | 20,000,000 |
| Supply Storage | 16,600,000 | 26,000,000 |
| Total | $95,400,000 | $68,000,000 |

# Chapter 12
# Soaring Water Rates

A well managed municipal water utility must have adequate revenues to properly maintain existing infrastructure. This means replacing systems with modern components on a perpetual life schedule. In other words, replace and maintain so the system never wears out and all increasing federal and state regulations are met without compromise. It is unconscionable for any municipal water utility not to have perpetual life as an ongoing policy. To do otherwise is passing the financial burden to their children and grandchildren. This is the sermon the public works and finance departments in Salem have preached to city councils and the public for many years. However, as we see in this chapter this advice has only recently been followed.

The cost of maintaining, replacing, and modernizing a water utility constantly increases as regulations become more strict and inflation eats up the rate base. Constant rate increases to the customers of the utility is a necessity if the utility is to be well managed to provide water quality that meets all federal and state standards, to provide the water quantities to growing service areas, to properly maintain the existing system, and to provide well motivated, well trained, and productive utility employees and contractors.

In Salem water rate increases must be approved by the City Council after a process of informing the public about proposed rate increases and obtaining public testimony in a formal public hearing. The process in Salem, as in many cities and water districts, guarantees uncertainty because few customers are pleased with increased water rates even if it means they are supporting a well managed water utility. This puts the City Council in a very awkward situation—raise the rates because staff believe it is needed or follow the advice of many customers which is to lower the rates, or at least not raise them.

Lets now look at the history of water rate increases and decreases in Salem and political environment that motivated such changes.

In 1957 city staff proposed the first ever water rate increase since purchasing the private system in 1935. The proposed rate increase was 10% which seems like an incredibly low increase after 22 years of ownership. But local politics took over and the City Council decided to lower the water rates instead of raising them.[105] And the same water rates had been in effect since 1916 when the water system was owned by Salem Water Company!

This extraordinary action by the City Council ignored the reality of a rapidly growing city that needed major expansions of the water distribution system, transmission lines to Stayton Island and an upgrade to the treatment system at Stayton Island.

The same year, 1957, the City Council had already agreed to construct a new 54 inch transmission line to Stayton Island and to build the first slow sand filtration system to supplement the existing infiltration galleries. These new facilities were critically needed because of the rapid growth of the city and the lack of water capacity during the summer when irrigation had a large demand and the food processors were peaking in their use also.

The action of the City Council to lower the water rates decreased yearly water revenues from $555,000 per year to an estimated $519,000 per year. The action the City Council took was to decrease the commodity rate ( dollars per 100 cubic feet of water) from $0.40 to $0.30 per 100 cubic feet (100 cf) for the average residential customer. The City Council did increase revenues a small amount, by raising rates for very large water users from $0.05 per 100 cf to $0.06 per 100 cf. Even though the very large water users, primarily food processors, suffered a small rate increase, they were still greatly benefited by the declining block rate structure where the more water was used the cheaper the water became per 100 cf (declining blocks were finally eliminated by the City Council in 1992).

The City Council also continued an "irrigation rate" for residential customers by charging only $0.15 per 100 cf for all water used over 400 cf in a month and $0.10 per 100 cf for water used above 2000 cf in a month. Apparently, green lawns watered at a very low cost during the very dry Willamette Valley summers was demanded by Salem residents. The City Council heard this desire and delivered the goods even though the water system could not afford it.

The 1957 rate adjustment did result in one positive thing for water revenues. It established for the first time a minimum water bill of $1.20 per month which bought 400 cf of water. This minimum bill tended to stabilize revenues and was a benefit to the utility but it did generate a lot of criticism from customers who used less than the 400 cf in a month.

The capital expenses in 1957 for increasing the water supply was financed by the sale of a $3,750,000 bond issue. The 10% rate increase proposed by staff was intended to pay for this bond issue. Because the City Council had approved the bond issue, it was assumed by staff that the City Council would increase the rates, but they decided not to. Therefore the debt payments had to be absorbed by the very lean water utility budget which was forced to eliminate valuable maintenance and replacement projects.

The effect of this loss of revenues meant that during this crucial time of rapid city growth and large capital expenses, the City Council decided to defer to the future the necessary maintenance of the system. And as we see, this tight fisted policy of insisting on extremely low water rates resulted in a large inventory of unmet maintenance needs and contributed to soaring water rates later. Using a well worn phrase, "pay me now or pay me more later" certainly turned out to be true, because when needed maintenance is deferred for many years the costs escalate tremendously.

And on top of the water utility having to pay for an expensive capital project bond issue without additional revenues, the utility was required by city policy to extend water lines to new developments outside the currently developed area. The requirement to do these service extensions was a first priority and could bump planned maintenance projects.

Thankfully in 1979 there was a major change in this policy. The City Council adopted a new and rather radical policy for urban growth management. The urban growth management policy required developers at their own expense to provide all the infrastructure for new development outside the currently developed area (CDA). The CDA was a strange new line that approximated the city limits in many parts of the city but did not cover some undeveloped areas within the city limits. This very controversial urban growth management policy and enacted ordinance saved the utility system some expenses each year that could be and were diverted to much needed deferred maintenance and replacement programs.

From 1957 to 1980 the City Council approved several small rate increases resulting in a monthly minimum bill of $2.80 with 400 cf of water. These small rate increases did not keep up with inflation and the system continued to suffer from lack of maintenance.

Finally, in March, 1980, the City Council agreed to a 12.5% water rate increase. The Council agreed to the hefty rate increase because of the obvious need to greatly increase the maintenance and replacement of the aging system. The problem of not maintaining the system had become acute during the past decade partially because the city had inherited two private water systems: the Salem Heights system in

South Salem; and, the Jan Ree system in East Salem. Both systems had distribution systems—wells and pump stations far below the City of Salem standards. In Salem Heights the distribution system was built entirely of galvanized and wrought steel pipe that needed to be replaced in its entirety. In Jan Ree the distribution system was asbestos cement pipe that was heavily clogged with iron and manganese bacteria. This system also needed total replacement.

In addition the city had miles of leaky pipes with a system leakage rate of 20% compared to a well maintained system of about 5% to 6% leakage. The needed maintenance improvements, and the fact that inflation over the years had greatly decreased the buying power of the utility, convinced the City Council to approve the water rate increase.

The 1980 rate increase set the minimum bill at $6.30 bimonthly which purchased 800 cf of water. The City Council also greatly increased the commodity rate for large water users. The new commodity rate for the large users was set at $0.28 per 100 cf up to 100,000 cf and $0.24 per 100 cf over 100,000 cf.

The commodity rates for the large users, even though much lower than other Willamette Valley cities was an increase of over 100% compared to the 1957 rates ($0.10 per 100 cf up to 100,000 cf in 1957).

The 1980 water rate increase plus a large increase in the sewer rates may have played a role in the major food processors leaving Salem. Some of the food processors claimed the utility rate increases in Salem tipped the balance for them in deciding to close their plants. Since a major recession started in Salem about this time it was believed by some that utility rates and a very controversial new development fee contributed to the recession.

The 1980 rate increases also included large surcharges for areas outside the Salem city limits receiving city water. In Jan Ree (East Salem) and Chatnika Heights (West Salem) a 100% surcharge was approved for these retail customers. The wholesale customers in the City of Turner and the East Salem Water District were charged a commodity rate surcharge of 25%. The Keizer Water District had been a wholesale customer of the city since it was created in the early 1970's. However, when the residents of the district formed the City of Keizer they chose to develop their own water supply system with deep wells.

In 1984 the public works and finance department staff completed a major refinement to past water rate studies. A cost of service analysis (COSA) was completed where the costs to serve each geographic customer group was evaluated. Johnnie Jordan, assistant finance director, led the COSA preparation. All City of Salem customers were considered one group and each of the outside the city limits areas were evaluated as a COSA group.[106]

In the COSA it was decided to do away with the arbitrary surcharges for the outside areas and to initiate a utility basis rate process for outside the city customers. The utility basis accounting system allowed the city to collect from the outside customers a rate of return on the city's investment to serve them and to charge a depreciation charge for all system components they use and which the city had the responsibility to replace at a future time. The utility basis accounting system did not allow the city to charge bond debt expenses to the outside customers.

The COSA parameters for the outside-the-city areas were: distance from the source; elevation (was pumping required?); demands during peak water use months; the rate of return on the city's investments; and, depreciation to the system used by the outside area.

The city believed, and it was accepted by the outside customers, that the COSA and the utility basis system was a fair method to set water rates for the outside customers.

The City Council approved the new COSA and the rate system in February, 1985. The new rates for City of Salem customers were set at $7.20 for a bimonthly minimum with 800 cf of water and commodity rates of $0.31 per 100 cf up to 100,000 cf and $0.27 over 100,000 cf. This was a 14% rate increase for City of Salem customers.[107]

The approval of the new COSA and the 14% rate increase was not an easy decision for the City Council. There was considerable discussion about everything in this staff proposal. For instance, staff proposed eliminating the declining block system of two tiered commodity rates. The Council disagreed and required the declining block system to remain. Mayor Sue Miller was concerned and agreed with staff about deferred maintenance and the catch-up that will be required. Staff included a new water line replacement program and water system improvements of $1.9 million. However, John Carney, Councilor, expressed having a difficult time with the water rate increase. He believed the proposed rate increase was directly related to the proposed capital improvements of replacements and system improvements and was not directed where it was needed for maintenance.

The hearings and deliberations by the City Council indicated the Council was very unsure about the need for a capital improvements program for replacing worn out and leaking water lines. Probably the

Council believed the replacement program was a bottomless pit that could justify very large rate increases every year and they were, as a Council majority, opposed to rate increases, period.

So, perpetual life replacements of the system would need to wait until a future Council could appreciate the need to stop deferring capital improvements to future rate payers. And, this was during a time when Salem had the lowest water rates in the Willamette Valley, with water rates far below market rates.

Three years later, in January, 1988, an additional 4% rate increase went into effect. Staff and City Council acknowledged the rate increase was far less than what was needed for proper maintenance and replacement of the system, but keeping water rates low was the continuing prevailing mood of the Council. This very small rate increase also required that the working capital of the utility be greatly decreased, but the Council still believed keeping rates low was more important.

Staff did not miss the opportunity during the rates hearing to remind the Council again that the capital water line replacement program was far below the level it should be and the Council was deferring the funding of this program to future rate payers. The Council was also shown comparative water rates in the region and how Salem was selling water far below the market. Following is Table 12-1 comparing water rates in the region of similar sized cities:

TABLE 12-1
WATER RATE COMPARISON FOR 1988

| CITY | BIMONTHLY MINIMUM FOR 800 CUBIC FEET | COMMODITY RATE FOR 100 CU, FT. |
|------|--------------------------------------|--------------------------------|
| Salem, OR | $7.50 | $0.32 |
| Olympia , WA | 11.52 | 0.69 |
| Vancouver, WA | 11.58 | 0.66 |
| Gresham, OR | 17.41 | 1.02 |
| Hillsboro , OR | 14.26 | 0.69 |
| Eugene, OR | 11.99 | 0.40 |
| Beaverton, OR | 18.80 | 0.60 |
| Spokane, WA | 10.62 | 0.37 |
| Yakima, WA | 7.79 | 0.51 |

During the public hearings for this rate increase the City Council appointed a Council committee to review possible future rate increases to increase rates sufficient to fund a perpetual life program for replacements. The committee of Mayor Sue Harris, and Councilors John Carney and Dick Berg met 10 times prior to the City Council making a decision on the 1988 rate increase.

The committee reviewed in detail revenue and expenditure forecasts, performance budgets, and needed capital projects. The committee agreed that a larger capital improvement program of replacing leaky and worn out water lines was needed. They agreed this enhanced program should be started the coming fiscal year and a rate increase was needed of 6% for at least the next four years. However, as stated earlier the full Council would not increase the rates 6% but did raise the rates 4%.

And, to make rate making very confusing, the Councils in 1989, 1990, and 1991 refused to raise rates at all, ignoring the policy recommended by the Council committee.

Finally, on April 6, 1992 the City Council approved a water rate increase of 12.5% that included a 5% water and sewer fund franchise fee that would be a general fund revenue. [108]

On April 7, 1992, the *Statesman-Journal* wrote a negative editorial on the city collecting a franchise fee from the water and sewer fund. Quotes from the editorial follow:[109]

> The City of Salem has no justification to assess franchise fees against Salem water and sewer customers and to use the money as general support for government.
>
> Salem will face a big expense in upgrading its water system in the near future. The city must keep today's costs as low as possible and build voter trust as it prepares for the big bill to come.

But, hold on, this issue had not been settled! On April 27th the City Council reversed itself and voted against the water rate increase.[110] But, more indecision was yet to come.

On May 4, 1992 the Council reversed itself again and approved the controversial rate increase of 12.5% that included a 5% water franchise fee to be paid to the general fund giving a net increase of 7.5% increase for the water utility. The Council also eliminated the declining block of commodity rates for the large users. The new water rates were a residential minimum charge of $8.45 bimonthly which purchased 800 cf of water and a single commodity rate of $0.36 per 100 cf. [111]

The editorial in the *Statesman Journal* on April 6, 1992, hit the target. A big water bill was soon to come. The political era of once in a while raising water rates a minimal amount and not building contingency funds for large future expenses would soon come to an end. The reason was that Salem's water piping system was wearing out due to neglect, Salem's growth rate was pushing the capacity of the water supply system, and the new Federal Safe Drinking Water Act requirements would all cost tens of millions of dollars. Soaring water rates were right around the corner and this would come as a shock to many residents and businesses. This pain could have been avoided if Council had chosen earlier to charge market water rates and build a sizable contingency fund. But they refused this seemingly excellent business plan.

And, of course the Council had second thoughts, again, about a huge 12.5% rate increase. On May 28, 1992 the Council voted to rescind the 12.5% rate increase they had previously approved. It is believed the Council took this unexpected action because several businesses believed the rate increase would damage their profitability. But, this water rate battle was not over yet! At their next meeting the Council again reversed fields and voted to approve the rate increase. And, believe it or not, this was the final vote.

At this point it seemed like a long shot that major improvements to the supply and distribution system could be financed in the near future because of the reluctance of the City Council to continue a program of significant increases in revenues that were needed.

For the next round of budgeting and setting water rates consistent with the budget, staff prepared a 20 year proposed capital improvement program, the initiation of a new *Water System Master Plan* (the existing plan was prepared in 1968 and was totally out of date), and a five year plan for water rate increases. The 20 year capital plan follows in Table 12-2.

Staff proposed that, due to the 20 year capital plan costs, water rates needed to be raised 7.4% per year. The 20 year capital plan must have finally impressed the Council that the needs were truly great and they did raise water rates 7.4% on December 21, 1992. The new rates were a residential minimum of $9.10 bimonthly for 800 cf of water and a commodity rate of $0.39 per 100 cf.

In late 1993 the city was concluding the preparation of a new *Water System Master Plan* with CH2M-Hill. As predicted in the 1992 Capital Plan, for a 20 year period, the *Water System Master Plan* confirmed there would be huge capital expenses for the water system in the very near future.

TABLE 12-2
20 YEAR WATER SYSTEM CAPITAL PLAN IN 1992

| | |
|---|---:|
| Water Master Plan | $178,000 |
| Needed water projects in 1994/95 | 5,259,000 |
| Water line replacements | 45,264,000 |
| Water supply expansion | 40,000,000 |
| Water distribution improvements | 3,500,000 |
| Total: | $94,201,000 |

As a supplement to the *Water System Master Plan,* the city let a contract to Black and Veatch Corporation to prepare a Financial Feasibility Study. This study would be required by bond rating agencies when large bond issues were to be rated and sold. The Financial Feasibility Study was completed in November, 1993 and was reviewed by the City Council in December, 1993.

The Financial Feasibility Study recommended annual water rate increases of 9% starting in January, 1994. This proposal sent the City Council into rate making shock. The Mayor, R.G. Andersen-Wyckoff, decided the Council needed to convene a committee that would be represented broadly in the community. The committee was named the Water/Wastewater Task Force and was intended to be short term and not a permanent standing committee. The Mayor appointed himself as chair and also appointed all the members which included the Chamber of Commerce, the food processors, neighborhood representatives and three City Councilors. The Task Force reviewed the proposed rate increases and reluctantly agreed that they were needed.

The full City Council was still very reluctant to agree to the Financial Feasibility Study and annual rate increases of 9%. However, they changed their minds when at the public hearing a member of the Water/Wastewater Task Force, David Truitt, (owner with his brother of Truitt Brothers Food Processing Company), testified that the rate increases would certainly hurt his independent company financially, but he thought it was the right thing to do because he was convinced the rate increases were needed to pay for necessary improvements to the system. However, he appealed to the City Council to cap the rate increase for food processors at 3% because of the general unprofitability of his industry and the need to preserve jobs. This testimony tipped the balance at the Council and they approved the 9% rate increase but, unfortunately for the food processors, the rate increase would be applied to all. As a result the new water rates were a $9.90 minimum bimonthly charge and a commodity rate of $0.43 per 100 cf.

The approval of the Financial Feasibility Study by the City Council and the adoption of the annual rate increases of 9% removed the political barrier of modernizing the Geren Island treatment system and systematically replacing the water distribution system on a perpetual life basis.

In January 1995 and 1996, the City Council increased water rates by 9% each year. The new rates approved in January, 1996 were a $11.80 bimonthly minimum and a commodity rate of $0.512 per 100 cf.

In 1997 after retaining Black and Veatch to design the modernization of Geren Island and the replacement water transmission line from Geren Island to Franzen Reservoir, the Financial Feasibility Study was updated with new cost estimates. To everyone's embarrassment the costs were significantly higher than the adopted *Water System Master Plan* and the Financial Feasibility Study had estimated. It was found the estimated cost of building the new transmission line from Geren Island to Franzen Reservoir had escalated from $25 million to $45 million and the cost of modernizing the slow sand filters had escalated from $15 million to $30 million. Therefore the annual water rate increases that were needed went up to 14% per year.

The big question was now would the City Council go for these even more soaring water rates? The city had elected a liberal mayor, Mike Swaim, in 1996 and he took office in January, 1997 just in time for a 14% water rate increase. The majority of the Council were conservative and were led by Councilors George Puentes (who was defeated by Swaim in the mayor's race), David Glennie and Tom DeSouza, but all true friends of the utility system. Would there be a split vote on the water rate increases? There was not. Both the liberals and the conservatives voted to approve the water rate increases from 1997 to the year 2000 with 14% rate hikes (except for one year when liberal Councilor Wes Bennett convinced the Council that only a 5% increase was prudent because of soaring utility bills). As a result of four years of water rate increases the water rates were $18.36 for a bimonthly minimum and a commodity rate of $0.80 per 100 cf.

In 1999, the city greatly increased their systems development (SDC) fees for water projects serving growth. As an example the new SDC fees greatly reduced the water rate obligation to pay for the new 75 mgd transmission line. For this line the SDC fees would pay 68% of the capital costs and water rate payers would pay the remaining

32%. Each component of the *Water System Master Plan* was evaluated for its growth component in a detailed methodology. The new SDC fees would decrease the future water rate increases related to capital facilities to a new annual rate slope increase of about 8%.

However, future rate increases would be very difficult to compare with previous rates because the rate system was to be completely amended with a new Cost of Service Analysis (COSA). In the year 2000 the city after evaluating its 1984 COSA, decided it was out of date and decided to reinvent cost responsibilities for all customer classes. Eric Rothstein of CH2M-Hill and Debbie Galardi of Galardi Consulting headed up this major consultant and staff effort. The City's effort was headed by Jack Merritt, Director of Finance, and Paul Eckley and Diane Taniguchi-Dennis of the public works staff.

The COSA was completed in three major steps:

Step 1. Determine system wide revenue requirements to be recovered from rates.

Step 2. Allocate revenue requirements to customer classes.

Step 3. Determine the rate structure and specific rates.

The completed COSA resulted in some shifts of rate responsibilities for some classes but nothing drastic. There were small shifts upward for customer classes that had high peaking demands which coincided with the system peak in the summer, such as irrigation. Low peaking industries and the wholesale customers of the City of Turner and the East Salem Water District were winners with their rate responsibilities decreasing significantly. This COSA was cash basis and therefore the previous complex utility basis was retired. This meant also that the premium rates charged to outside customers with the previous COSA went away with the new COSA.

An additional major change with the new COSA was the bi-monthly minimum charge. The minimum charge over the years had become progressively larger with every percentage rate increase. The minimum charge was considered unfair by customers who used considerably less than 800 cf of water in a two month period.

The new COSA did away with the large bimonthly minimum charge and settled on a bimonthly minimum charge of $1.35 to pay for billing and customer service with no water allowance. The downside of this new enlightened policy of low minimums was the commodity rate greatly increased. Rate making is a zero sum game where the cost of the utility must be paid by its customers and, if one class has a rate decrease the other classes must have an increase.

The new commodity rate was set at an astronomical $1.41 per 100 cf. This meant all operational and debt expenses must be collected through a commodity charge where in the past a large amount of revenue was collected with the minimum charge.

The City Council, now with a liberal majority headed by Mayor Mike Swaim, was very pleased with the new COSA, especially the new method for charging minimum rates. The Council as well as staff had received many complaints from customers who conserved and were unable to control their bills because of the high minimums. The Council at adoption had not heard from the large residential and industrial customers who would see significantly higher water bills because of the much higher commodity rate. So, this new COSA is probably still politically sensitive and may need to be revised when the large use customers weigh in with their concerns.

In January, 2003 a new Mayor, Janet Taylor, took office along with three new City Councilors. The elections created what was believed to be a conservative majority. In May, 2003 the new Council was faced with a staff proposed water rate increase of 8.3% to continue the annual rate slope started in 1999. At the public hearings for water rate increases, the food processors appealed to the Council to cap their rates at a lower increase. However, the Council along with Mayor Taylor voted 5 to 4 to approve the 8.3% increase for all customers. This vote of the Council confirmed again their commitment to continue water rate increases to pay for needed system improvements.

In conclusion, major improvements made to a water system and perpetual life maintenance are both expensive and must be paid by the customers of the utility, assuming no subsidies from federal and state governments. In Salem the water utility is an enterprise financial fund with no subsidies from general fund revenues.

Looking back, the City Council in the early 1930's certainly went way out on a political limb in approving the mountain water system with its very large costs for its time. This gamble was a winner. The North Santiam River supply has benefited the City's industries and citizens with extremely good and healthy water. In the 1950's, 1960's, 1970's, and 1980's the City Councils were very tight fisted and refused to implement water rates sufficient to properly maintain and modernize the system. This period of time created a huge backlog of deferred maintenance and deferred capital improvements. This put a burden on staff to keep the system going and a political burden on the

City Councils in the 1990's to create soaring water rates. The Councils in the 1990's and early 2000's did what was needed and experienced the political criticism that followed.

The Council in 2003 continued the needed rate increases for one year. Will the Councils continue the needed rate increases in the near future?

Finally, Figure 12-1 shows graphically the history of water rates in Salem. It clearly illustrates the "soaring" of recent water rate increases.

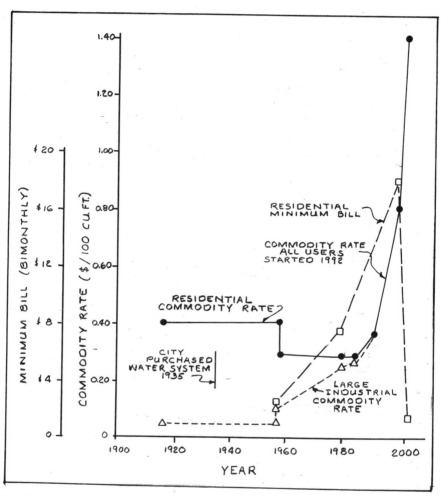

FIGURE 12-1: Commodity water rates soared while minimum bills dropped in 2001 due to a new cost of service analysis.

# Chapter 13
# Fish Exert Their Rights

In the 1990's Salem's comprehensive planning for the future, along with many other cities in the greater Columbia basin, could require extensive amendments. The comprehensive plans, water rights, property protection rights along fish bearing streams, development plans and many other impacts were left in limbo because of the decisions by the federal fish agencies that several species of fish were either endangered or threatened. The fish were exerting their rights to survival and the region would never be the same again!

This chapter explains the impacts on the city's water supply system and one of the most valuable assets of the City of Salem—its water rights. Fish need water to survive, but so does a city and so does agriculture. How do we balance a finite amount of river water among all the competing needs? This chapter suggests some strategies that are open to the fish agencies. Hopefully they are open to these suggestions. Salem's future may depend on it.

When the 1994 *Water System Master Plan* was being prepared it was known that the U.S. Fish and Wildlife Service (USFWS) had listed on October 18, 1993 the Oregon chub as endangered under the federal Endangered Species Act (ESA). [112] However, it was not known until 1998 that the National Marine Fisheries Service (NMFS) intended to list spring Chinook and winter steelhead as threatened under the ESA in the Willamette River and its tributaries, including the City of Salem's water supply on the North Santiam River. (This book continues the use of NMFS instead of their recent new name, National Oceanic and Atmospheric Administration Fisheries or NOAA Fisheries.)

The U.S. Supreme Court has described the ESA as the most comprehensive legislation for the preservation of endangered species ever enacted by any nation.[113]

The ESA is comprehensive and extremely complex. Basically, the ESA defines two levels of protection: first, for endangered species, and, second for threatened species. The definitions of each are:

Endangered species:   Any species which is in danger of extinction through all or a significant portion of its range (example: Oregon chub).

Threatened species:   Any species which is likely to become an endangered species within the foreseeable future throughout all or a significant portion of its range (examples: Chinook salmon and winter steelhead).

Generally, the ESA allows more administrative flexibility for regulating harm to threatened fish than for endangered fish. For endangered fish an "incidental take" (defined later in this chapter) can only be authorized by USFWS if an approved permit is issued under Section 10 of the ESA. Section 10 defines a  habitat conservation plan (HCP) acceptable to the fish agencies including comments from the general public after publication in the *Federal Register*. Incidental take permits for endangered fish are very, very difficult to obtain. This chapter describes Salem's attempts to obtain one for Oregon chub on Geren Island.

For threatened fish the ESA has included under Section 4 a little gem titled "protective regulations." This allows the federal agencies to create 4(d) rules. The ESA states: "the Secretary shall issue such regulations as he deems necessary and advisable to provide for the conservation of such species." Prior to fish biologists issuing 4(d) rules there was much confusion with local governments trying to do their thing like treating water and delivering it to their customers. But, in fairness to the fish folks, the 4(d) rules do allow incidental takes of threatened fish for essential utility operations. The existing NMFS 4(d) rules for Chinook salmon and winter steelhead in the Willamette system will be described later in this chapter.

Lastly, Section 7 of the ESA requires that all federal agencies shall consult with the fish agencies when issuing permits that may affect the habitat of threatened or endangered fish. If the fish agencies believe the permit will adversely affect the threatened or endangered fish, they must use the best scientific information available and "suggest reasonable and prudent alternatives" that will not adversely affect the fish or its habitat.

However, as we shall see in this chapter, the reasonable and prudent alternatives to a fish biologist may not seem reasonable and prudent to a water system manager for an urban area.

The listing of the fish has for the first time created a real threat to Salem's 147 cfs of 1856 and 1866 priority water rights on the North Santiam River. Until the listings, Salem had iron clad legal rights under water rights prior appropriations laws in Oregon which were passed into law in 1909.

The Oregon water code established four general principles which are still the basis of water law in Oregon. They are:[114]

1. The water belongs to the public;

2. Any right to use it is assigned by the State through its permit system;

3. Water use under the permit system follows the "prior appropriations doctrine" i.e., older water users get priority over newer water uses; and,

4. Permits may be issued only for beneficial use without waste.

Oregon's prior appropriation doctrine encouraged the diversion of water and delivery of it where it was to be used. Obviously the City of Salem was diverting water legally and was putting it to beneficial use.

But, the listing of the Oregon chub and the two salmonid species with their need for sufficient water put into question the value of early water rights permits that were not fully perfected. Therefore the listings became an issue of fish habitat protection versus the future growth and economic viability of the City of Salem and other cities dependent on surface water supplies for municipal use.

The crucial question is: how did this situation occur and what are the possible solutions for both preserving the fish and providing water to a growing metropolitan area?

First, lets examine the endangered listing of the Oregon chub because it may be the most difficult ESA issue for Salem.

## THE ENDANGERED OREGON CHUB

The Oregon chub is a very small minnow sized fresh water fish that is less than 3.5 inches in length. Its taxonomy was first described in 1908 as *Hybopsis erameri*. Later taxonomic revisions placed it as *Oregonichthys crameri* or *O. crameri*.

Figure 13-1 is a photo of an ideal habitat for the Oregon Chub which are flooded wetlands off the main channels of rivers. Figure 13-2 is a photo of the Oregon chub.

The Secretary of the Interior who delegates fish management to the USFWS has jurisdiction for protecting fresh water fish from extinction under the authority of the ESA.

The USFWS on October 18, 1993 issued their "final rule" for listing the Oregon chub as endangered.[115] Unfortunately, there was very little public or scientific interest in the listing. After publishing the proposed rule on November 19, 1993, no requests were made for a public hearing and only one comment was received. The comment was that the endangered listing was not needed because there existed a conservation agreement for the Oregon chub signed by USFWS, Oregon Department of Fish and Wildlife (ODFW), Oregon State Parks, the Corps of Engineers (Corps), the Bureau of Land Management (BLM), and NMFS.

FIGURE 13-1: Ideal habitat for Oregon chub.

The goal of the conservation agreement was to reverse the declining trend of Oregon chub populations and increase the abundance of this species in healthy wild populations through protection of habitat; to reintroduce to suitable habitats within its historic range; and, to provide public education and involvement. A task force of the signatory agencies was to be established to oversee and coordinate actions to achieve these goals.

This seemed like an ideal cooperative agreement between the resource agencies that could significantly achieve the goals. However, the USFWS rejected this approach and decided to list the Oregon chub as endangered. This required the USFWS to produce a "Recovery Plan" which then gave the USFWS regulatory power over

FIGURE 13-2: Oregon chub shown approximately 1.5 times actual size.

all government agency activities that may further endanger the fish!

Meanwhile in January, 1997 back at Geren Island the public works staff and the consultant, Black and Veatch, were applying for permits to the Corps of Engineers to construct the new raw water intake and the new slow sand filter #3.

Black and Veatch examined the site where the proposed construction would take place and found wetland areas. They then prepared the appropriate documents for applying for a Section 404 permit with the Corps. The Corps then consulted with both the USFWS and the NMFS. After this consultation the Corps requested the City to prepare a biological assessment as required in Section 7(c) of the ESA.

The biological assessment was then prepared and it found the Oregon chub in the raw water inlet channels and the ponds on Geren Island. Since Oregon chub was listed as endangered, the ESA allowed only one route for any "incidental takes" that may occur in constructing the improvements on Geren Island. This route was the preparation of a formal environmental assessment (EA) and a habitat conservation plan (HCP).

In addition to the Oregon chub, it was determined the EA/HCP would also include the federal "species of concern" the northern red legged frog which was also protected by the USFWS. Additionally the EA/HCP would include the federal "candidate species" of winter steelhead and the spring run Chinook salmon, which as anadromous fish, would be regulated by the NMFS.

The City of Salem never dreamed in its wildest nightmares that improving Geren Island could possibly get caught up in the federal fish regulatory powers that could trump all other laws and permits. But it happened.

The development of the EA/HCP was started by the consultant after receiving a very hefty change order because this work was never contemplated in the original design contract. The EA/HCP was to include everything wanted by the two fish agencies and the ODFW. Since completion of this very complex study along with the regulatory agencies approval process would take years and hundreds of thousands of dollars, the city was able to convince the fish agencies that work needs to be started very quickly on the modernization projects. The fish agencies then agreed to an interim memorandum of understanding (MOU) with USFWS that would ensure protection of the Oregon chub in the short term, while the EA/HCP was being prepared. The city agreed to make revisions to their modernization plans to accomplish this protection.

To gather information for preparing the MOU, Oregon chub were trapped, identified, and relocated to a north pond area of Geren Island. It was agreed the north pond would become a permanent habitat for Oregon chub. At this point disaster struck for the happy little Oregon chub in their contrived new habitat. Blue gill bass, a nonnative predator of the Oregon chub entered the north pond from the lower intake and destroyed most of the Oregon chub population.

City staff and the consultants worked intensely with the fish agencies to complete the EA/HCP and the implementing agreements. Long delays from several months to a year were experienced in obtaining reviews by the fish agencies.

However, by 1999 the NMFS was not interested in including steelhead and Chinook salmon in the EA/HCP because in March, 1999 they proposed a threatened listing under the ESA for both winter steelhead and spring run Chinook salmon. Because their listing was as threatened rather than endangered, the NMFS had more flexibility in issuing incidental take permits. They could do this by issuing Section 4(d) rules under the ESA. This very confusing regulatory process will be discussed in more detail later in this chapter.

Meanwhile, city staff and the consultants continued attempts to get approval of the draft EA/HCP from the USFWS, which continued to insist on revision after revision.

On January 4, 2001 city staff and the consultants met with USFWS and NMFS officials. The USFWS was concerned that the north pond habitat for the Oregon chub was not working because the city had not created a physical barrier for the blue gill bass and other predators from entering the pond. The city agreed to construct a screen that would keep the Oregon chub in the pond and deny access of the predators to the pond. This seemed to solve the final problem of the USFWS in completing the EA/HCP.

However, in early 2003 the city was still waiting for approval of the EA/HCP. Meanwhile all modernization projects at Geren Island including restoration of a wetland on the western side of the island had been completed.

The author believes the performance of the USFWS in reviewing the EA/HCP and working with the City has been overly expensive to residents of Salem. The agency probably defends itself with the excuse that "they are so busy that they just don't have the time to do timely reviews." The City and their consultants have worked extensively with many federal agencies with most appearing to have much heavier work loads than the USFWS and also able to work successfully with local governments. It appears to the author that USFWS has quite an attitude problem and they just simply don't care if they are responsive or timely. It seems appropriate that a member of Congress should request a General Accounting Office audit of their performance in protecting the Oregon chub.

The USFWS took five years to publish their ESA required *Oregon Chub Recovery Plan* after they listed the species as endangered in 1993. The recovery plan was published on September 3, 1998.[116] The recovery plan's objective as stated by the USFWS was: "The ultimate objective of this plan is to delist the Oregon chub, however, criteria for down listing to threatened are also established."

The *Oregon Chub Recovery Plan* will hopefully over time create better habitat conditions for the species, but at the same time, places the responsibility on the City of Salem to maintain the populations on Geren Island. The recovery plan states for the Geren Island population:

> Protect Oregon chub habitat through an agreement with the City of Salem by setting aside the north pond and north channel as habitat for Oregon chub. Protect and manage these sites in perpetuity.

The recovery plan also states some requirements for logging in habitat areas:

> Reduce the threat of logging related sedimentation by pursuing agreements with the USFS and commercial timber companies in the watershed to reduce the risk of degraded water quality resulting from logging induced sedimentation.

The City of Salem is certainly willing to do their part in conserving Oregon chub and it greatly appreciates USFWS involvement and regulatory clout to reduce "logging related sedimentation." This will be of benefit to water quality in the North Santiam watershed. But, in 2003 we know of no action by USFWS to start this process. We also know the USFWS has shown no interest in Salem's monitoring the river for sediment during storm events with the assistance of the U.S. Geological Survey. The agreement with the U.S. Geological Survey has cost the City of Salem several hundred thousand dollars and was not required by regulatory agencies. Perhaps the USFWS are monitoring the Geological Survey's web site and going ho-hum. Perhaps again they are just not interested.

However, on a positive note the USFWS will find when they get around to pursuing agreements on logging related sedimentation that the USFS and the BLM have made great strides in reducing sedimentation after the implementation of the 1993 Clinton Forest Management Plan.

On a negative note the USFWS will find the Oregon Forest Practice Act does little to control sedimentation from logging on private lands. The Oregon Department of Forestry has done a progressively better, but minimal job, when logging state forests but has a long way to go to equal the Clinton Forest Plan protections. So, USFWS when are you going to take on the private land owners in the watershed to control logging related sedimentation? Remember your recovery plan says: "U.S. Forest Service and *commercial timber companies*".

The recovery plan lists for the Geren Island north pond habitat the "threats" to Oregon chub. The listed threats are:

1. Non native fish present;
2. Threat of non native fish introduction;
3. Bull frogs present;
4. Possible agricultural chemical runoff; and,
5. Possible sedimentation from logging in the watershed.

This list does not include water diversions for agricultural and municipal purposes that may create slightly lower water elevations in the summer. This is a good decision by USFWS because of the substantial releases of water by the Detroit reservoir system in the summer. Historically during drought years the North Santiam River's natural flow prior to the dams construction was approximately 450 cfs. With flow augmentation the minimum flows are approximately 900 cfs during drought years. Thus no problem exists because of lowered flows in the summer even with the City of Salem's future full diversion of 147 cfs using all of the early 1856 and 1866 water rights. Even with this full diversion the flows will still be considerably higher than historic low flows when Oregon chub were thriving in the North Santiam prior to the construction of the dams.

It seems to the author that because the Oregon chub's native habitat was the wetlands and ponds created by winter time high flow events that the problem now is that the Corps of Engineers controls the river and does not allow it to overflow its banks. It seems the recovery plan should prioritize the need to allow the river to take back its flood way and flood plains. This in the author's humble opinion will do more to recover the Oregon chub than all the highly managed methods mandated by the USFWS.

In conclusion, it appears to the author that dealing with USFWS in protecting Oregon chub has been very cumbersome, incredibly expensive for City of Salem water customers and overly time consuming. The author wonders if there is not a much more efficient and economical way both for the federal government and local officials to accomplish the same objective, which is recovery of an endangered fish.

Section 6 of the ESA allows state government to take regulatory authority of conserving endangered and threatened species. In other words, if the State of Oregon met the requirements of the ESA, they could get primacy over the regulation of the ESA within Oregon. The state could also receive federal funds for this work. The author believes the ODFW could manage the endangered and threatened species much more efficiently than the federal agencies and recommends the state apply for primacy as soon as possible. I know that local governments who have responsibility for providing basic services to cities, like drinking water, would be a lot happier and the water rate payers would be happier as well.

## THREATENED SPRING CHINOOK AND WINTER STEELHEAD
Both the spring run Chinook salmon and the winter steelhead are anadromous fish. This means they start their lives in fresh water, migrate to the sea, where they spend most of their lives before returning to their fresh water stream birthplace to spawn and die.

Figure 13-3 shows a typical Chinook salmon. Both the spring Chinook salmon and winter steelhead are of the salmonid family and the same genus; *Oncorhynchus*. The spring Chinook salmon is of the species *tshawytscha* and the winter steelhead is of the species *mykiss*.

Chinook salmon spawning in the upper Willamette River system start their homeward migration up the Columbia and Willamette Rivers in the winter or early spring when river flows are high and they can negotiate Willamette Falls. They then progress upstream, mysteriously orient to their original birth place stream, spawn and die. The decaying carcass provides nutrients for the aquatic system which helps feed the next generation of salmon.

Steelhead have similar patterns of spawning as spring Chinook but their spawning season is usually in the winter.

FIGURE 13-3: A typical spring Chinook salmon of up to 36 inches in length and up to 20 to 30 pounds.

The upper Willamette River does not have a native run of fall Chinook salmon. These salmon runs start their homeward journey in the summer and spawn in the fall. Because Willamette Falls is a barrier during the late summer low flow season, the fall run chinook are not able to proceed upstream.

In the 19th century there were millions of salmon in the Columbia and Willamette systems. In the early 21st century only about 5% remained.[117] The loss of salmon was initially due to commercial fishing. Figure 13-4 is a photo of a commercial fishing operation in around the year 1900. Figure 13-5 shows a fish wheel that was commonly used in the late eighteen hundreds and early nineteen hundreds to harvest huge amounts of spring Chinook. Now with fishing regulations in place, the losses still continue because of adverse ocean conditions, non native predators, and a decrease of habitat due to dam building and development caused primarily by increased human populations.

The Willamette River in particular, and to some extent its tributaries, has been turned into a river highway crafted to efficiently carry flood waters away from developed areas. Prior to 1900 rivers and creeks in the region were complex and ribboned with vast flood plains and wetlands. The waterways were in many places full of tangled logs and overhanging vegetation to both pool and cool the waters, making ideal habitat for the salmon.

FIGURE 13-4: A typical commercial salmon fishery operation around 1900 on the Columbia River.

Picture Jason Lee and his small party of Methodist missionaries paddling up the Willamette in 1834 looking for a suitable site for their mission. What they encountered was a multi-channeled Willamette

River that was probably very confusing with its complexity. They did not see nor could they visualize the Willamette ditch of today. No wonder the fish are struggling to survive! But now the flood waters face little friction or obstacles in traveling to the Pacific Ocean. Can we regain the vitality the salmonid exhibited for thousands of years by creating manmade artificial habitat areas for these wild fish? The federal ESA mandates that we must try, regardless of the cost. And trying is what Salem is committed to do.

In 1996 when the City of Salem started their modernization program at Geren Island, the NMFS had Chinook salmon and winter steelhead listed as "candidate species" for listing under the ESA. At that time the NMFS was being pushed by environmental groups to list both species under the ESA.

A FISH WHEEL ON THE COLUMBIA RIVER

FIGURE 13-5: Typical fish wheel used in the late 19th century and early 20th century to harvest huge amounts of spring Chinook.

The 4(d) regulation concept is part of the ESA. When a species is listed as threatened, the ESA gives the Secretary (NMFS is under the Commerce Secretary) the authority to "issue such regulations as deemed necessary and advisable to provide for the conservation of such species."

The NMFS publishes an excellent citizens guide for understanding this strange and complex 4(d) rule.

The NMFS 4(d) rule introduces a term they call "limits" that are actually specific programs that allow for incidental take of the threatened fish. The final 4(d) rule contained 13 limits with limit #12 impacting cities directly. Limit #12 was titled "municipal, residential, commercial, and industrial development and redevelopment" with the acronym "MRCI" pronounced "mercy". (Please fish regulators have mercy on us poor local governments.) This limit "encourages" (that means requires, or you open the city to private citizen law suits) each city to develop a specific MRCI ordinance.

The MRCI limit specifies that an acceptable ordinance would include the following: development will avoid sensitive areas; prevent storm water discharges from impacting water quality; protect riparian areas; avoid stream crossings; protect historic stream meander patterns; protect wetlands; promote landscaping with native vegetation; prevent erosion and sediment runoff; avoid demands on water supply that would adversely affect fish; and, screen all water diversions.

Can the City of Salem recreate itself to satisfy the requirements of a MRCI limit? It may be more economical just to abandon the existing city and build a new one that NMFS approves of! However, on a serious note, it would be incredibly difficult for Salem to politically adopt a MRCI ordinance with all the suggested prohibitions. The cost impacts of doing so on both existing property owners and utility rate payers would be huge and quite possibly prohibitively expensive.

The 4(d) rule prohibits anyone from "taking" a listed salmon or steelhead, except in cases where the take is associated with an approved program (such as the thirteen 4(d) limits). Unfortunately the term "take" is defined in Section 3 of the ESA with little flexibility for interpretation. The ESA defines "take" as:

> The term take means to harass, harm, pursue, hunt, shoot, wound, kill, capture or collect or to attempt to engage in any such conduct.

Apparently the definition of all these terms were clear enough for everyone to prudently avoid a take except the term "harm." This word was apparently so ambiguous that a special rule had to be proposed by NMFS to properly define it. On May 1, 1998 the NMFS published in the *Federal Register* a draft definition of the term "harm" which is contained in the definition of "take." The NMFS final rule was published in the *Federal Register* on November 8, 1999.[118] A summary of the final rule follows:

> This final rule defines the term "harm" which is contained in the definition of "take" in the ESA. The purpose of this rule making is to clarify the type of actions that may result in a take of a listed species under the ESA. The final rule is not a change in existing law. It provides clear notification to the public that habitat modification or degradation may harm listed species and, therefore constitute a take under the ESA as well as ensuring consistency between the NMFS and the USFWS. This final rule defines the word "harm" to include any act which actually kills or injuries fish or wildlife and emphasizes that such acts may include significant habitat modification or degradation that significantly impairs essential behavioral patterns of fish or wildlife.

The rule is very clear on "harm" when a fish is killed. However, it is not clear when a fish is injured. If a fish bumps its nose on a man-made structure, is the fish injured? Some regulators would like to think so. If a fish is hooked and then released by a person fishing, is the fish injured? The regulators say no, but if the fish could talk, I'm sure it would say yes. This is still very confusing for poor local officials trying to improve essential services and being faced with this incredibly confusing rule.

Additionally, this rule of harm, when applied to habitat, depends entirely on the definition of "significant." If essential behavioral patterns are impaired significantly or there is a significant habitat modification or degradation then there is a take. I assume if these factors are not significant, then there is no take.

The final rule very bravely attempts to define "significant modification" to be:

> If significant it must be capable of resulting in the death or injury of fish or wildlife. Habitat modification or degradation will depend on an evaluation of all the available evidence of a specific situation or action(s) and will most often be determined on a case by case basis.

The definition of "significant" is circular to the definition of harm and to "be determined on a case by case basis." Obviously these definitions create no feeling of confidence by local officials when planning critical public facilities when endangered or threatened fish or wildlife have any possibility of being harmed. Definitions with more certainty are needed.

I firmly believe its essential that the fate of a planned public facility must not be at the discretion of a fresh graduate in fish and wildlife management with no experience or understanding in state and local laws governing the planning and management of urban areas. Environmental management must take a broad view with decision makers representing the spectrum of disciplines used for urban situations. Fish agency staff usually lack this broad view. Maybe Congress should amend the ESA and give local officials more discretion in carrying out this most important environmental act.

## ARE WATER RIGHTS AT RISK?

The bottom line for Salem is how does the ESA and the multitude of federal regulations relate to the city's modernization program at Geren Island and the construction of a new water transmission line?

First, as previously discussed, construction in a wetland area of Geren Island triggered the application of a Corps of Engineers 404 permit which in turn triggered consultation with the USFWS because of the endangered Oregon chub and the species of concern, the northern red-legged frog. The USFWS required an EA/HCP for an incidental take permit for the Oregon chub. The city has mitigated any harm to the Oregon chub by creating and maintaining a protected habitat on Geren Island in perpetuity. After several years the city is still waiting for final approval of the EA/HCP.

It must be emphasized here that the City of Salem did nothing to create the demise of the Oregon chub. Their demise has largely been created by loss of habitat after the Corps of Engineers started operating the Detroit Dam system to prevent annual high flows from entering the flood plain and preventing the creation of excellent habitat pools. Their demise has also been accelerated by the introduction of nonnative predators such as blue gill bass. Never the less, the USFWS used their regulatory power to require the City of Salem, at considerable expense and frustration, to take responsibility for the survival of the species in the North Santiam River.

A lingering question is whether or not the USFWS is now satisfied or will they require even more of the City of Salem? Will they try to exact some of Salem's earliest water rights and dedicate the water to the fish instead of canceling some very junior water rights? This is still an open question because the city still has more wetlands to contend with when constructing the new replacement water transmission line.

As mentioned above, the City's *Water System Master Plan* recognizes the need to replace a 1937 water transmission line, a 36 inch concrete pipe. Since the existing two transmission lines have a peak capacity of 66 mgd the City has the objective of replacing the 36 inch line with a 75 mgd line when peak demands are above 60 mgd. Water conservation in the city has recently reduced the peak demands to less than 60 mgd but this demand is expected to be exceeded between the years 2005 and 2010. The city would then start the permitting and construction so that the new line is operational within two years. With the new 75 mgd line, and the existing 54 inch line with capacity of 50 mgd, this would give the city a peak capacity of 125 mgd or sufficient capacity for at least the next 30 years.

The design of the new 75 mgd line depended on obtaining a Corps of Engineers 404 permit so pre-permit discussions were started with the Corps, NMFS, USFWS, and State of Oregon agencies. The fish agencies warned there could be a take if additional water were to be diverted from the North Santiam River for municipal use. In other words if no other water sources were available to Salem, the fish agencies were saying any population or industrial growth in Salem that requires more water from the North Santiam would be a take. This possible interpretation of the ESA set off alarm bells in the minds of city staff.

The city has been diverting on a peak day about 50 mgd while owning the earliest senior water right certificates and water right permits of 147 mgd. By state law these senior rights of a municipality were gold plated. They were guaranteed because the state understood the need for a city to have a reserve of water rights for inevitable future growth.

In discussing the possibility of losing water rights with private attorneys with special knowledge of the ESA, the City was informed that ESA trumps all state laws including state prior appropriation laws for water rights.

Why did the fish agencies believe that diverting more water in conformance with state laws may constitute an ESA take? The answer appears to be incredibly confusing but if this power does exist it must be part of the ESA or be defined in the Federal Register as adopted regulations. There is a possibility that it may be legal if it is defined in an agency "Procedures" which were never published for public comments. The Procedures explain in detail how the federal services will administer the ESA. A discussion of each guiding document for federal agencies follows.

ESA  The Act defines "take" which includes the term "harm"

Federal Register  The final rule defining the term "harm" was published November 8, 1999. This final rule includes a comment #14 which states: "Several commentators stated that the current owner of a dam lawfully installed before a species is listed should not be liable for a take based on a subsequent listing. In the view of these commentators liability for take must be based upon some action occurring after the effective date of listing. Response: "any person who engages in diverting water may by engaged in a take if the diversion of water injures or kills listed species by significantly impairing essential behavioral patterns."

Procedures for Conducting Consultation[119] This 1998 Handbook for the NMFS and USFWS biologists gives a detailed procedure both for conducting a consultation and how to evaluate a proposed action for harming fish. Whether decisions that come from using the Procedures have been tested in the courts is not known. The fish agencies apparently use this handbook as their bible because there is a considerable amount of turnover within the agencies and therefore many staff are very inexperienced but still carry a huge amount of authority. The Procedures include a detailed explanation of their "but for" test which tests the interdependency and interrelatedness of actions to determine whether one action which in itself does not "take" could lead to another that would. The "but for" test appears on the surface to be overly confusing. Most non-agency people find this test to be totally non-understandable.

Following is the explanation quoted from the Consultation Handbook for the "but for" test:

> ..as a practical matter, the analysis of whether other activities are interrelated or interdependent with the proposed action under consultation should be conducted by applying a "but for" test. The biologist should ask whether another activity in question would occur "but for" the proposed action under consultation. If the answer is "no" that the activity in question would not occur but for the proposed action. If the answer is "yes", that the activity in question would occur regardless of the proposed action under consultation then the activity is not interdependent or interrelated and would not be analyzed with the effects of the action under consultation.

Obviously this test which can decide whether a simple informal process of consultation is required or an incredibly complex formal process is required is crucial to applicants trying to obtain a permit to complete their projects.

The City of Salem applied in 2001 for a 404 permit with the Corps of Engineers to install twin 75 mgd pipelines from Geren Island across the north channel of the North Santiam River. The two pipelines were to be terminated just after the river crossing and connect to the existing two transmission lines. These crossings the City stated in their permit application would not have the potential to divert more water from the river. The Corps issued the permit after informal consultation with the NMFS and the USFWS which included the determination that the direct effects of construction would not harm the fish (the city passed the "but for" test because the pipelines carrying water to the city did not increase the quantity of diverted water, therefore no other relative action would occur that would harm fish such as maybe the water demands of a new major industry in Salem).

After the year 2005 the city will apply for continuing one of the 75 mgd transmission lines to Franzen Reservoir. This pipeline will create the potential for increased diversion of water with the potential it will produce a negative "but for" test and therefore trigger a formal process of consultation with NMFS and USFWS. The "but for" test will determine the effects of increased diversions that are interrelated to or interdependent with the construction of the transmission line. Depending on this determination and decision to mitigate the harmful action, future increased diversions may not be possible according to the fish agencies.

The City of Salem hopefully would strongly object to the fish agencies taking (this is taking property and not the same as taking a publicly owned fish) senior water rights as mitigation for possible future low flows created by cumulative actions of all users of river water, many of which have very recent junior water rights.

There are several options open for the fish agencies if they believe water right diversions are taking fish. They are:

1. If ESA trumps all other laws, then the federal fish agencies could order the Corps of Engineers to increase augmented flows from Detroit Reservoir during the crucial spawning and migration times. This option should be looked at first and would be the easiest to implement. The Corps of Engineers have a federal authorization to provide water for conservation but no authorization to provide water for recreation such as keeping Detroit Reservoir full to the brim for the pleasure of the boaters. The question is what is more important, the

fish having enough water, or a full reservoir all the way to Labor Day? This would be a very politically charged option because the boaters can get very loud when their recreational playground is threatened.

2. Section 5 of the ESA gives the fish agencies the authority to acquire by purchase, donation or otherwise, lands, waters, or interest therein. The fish agencies could buy or if necessary condemn water rights sufficient for providing minimum flows for the fish. If this strategy were used it would make good economic sense to buy junior rights because their value is far less than senior rights.

3. The federal fish agencies use Section 7 of the ESA as their only method to force agencies that apply for federal permits to mitigate problems with habitat or water conditions. The example of the USFWS requiring the City of Salem to maintain habitat for the Oregon chub in perpetuity is a good example.

Section 7 does not have to be the primary weapon of the fish agencies. The fish agencies have the authority under the ESA to regulate any person or agency doing harm to fish protected by the ESA. The fish agencies could regulate the worst offenders first. Who is responsible for the low numbers of the Oregon chub? Is it the Corps of Engineers? If so, regulate them first. If the regulated parties object, then let the courts decide if they have harmed or taken protected fish. This option would redirect the fish agencies to do analysis, identify the takers of fish, and take appropriate actions.

## CONCLUSIONS

The listing of the Oregon chub, spring run Chinook salmon and winter steelhead in the upper Willamette basin has created a variety of unanticipated problems for a future city water source. It also brings the State of Oregon with their land use laws and the City of Salem's "Salem Futures" long term planning effort back to square one.

The city has a solid objective to protect and conserve the protected fish and has started a very proactive process for finding solutions for saving fish and to provide the city with sufficient water for a healthy economy and normal growth. The city has initiated a very proactive "Water Management Plan" that is intended to analyze the legal, biological and engineering options of a future water supply for the City with the full knowledge of the expectations of the federal and state fish agencies. Hopefully the fish agencies can take off their regulatory hat and be full partners in developing this plan. The Water Management Plan's major elements are planned to be:

1. Description of the Water System

The plan shall provide a detailed description of the City water system including sources, water rights, storage, contracts and agreements, system capacity limitations, water use and demand, customer base profile and schematics of the system.

The plan shall provide a thorough assessment of current and future supply, including sources of supply, sizes, kinds, historical measurements, reliability, permits, system limitations and capacity, and overall production.

The plan shall focus equally on the demand component of water management by reviewing production, delivery, annual water use, rate structure, and projected future need.

2. Environmental Issues

The plan shall analyze the impacts of the ESA and the associated species of concern (candidate, threatened or endangered) with regards to current and future water withdrawals, Water Master Plan projects and provide a recommended strategy to deal with ESA issues.

3. Conservation Measures

The plan shall review the current conservation strategies, determine effectiveness, and develop a revised conservation program to address the community's future water needs.

4. Water Curtailment Planning

The plan shall analyze and develop options for handling situations of severe water shortage or need. The analysis shall consider the likelihood and frequency of severe water shortages or need and account of options for curtailing water use during these times.

Other elements of the plan shall address emergency and contingency plans for water management (environmental and habitat needs, natural disaster system failures) prioritization of water uses and health and safety issues.

5. Management Strategies

After assessing and analyzing the supply, demand, and environmental components of the City's water system, the plan shall address management strategies for meeting demand and addressing any issues resulting form the assessment.

The strategies shall include "supply management" tools such as development of new, alternative or secondary water sources or securing new technologies for water supply. "Demand management" strategies shall consider conservation measures, changes in rate structures or delivery systems, or improved technology for water use.

6. Completion of the required EA/HCP as required by the USFWS to mitigate the impacts on the Oregon chub (later negotiated change order).

The city has retained HDR Engineering along with several specialized fisheries and legal sub consultants. The "Water Management Plan" is scheduled for completion in 2003. Hopefully in completing this plan with the intensive coordination it will require with fish agencies, an agreed plan for the future can be found.

Latest Fish Issues

The fate of listing the salmon as threatened throughout the western United States has recently been put in question by the U.S. District Judge, Michael Hogan His ruling was specifically for coho salmon in coastal rivers of Oregon but conceivably could be applied to all listed salmon.

The *Oregonian* newspaper in Portland on their web page on September 14, 2001 reported:

> Hogan said the fisheries service erred by considering only wild fish and by not counting the far more numerous hatchery born Coho for protection. This finding knocks the legal legs from under two dozen West Coast salmon and steelhead listings made by the fisheries since 1991.
>
> Hatchery born salmon are rarely counted when the fisheries service decides whether to list stocks under the ESA. Fisheries service officials say they are most concerned about wild salmon and worry that hatchery salmon threaten wild stocks by contaminating their gene pool or taking food and habitat.
>
> An attorney with the San Francisco based Pacific Legal Foundation which brought the action said hatchery fish are genetically indistinguishable from wild fish. Not considering abundant runs of hatchery fish when making listing decisions, Russ Brooks said, allows the federal government to use the ESA to impose unnecessary and Draconian land use controls.

On July 25, 2002, the *Statesman-Journal* reported that the NMFS has proposed a new policy that would give hatchery salmon endangered species status. NMFS said the proposal was in draft form and won't be finalized until the end of 2002. ( By 2003 the proposal has still not been finalized.)

However, regardless of any federal action by NMFS that may include the delisting of wild salmon on the North Santiam, the endangered listing of Oregon chub must still be dealt with by the City of Salem if further modernization projects are to be continued.

The Water Management Plan became after review of the scope of work by the USFWS the mechanism to wrap up all remaining issues with the fish agencies. A huge issue that still remained undecided was completion of the EA/HCP required by the USFWS to mitigate any takes of the Oregon chub. The city and USFWS agreed to wrap this requirement into the Water Management Plan and thereby probably greatly increasing the scope of the EA/HCP and the cost of the Water Management Plan.

Because the USFWS diddled with the approval of the EA/HCP for five years, it appears that with the increased scope, all bets are now off as to how long in the future it will take to complete this requirement. Is this incredibly technical nitpicking necessary, and is it fair to Salem water rate payers who are paying the consulting bills? I doubt it.

# Acknowledgments

Salem history is the story of the Kalapuya "people of the land," missionaries, the Oregon trail pioneers, entrepreneurs, hustlers, land speculators, farmers, industrialists, government workers, environmentalists, and everybody that has called home the area around the capital city of Oregon. So, thanks to every past and present resident for supporting the evolution and modernization of what I believe to be Salem's most prized possession—one of the most pure and healthy water systems in the world. Truly a sweet water system.

Special thanks for assisting in the researching of background materials and editing of the book to Tina Schweickert. Without her this book could not have been written. And also thanks to Zeb Schweickert for his participation and expert assistance in desktop publishing software.

Thanks also to Monica Mersinger, the head and inspiration of the Salem History project. She first encouraged me to write a very brief history of the water system. Monica, I'm very sorry it did not turn out to be brief, but at least I finished my assignment as a dedicated Salem History volunteer. Thanks to Don Christensen, the ultimate Salem History volunteer, who assisted me in making some historic photos available for the book. And, thanks to Hudson Schweickert for scanning the maps and photos.

Salem staff that assisted me in locating valuable water system information and materials were Tim Gerling, Dean Bartell, Jon Bolliger, Louise Klukus, Jim Bonnet, Paul Eckley, Sofia Hobet, Deborah Herman, Dave Prock, Sandy Olds, all in the public works department, and Jane Kirby, reference librarian with the Salem Library.

Thanks to retired City Manager Bob Moore for filling in some gaps of information on previous city managers, Kent Mathewson, Doug Ayers and himself (the three city managers who all knew each other before coming to Salem and all graduates of Syracuse University).

The success of Salem's water system owes much to elected officials dedicated to protecting Salem's watershed. First is the former Governor of Oregon and the retired distinguished and Honorable U.S. Senator Mark Hatfield. Senator Hatfield sponsored federal legislation to protect much of the watershed, including its crown jewel—the Opal

Creek Wilderness area. The residents of Salem owe a tremendous debt of gratitude to the Senator for his dedication to the watershed.

Thanks also to the Honorable U.S. Representative Darlene Hooley who has taken a keen interest in the health of the watershed and has met several times in the field with USFS staff, environmentalists and Salem staff to mediate differences of opinion about forest management and its affects on drinking water.

Probably surprising to Chuck Bennett that I remember this, but in 1982, State Representative Bennett sponsored legislation to stop the Eugene Water and Electric Board from building a hydroelectric dam on the North Santiam downstream from the present Big Cliff dam. The City of Salem was opposed to this dam because of the devastation of the river during construction and the long term impacts to water quality. The city appeared to be getting nowhere in their opposition until Representative Bennett's bill passed the Oregon State Legislature successfully stopping the dam development. Thanks Chuck, please keep up the good work. Maybe in the future you can assist in stopping any copper mines from locating in the watershed.

Special thanks to Bryan Johnston, State Representative in 1995, who led the fight to stop a Canadian copper corporation, Kinross Copper, from developing a large copper mine in the Opal Creek area. If developed, this mine would have left a mountain of toxic mine tailings. Also Susan Smith of the Willamette law school and Al White of Oregon Watersheds led the legal fight to oppose Kinross' "taking" law suit. Keeping this large mine and huge toxic tailings pile out of the watershed's national forest area was of utmost importance in preserving the watershed. Thanks to Dr. Louisa Silva for her expert testimony at public hearings. Thanks to Dr. John Currie for his support in stopping the copper mine and special thanks for his encouragement in writing this book and the continuation of a sweet water supply for Salem.

Several mayors of Salem have been supporters of the water system including P.M. Gregory who was elected in May, 1930 as the head of a Mountain Water Party who successfully put on the ballot and secured the election victory of a $2.5 million bond issue to purchase the private water system and construct the mountain water system.

Mayor V.E. Kuhn in 1936 championed a Stayton Island water source and defeated the energetic opponents of this source. Mayor Al Loucks in 1951 completed an agreement with Oregon Pulp and Paper Company to acquire a desperately needed 1856 priority water right of 60 cfs. In 1957, Mayor Robert White led the City Council in approving a $3.75 million bond issue for expanding the Stayton Island water source.

Mayors Kent Aldrich, and Sue Miller, highly supported the water system by leading the City Council in the purchase of all of Boise Cascade's 1856 priority water rights. Mayors Roger Gertenrich and Mike Swaim were very active in advocating protection of the watershed. Mayors R.G. Andersen-Wyckoff, Roger Gertenrich, Mike Swaim and Janet Taylor courageously supported water rate increases so that the modernization of the water system was financially possible.

Thanks to the Salem Public Library's photographic collection. The following photographs are from their collection: Oregon Pulp and Paper aerial opposite the title page, Figures 1-2, 1-3, 1-4, 2-1, 2-2, 2-3, 3-2, 4-1,4-2, 5-1, 5-2, 10-2, 13-4, 13-5, and photographs in the Appendix of Bob Moore, Russ Abolt, Larry Wacker, and John Geren.

Thanks to the public works department for generously furnishing historical reports and photographs. Photos shown as Figures 6-1 and 6-2 were furnished by Sofia Hobet, Water Superintendent.

Thanks to the Oregon Department of Fish and Wildlife for the photographs copied from their web page and shown as Figures 13-1, 13-2 and 13-3.

And, finally, thanks to all mayors, city councilors, members of the public, and city staff who have stood in support of protecting the valuable mountain watershed it that may continue to provide pure waters for generations to come.

# Epilogue

> Of all our natural resources, water has become the most precious . .
> . . In any age when man has forgotten his origins and is blind to his
> most essential needs for survival, water along with other resources
> has become the victim of his indifference.
>
> Rachel Carson, *Silent Spring*

I am fascinated with this indifference so elegantly stated by Rachel
Carson, who almost single handily created the modern environmental
movement.

Today, Salem citizens turn on a water tap and drink, bath, and
cook with little thought of where the water comes from or how the
water system became a reality. Does that mean that Salem residents
are indifferent to this precious resource—pure, sweet, and healthy
water? Undoubtedly, this resource will become increasingly rare in
coming years as the Willamette Valley bursts at the seams with development to serve an ever increasing population. Indifference, my dear
Salem residents, will surely compromise in the future this great water
resource that we all today enjoy.

Hopefully, this book has identified the present and possibly future
problems the water supply is faced with.

Regardless of future problems, Salem city government has accomplished a miracle in this time of government distrust. It has provided
a service to its citizens that is accepted without criticism of its quality. The recent soaring water rates has, however, caused considerable
concern with local industry and the City Council, but not to the extent
that they fear recall petitions, which has happened in many communities. Hopefully, the cost of continuing this pure healthy water system will not lead to a political reversal of continuing to adequately
fund an excellent water system.

It seems fitting to end this book with stating my commitment while
public works director and the people who motivated me during my
career. Hopefully, I have been able to motivate a very fine public
works staff to continue this tradition.

I am very proud that for 24 years I was privileged to contribute as an engineer and manager for the City of Salem's public works department—14 years of this time was spent as the public works director providing communications to the public and the City Council, and best of all working with a very dedicated and motivated city staff.

I was motivated early in my career by three remarkable city employees: the heart and soul of the developing water system, John Geren; the first city manager I worked under, Ralph Hanley; and, the best city manager I worked for, Larry Wacker.

The citizens of Salem owe a huge gratitude to John Geren who guided the development of the water system. He was water department manager from the 1950's to the 1970's . Geren, as a young engineer in 1937, participated in the conception and construction of Stayton Island (later named Geren Island in his honor). He gave the citizens of Salem expertise and dedication to the water system until his retirement in 1974.

I was very fortunate to have known Mr. Geren after his retirement. He was a crusty disciplinarian and very displeased with the direction of the "new" utility/public works department (later shortened to public works department after Geren's death) that I was part of in 1978. He let me know in terms John Geren was infamous for that "we were incompetent and the water system was going to hell."

At one of our meetings at his house he asked me if "the engineers" at city hall were still made to operate the Stayton Island system and the water supply reservoirs on the weekend. I knew of this custom from the person who hired me and was my boss for a couple of years, Herb Arnold. So it did not surprise me that Mr. Geren was interested in this, because knowing how to operate the system by the city hall staff was a deeply held value. Mr. Geren, Herb Arnold and the other staff at city hall knew every valve in the supply system. Mr. Geren made everyone except the "girls" do this duty when their turn came up on Saturday and Sunday. Mr. Geren had total dedication to the system and he expected the same from his staff.

Anyway, I confessed that I was not required to operate the supply system. I told him that Keith Farrow, the water superintendent and Lyle Huffaker, the water quality supervisor operated the system with their staff. Mr. Geren then told me that "engineers" should never design or be involved in a water system in any way if they did not know where the valves were located and know how to operate them. I said nothing at this point because I only vaguely knew how to operate the system and I had never held that responsibility on the weekend. I did regret this, but holding down a desk at city hall had become a full time job.

I defended myself and the department as well as I could during these discussions, but I knew I was out classed and it was best if I just listened. And listen I did. I came away from these sometimes vitriolic discussions with a deep feeling of John Geren's passion and caring for his baby—the water system. I can only hope that when he died in the early 1980's that he was feeling better about the new generation of water managers in Salem.

A most memorable teacher was City Manager, Ralph Hanley. Ralph and I started to work at the city on the same day, June 1, 1978. I was one of the engineers in public works and Ralph with his aggressive management style was "the boss." Immediately after arriving in Salem, Ralph started working on a pet project: urban growth management to the extreme chagrin of the land developers in Salem. I got the short straw in public works and was assigned to Ralph's staff committee to produce this plan along with Roger Budke in community development, Glen Hadley in parks, John Elegant of the city managers office and Bill Blair, assistant city attorney. We were Ralph's urban growth storm troopers. After the political war ended between Ralph and the land developers, Ralph of course won a complete victory. But I was exhausted. Ralph had given me a great introduction to city government by cramming it down my throat all the way.

I questioned Ralph's way of treating people, but I've never learned more so quickly in my entire life. Ralph was a shooting star and only lasted five years as city manager but he left a lasting impression and taught me a lot of skills that came in real handy over the years. He also taught me how not to deal with people and I hope I was true to that throughout my career. But only my colleagues know the truth of that.

Larry Wacker is a life long resident of Salem and understood the culture of the capital city better than anyone. However in my opinion the biggest mistake in his life was studying psychology at the University of Oregon. He would have probably been a better city manager if he had studied civil engineering at Oregon State University (just half kidding, Larry).

Larry started his career with the City of Salem with the personnel department, moved to the city managers office as assistant city manager and was appointed city manager in the early 1990's. Larry and I worked closely together on several projects before he became city manager and he learned quite a lot about public works. However, I have to admit he and I did not have a perfect working relationship, but he always, and I mean always helped me through crisis situations.

Larry was a straight communicator and department heads and the City Council respected that very much. When he retired in the year 2000, I knew that things would never be the same for me at the City of Salem. I was right. I retired about one year later.

After retiring on January 31, 2002 after 14 years as public works director, and, because of my link with John Geren, I started to think I was probably the last person who would ever want to write the history of Salem's water supply system. Coincidentally, the City of Salem's library was beginning a Salem History Project. Monica Mersinger, the project director requested I furnish a very small piece of Salem's history—the water system. I, of course accepted the assignment as an unpaid volunteer of the library. What a switch for a public works person! So, many thanks to George Happ the library director who started the Salem History Project and retired before I did, and to Gail Warner the current library director for leading this project.

As a final note, I hope this book will provide the citizens of Salem a feeling of pride of having the earth's most precious resource—pure healthy water with just a turn of their water tap, and at a very affordable price of about $2.00 per 1000 gallons. Salem residents, that's compared to about 8,000 pints of bottled water that may not be as pure as Salem's tap water. And, at about a buck for a pint of bottled water, that's $8,000 for bottled water of questionable quality, compared to $2.00 for one of the best quality drinking waters in the world. Salem residents, I sure hope you insist on keeping it that way.

# Appendix A
# A Very Brief History Of Salem
# Emphasizing Water Development

The first residents of the Salem area were Kalapuya "people of the land" (term supplied by Calvin Hecocta of the Klamath Tribe). Archaeological evidence shows the Kalapuya camped at several locations along Mill Creek starting about 4000 B.C. The Kalapuya occupied the entire Willamette Valley prior to settlement by Canadian trappers and American pioneers. The Kalapuya were dependent on the common camas plant *(Camassia quamash)* which grew in and near the luxuriant wetlands in the valley. Meriwether Lewis's journal describes a meadow of purple camas seen from the distance as "resembling a lake of fine clear water." The Kalapuya subsistence economy was based primarily on the collection of camas roots which were ground into flour and other wild plant products such as acorns and berries. Wild game, insects, and salmon were also part of their diet but of secondary importance.

Since the Kalapuya were dependent on wild plants, they managed their environment by improving the plant's growing conditions by burning competing brush and trees. This helped to maintain open meadows and oak savannas which produced plentiful growth of edible plants that were much more easy to harvest.

The first European descent settlers to the Willamette Valley area were retired trappers from the Hudson Bay Company whose base of operation was at Fort Vancouver, Washington. Unfortunately for the Kalapuya these first settlers brought a variety of European diseases from which the Kalapuya had no natural immunity. Most of the Kalapuya died from smallpox and malaria in the 1820's and 1830's prior to the first American settlers.

Jason Lee, a Methodist missionary started the first mission in 1834 in an attempt to Christianize the Kalapuya. The mission was located on the east side of the Willamette River about 10 miles to the north of present Salem. (The Willamette Mission Park was created over a century later by the State of Oregon to honor this historic site.) However, the Lee mission found the site to be very flood prone and unhealthy.

In 1837 Anna Marie Pittman arrived at the mission from Boston. After a short engagement, she and Jason Lee were married July 16, 1837.

On the arrival of the "great reinforcement" in 1840 of about 40 additional missionaries, along with machinery for a flour mill and a sawmill they moved the mission to the "Chemeketa Plain" (now the City of Salem).

The missionaries then constructed a water powered flour mill and sawmill on Mill Creek close to its confluence with the Willamette River at what was called Boones Island. (The original site was located at about where Broadway Street crosses Mill Creek.) The missionaries also built a school for the Kalapuya called the Manual Labor School.

From 1840 through 1844 the Methodist Church in Boston sponsoring the mission became progressively dissatisfied with the progress and the great expense of the Manual Labor School. Jason Lee was recalled back to Boston and the church sent Reverend George Gary to liquidate the holdings of the mission. Since the flour mill and the sawmill could only operate during the high water period on Mill Creek, it became an uneconomical operation. Reverend Gary then sold the mills to John Force in 1844 for $6,000.

In 1844 the Methodist Mission sold the original school building and the site of the Manual Labor School to the Oregon Institute trustees with David Leslie as chair. The Oregon Institute eventually evolved into Willamette University, the oldest college west of the Mississippi River.

In 1844 William Willson moved to the Chemeketa Plain from Tacoma, where he had been stationed as a Methodist missionary. Willson arrived in the northwest in 1937 as part of the second reinforcement of the Methodist Mission along with David Leslie and Leslie's wife. Willson was an experienced carpenter and self proclaimed physician. He called himself Dr. William Willson. Willson married Chloe Clarke in 1840 shortly after she arrived in Oregon as part of the great reinforcement. Later William and Chloe played extremely important roles in the early development of Willamette University and the City of Salem.

In 1846 the name "Salem" was chosen instead of Chemeketa as the name for the growing tiny village. In 1846 William Willson was appointed by the Oregon Institute as their agent to create a town plat with lots to sell that would provide needed revenue to the Institute. A newspaper in Oregon City the *Oregon Spectator* advertised the lots to be sold by auction on August 20, 1846.

In 1848 Thomas Cox opened the first dry goods store in Salem at the corner of Commercial and Ferry Streets. In 1849 J.B. McClane opened the second store in Salem. Salem then had 16 buildings.

In 1850 the United States Congress enacted the Oregon Territory Homestead Act. This act allowed an individual to claim 640 acres of land. In 1847 the Oregon Institute, in anticipation of this act, transferred most of its land holdings including most of the present downtown of Salem to Dr. Willson. Willson made his final proof of his claim in 1853 and title of the 640 acres was awarded to him. Half of this claim under provisions of the federal act went to Willson's wife Chloe who was not bound by any prior agreements with the Oregon Institute. Therefore Chloe ended up with title to 360 acres of prime Salem real estate.

After all donation land claims were completed in Salem, the Willson's, David Leslie, Josiah Parish, Alvin Waller, and the Oregon Institute all had obtained large land parcels in what is now the heart of Salem.

In 1849 the Oregon Territorial Government was authorized by the U.S. Congress. In that year John Force obtained a water right from the Territorial Government to divert North Santiam River water to Mill Creek through a dug ditch which was later called Salem Ditch. Force, who had purchased the water powered saw mill and flour mill from the Methodist Mission in 1844, soon realized that Mill Creek had insufficient water in the summer to power the mills.

In 1850 Force hired laborers to start digging a ditch of about six miles connecting the North Santiam and Mill Creek upstream from Salem. However, Force forgot to get the approval of the residents in the area who hotly protested this farsighted venture by a business man from the "big" village of Salem. Apparently the protests were especially caustic because even though Force obtained easements from the property owners along the route, he abandoned the project.

In 1850 the Territorial Government designated Salem as the capital of the Oregon Territory.

In 1851 Salem's first official steamboat, the Hoosier, arrived. The territorial capital moved from Oregon City to Salem and the first legislative session met in Salem. Asahel Bush started the *Oregon Statesman* newspaper.

In 1852 Salem was named capital of the Oregon Territory by the U.S. Congress. The First Methodist Church erected its first building on State Street. Oregon Territorial delegates and all the official territorial documents traveled to Salem from Oregon City by steamboat. The Oregon Territorial Legislature was forced to meet in a private residence during their first session in Salem. However the delegates were anxious to build their own capitol and in 1853 construction started on a frame building at about where the existing capitol now stands.

In the 1850's Salem grew much more prosperous with a thriving economy built around farm exports to Portland and California. In 1853 one store was robbed of $5,000 in coin and gold dust. What a difference the California gold rush made to the prosperity of Salem.

In 1855 Salem almost lost its home as the Territorial Legislature. The legislators packed up and went to Corvallis. They later decided to move back to Salem but at least one person was not happy with that decision because shortly after an arsonist burned down the first capitol building.

In January, 1857 the Territorial Legislature attempted to grant the city an official city charter. On February 9, 1857 an election was held in this city of 700 pioneers and Willie Kenyon, a photographer, was elected mayor. That election was ruled invalid because both houses of the Territorial Legislature did not properly pass the charter bill.

Oregon was recognized as a state in 1859. In 1860 a bill was proposed to grant Salem a city charter. However, Salem residents could not wait until the charter was official as they initiated a mayoral election in May, 1860.

Lucian Heath was elected the first mayor of Salem on May 19, 1860. The charter was granted October 22, 1860 by the state legislature which made the election legal.

Heath took office on November 22, 1860. An important event had already occurred in 1856 when John Force started Willamette Woolen Manufacturing Company and had Salem Ditch dug to divert North Santiam River water to Mill Creek. The mill on Boones Island was water powered and was the largest industry in Salem. Mayor Heath realized the shallow wells used by most residents and businesses in Salem were unhealthy and he initiated a committee of aldermen to discuss with John Force the use of the diverted water for city use. However, negotiations with Force, who held the water right, failed.

E.N. Cooke was elected mayor in May, 1861 and took office in January, 1862. He continued negotiations with Force but no progress was made. Meanwhile, the Willamette River started to become pol-

luted with human and industrial sewage which affected the health of
Salem residents using the Willamette River for drinking water.

In the winter of 1861 the Willamette River flooded the small city
and created extensive damage in the downtown area and along the
creeks. The 1861 flood was one of the largest on record.

H.M. Thatcher served as mayor in 1863 and 1864. During his tenure drinking water conditions continued to deteriorate as individual
wells became more and more polluted. Salem was probably a very unhealthy place during this time. During his term the Mill Race or South
Power was dug and connected Mill Creek to the site occupied presently by Boise Cascade. Since there was a about a 30 foot drop near
where the Mill Race crossed Liberty Street, it gave the city a great opportunity to use this drop to power a hydraulic ram and pump water
to four cisterns in the downtown area. This provided the volunteer
fire companies a ready supply of fire fighting water which was desperately needed.

John H. Moores was mayor from 1865 through 1868. The city continued to prosper during his term. The Mill Race was completed which
provided power for Salem Woolen Mill and Salem Flour Mill at the
foot of Pringle Creek where the existing Boise Cascade plant is now
located. The volunteer fire companies continued to grow with additional equipment and with water from the downtown cisterns available for emergency use.

During his term the city's water supply continued to be individual
wells. However in 1868 an entrepreneur Chinese resident, Lee Tong,
initiated a water service by delivering Willamette River water to residents and businesses in discarded oil tins. Tong's water service was
the first private water service in Salem, however modest it was.

Salem's economy continued to grow. In 1868 the Ladd and Bush
bank building was built on the corner of State and Commercial
Streets.

(There is uncertainty about who was mayor between 1864 and
1868. The version above is from the *1871 City Directory*. However the
City of Salem's web site, the Online History Project, lists H. Moores
as mayor in 1864, Q. Wilson as mayor in 1865 and John H. Moores as
mayor from 1866 through 1868.)

L.S. Scott was mayor in 1869 and 1870. During his tenure the city's
Board of Aldermen authorized the first piped water system in Salem
by granting a franchise to the Salem Water Company for the purpose
of supplying water to the businesses and residents in what is now the
downtown area of Salem. Salem Water Company was owned by J.M

Martin and David Allen, local downtown merchants; W.F. Boothby, an engineer; and N. Stapleton, an investor. The business plan of Salem Water Company was very optimistic. They hoped to make the water company a profitable business venture by constructing a deep cistern near the Willamette River where the existing Riverfront Park is now located. They believed the water seeping into the cistern would be filtered by the sandy soils and be clean and healthy. They planned to pump water from the cistern to an 80 foot high wooden water reservoir and lay steel pipe throughout the downtown area.

In 1870 the population of Salem was 1139. That year the first railroad reached Salem from Portland. The first volunteer police service was formed.

W. Smith was mayor in 1871. During this year the Salem Water Company completed the construction of their steam powered water pump station, the elevated wooden tower, and about one mile of steel pipe. The elevated tank supplied sufficient water pressure for new buildings of up to three stories. This prompted the construction of a high rise three story building—the Chemeketa House Hotel at the corner of Trade and Commercial. Finally, state legislators had a decent hotel in which to stay when the legislature was in session and much better quality water to drink.

Salem received a valuable new service when a coal gassification plant was built in 1871 near the riverfront. The coal gas was used to light the street lights and provide relatively clean power to downtown businesses and residents.

Daniel Payton was mayor in 1872. The water system was already developing serious problems. The elevated tank developed large leaks and became a public nuisance. The tank had to be removed. Also, Salem Water Company's cistern water supply did not supply sufficient quantities of water. The cistern was abandoned and a suction line for the steam powered pump was extended into the Willamette Slough, which was becoming more and more polluted each year due to the mills just upstream. Since the elevated tank was taken down the water pump was required to run 24 hours a day to provide the water pressure that the water company had promised. These problems greatly reduced the water company's profits.

A. Monroe was mayor in 1873. The city continued to grow and prosper with their new Salem Water Company service.

Salem in 1873 was not the law abiding city that it is today even with their volunteer police service. In August, 1873 the *Oregon Statesman* reported a vigilante group took a prisoner out of the city jail and treated him to a coat of tar and feathers free of charge. It must have been quite a party!

John G. Wright was mayor from 1874 through 1876. In 1874 a competing water company was formed in the city. The majority owner was a Mr. Griswald who owned a flour milling company housed in the Pacific Agricultural Works Building at Trade and High Streets. Griswald installed a water wheel in the Mill Race at a 30 foot drop in the Mill Race near High Street. The water wheel supplied the power to pressurize the new water system which served several blocks east of High Street. Griswald installed locally built wooden pipes to serve his customers.

A tragedy struck Salem in 1876 that made several hundred workers unemployed. Salem's leading industry, the Willamette Woolen Manufacturing Company, burned and was completely destroyed.

T.M. Gatch was mayor in 1877 and 1878. During his term, Santiam Water Company went bankrupt and the system was purchased by the Salem Water Company.

In 1878 the State Legislature appropriated funds to construct a state library in Salem.

G.M. Gray was mayor in 1879. Salem continued to grow and prosper. However there were complaints about the foul drinking water. The Willamette River was becoming progressively less than pristine each year and the Willamette Slough was very polluted with two industries upstream dumping all their wastes into this convenient open sewer.

T.B. West was mayor in 1880. Salem's population that year was 2538.

W. Crawford was mayor in 1881 and 1882.

Andrew Kelly was mayor in 1883 and 1884.

W.W. Skinner was mayor in 1885 and 1886. In 1885 Salem Water Company was sold to R.S. Wallace, a businessman with capital to invest in the water system greatly in need of modernization. In 1885 Wallace purchased the land at the southwest corner of Trade and Commercial Streets (present location of Salem's Fire Station #1). He then built a pumping station with the suction line in the Willamette Slough upstream of the flour and woolen mills. He also built a unique rope-transmitted power system driven by the water wheel on the Mill Race. These improvements greatly improved the quality of the drinking water.

Salem also enjoyed its first concrete sidewalks downtown, replacing the worn out wooden sidewalks.

William H. Ramsey was mayor in 1887.

J.J. Murphy was mayor in 1888.

George Williams was mayor in 1889 and 1890. In 1890 R.S. Wallace built a two million gallon reservoir on Fairmount Hill and installed a steam pump to supply additional pressure, beyond what the water wheel could provide, in order to fill the reservoir. The pump and reservoir provided added water pressure for all of Salem at the time.

In 1889 the Thomas Kay Woolen Mill was built and was water powered from the Mill Race.

Salem's population in 1890 was 2617.

P.H. Darcy was mayor in 1891 and 1892. In 1892 the original Thomas Kay Woolen Mill burned and was destroyed.

Claude Gatch was mayor in 1893 through 1896. In 1893 R.S. Wallace died and his brother J.M. Wallace assumed ownership of Salem Water Company. Wallace immediately initiated a major improvement to the water supply system. He started planning a primitive filtration system on Minto Island that would filter Willamette River water instead of relying on Willamette Slough water.

In 1893 a full time paid fire department was created.

J.A. Richardson was mayor in 1897 and 1898. The construction of the Minto Island water filtration system was started by Salem Water Company.

Charles R. Bishop was mayor from 1899 through 1903. In 1899 the Minto Island filtration system was completed. It consisted of a wooden crib that forced water entering the suction pipe to pass through the subsurface sands and cobble rocks, thus filtering the water. Again drinking water was improved but it was nothing to brag about. Not everyone was happy because the water was not sparkling clear and bacteria free.

In 1903 the 5th, 6th, and 7th wards were added to the city. The city charter at the time required two aldermen per ward, so the City Council was increased from eight aldermen to 14.

Salem's population at the turn of the century was 4,258.

F.W. Waters was mayor from 1904 through 1906. The City Council ordered that Salem's "Chinatown" be condemned. It was a half block of ramshackle buildings on the east side of Liberty Street between Court and State. The condemnation order was based on health and police concerns.

G.F. Rodgers was mayor from 1907 through 1910. In 1909 further improvements were made by Salem Water Company to the Minto Island filtration system. However the drinking water continued to deteriorate because of the increasing pollution in the Willamette River.

The concept of a mountain water system for Salem was initiated when Rodgers was mayor. In 1909 the City Council voted to approve a special election to authorize the city to approve the purchase of Salem Water Company. The voters of Salem then approved a bond issue of $400,000 for the purchase. A Mountain Water Committee was appointed with Rodgers as the chair. The committee was to study the feasibility of a water source on the North Santiam River. So, to the credit of Rodgers, the first steps were taken to create a water source with pristine mountain water and to stop using the polluted Willamette River as Salem's water source.

Salem enjoyed the news that a home town boy, A.C. Gilbert, won a gold medal and set a world's record in the pole vault in the 1908 Olympics.

In 1910 Salem's population jumped to 14,094.

Louis Lachmund was mayor in 1911 and 1912. On May 11, 1911 the City Council passed an ordinance authorizing the sale of voter approved bonds and the purchase of the Salem Water Company. However, the planning for a mountain water system and the positive vote by Salem voters to initiate the new system was invalidated by Lachmund when he vetoed the enabling ordinance. He believed "city taxes" had reached a maximum and the city could not afford this risky venture of developing a mountain water system. Salem's newspapers were highly critical of Lachmund's vote, but it stood. Salem would need to wait another 27 years to enjoy sweet mountain water and end up buying the private water company at three times the 1911 price.

The railroad bridge which currently stands over the Willamette River was completed in 1912.

C. Sigmund was mayor in 1913. The City of West Salem was incorporated in 1913 in Polk County.

B.L. Steeves was mayor in 1914. The Oregon State Supreme Court building was completed.

H.O. White was mayor in 1915 and 1916.

Walter Keyes was mayor in 1917 and 1918. A.C. Gilbert opens the world's largest toy factory in Salem. He markets his first chemistry set.

C.E. Albin was mayor in 1919. Salem has record low temperatures in December of six degrees below zero. Prohibition is approved as a constitutional amendment in the United States. Good-by to all the popular taverns in Salem!

O. Wilson was mayor in 1920. Many residents in Salem complained loudly about the bad drinking water quality that Salem Water Company was producing. Salem Water Company refused to make any further improvements because of financial difficulties.

Salem's population was 16,679.

Oregon Pulp and Paper Company, the predecessor of Boise Cascade, began operation with a huge new paper plant at the foot of Pringle Creek. The plant used water in the Mill Race for power production and manufacturing consumptive use. The water in the Mill Race was diverted from the North Santiam River via Salem Ditch. The plant had high priority 1856 water rights which it inherited from Salem Flouring Mills.

G.E. Halverson was mayor in 1921 and 1922. Salem General Hospital on Center Street was built during Halverson's term.

I.B. Giesy was mayor from 1923 through 1926. In May, 1923 with the Willamette River becoming more polluted each year, Giesy appointed a committee to investigate drinking water quality. The committee believed the future Salem water supply should be from the North Santiam River. The committee with City Council approval started filing for water rights at several sites on the North Santiam. The committee also recommended the city hire an engineer to study the financial and engineering feasibility of a mountain water supply. But, the City Council did not agree to hire the engineer. "Too expensive" was their conclusion—which was always the prevailing excuse for not developing a healthy water supply.

T.A. Lively was mayor from 1927 through 1930. In 1927 Salem Water Company was sold to Oregon Washington Water Service Company (OWWSC). OWWSC had the necessary capital to make improvements to the water supply. They made extensive improvements to the Minto Island infiltration system. But, since the Willamette River was polluted, the drinking water from this system continued to be bad, very bad.

Lively, a wealthy hop farmer, built the existing Mahonia Hall (now the governor's residence).

In 1930 the population of Salem climbed to 26,266.

P.M. Gregory was mayor in 1931 and 1932. Gregory headed a victorious Mountain Water Party in the 1930 elections. The Mountain Water Party won a majority of City Council seats. They pledged to buy the OWWSC private water system and to develop a mountain water source on the North Santiam River. Drinking water was so bad in Salem at this time that the city had a reputation of having the worst water in the state. State legislators refused to drink the water and insisted on having spring water to drink when in Salem.

Gregory and the City Council approved a special election to both purchase the private OWWSC system and to build a pipeline to the North Santiam River. In December, 1931 Salem voters approved a $2,500,000 bond issue expecting to be drinking pure mountain water in just a few months. But, it was not to be. It was remarkable that the voters approved this bond issue, because it was huge for a city the size of Salem and it was during the middle of the great national depression.

In 1931 the first dial telephone system was installed.

Douglas McKay was mayor in 1933 and 1934. McKay was later Governor of Oregon and Secretary of the Interior under President Dwight Eisenhower.

During McKay's term there were ongoing negotiations with OWWSC to purchase their water system. The negotiations dragged on and on, and Salem residents continued to drink foul Willamette River water.

V.E. Kuhn was mayor from 1935 through 1938. Kuhn was able, finally, to complete the purchase of the OWWSC system. But a sale price could not be negotiated, so the city was forced to condemn the private water system. The final court approved purchase price was slightly over $1,000,000, where OWWSC was demanding $2,000,000. Salem finally took possession of the water system on August 1, 1935. Mayor Kuhn showed great strength in pushing for the development of the North Santiam water source. However, the business community was generally against this "risky venture," as they called it. It was their opinion that it just cost too much. This of course was not the first time this argument was used to derail an excellent water source. The City Council continued to support the design and construction of the pipeline and the treatment system at Stayton Island, just upstream of the City of Stayton. Water from Stayton Island started flowing to the city in October, 1937.

In 1935 a great tragedy struck the State Capitol. It was destroyed by fire. By 1938 the new Capitol was completed and was dedicated on October 1st of that year.

W.W. Chadwick was mayor from 1939 through 1942. In 1940 Salem celebrated its centennial, marking 100 years of history since Jason Lee founded Salem in 1840.

Salem's population in 1940 was 30,908.

In 1939 Germany started World War II with the invasion of Poland. When the United States entered the war against Japan and Germany in December, 1941, Salem and the rest of the United States went on a war economy. Hundreds of Salem residents joined the military.

I.M. Doughton was mayor from 1943 through 1946. A Willamette River flood overflowed the Marion Street bridge in 1943 and caused flood damage in Salem and West Salem.

In 1945 the water rights were adjudicated by the courts on the North Santiam River. This court decision was extremely important for the City of Salem. The 1856 water right diversions of 254 cfs from the North Santiam River to Salem Ditch and then to Mill Creek and the Mill Race were given the early water right date of 1856, which was the earliest priority date possible. Later the city would acquire all of these water rights.

Robert L. Elfstrom was mayor from 1947 through 1950. In 1947 the city charter was amended by the voters to create a city manager form of government. J.L. Franzen was chosen as the city's first city manager.

The new city charter also reduced the number of aldermen per ward from two to one, thereby reducing the City Council to seven councilors and a mayor.

On November 14, 1949, West Salem voters approved a merger with the City of Salem. An 8th ward was added to the city with this merger and therefore increasing the number of councilors to eight.

In 1950 Salem's population had increased rapidly to 43,140.

Alfred W. Loucks was mayor from 1951 through 1954. Loucks played a key role in 1951 in negotiating the purchase of 60 cfs of 1856 priority water rights from Oregon Pulp and Paper Company. Salem, in 1951 was desperate for additional water rights and this purchase made it possible to expand the water system for a quickly growing population.

Turner Reservoir was built in 1952 and 1953. The 100 million gallon reservoir built in the City of Turner was a major improvement to the water supply system. The reservoir was later named Franzen Reservoir in honor of the city's first city manager.

The city's first sewage treatment plant was built in 1952. It was located on Front Street at the site of the existing Front Street Park.

The *Capital Journal* and the *Oregon Statesman* merged their business operations in 1953. The *Statesman* was distributed in the morning and the *Journal* was distributed in the afternoon.

The new Marion County Court House on High Street was built in 1953.

Robert White was mayor from 1955 through 1958. In 1956 the City Council approved referring to the voters a $3.75 million bond issue to expand the Stayton Island Water Treatment System and build a second pipeline to Stayton Island. The voters approved the bond issue.

In March, 1956 J.L. Franzen announced his retirement. Kent Matthewson was hired to replace Franzen with a whopping $14,000 salary compared to Franzen's $11,500 per year.

In 1957 the City Council refused to increase water rates that had been in effect since 1916, even with the added cost of large yearly bond payments. In 1957 the city's first slow sand filter was built at Stayton Island along with a second pipeline to the city.

Russell F. Bonestelle was mayor from 1959 through 1962. Salem's population in 1960 was 49,142.

In 1961 Salem was chosen an "All American City."

In 1962 additional water rights were purchased from Marion County Investment Company. The 50 cfs right had a priority date of 1866.

In 1962 Salem suffered one of the biggest disasters in its history. On October 12, the Columbus Day storm created heavy damage across the city with its 90 mile per hour winds.

The Thomas Kay Woolen Mill closed.

Willard C. Marshall was mayor from January, 1963 to August 1, 1965. He resigned during his second term due to illness.

At Christmas in 1964, a 100 year flood on the North Santiam River damaged the Stayton Island facility and washed out the upper Bennett diversion dam. The Willamette River and Mill Creek also flooded and backed up water throughout Salem.

In 1964 the Willow Lake Wastewater Treatment Plant opened north of Salem on Windsor Island Road. The treatment plant used a modern design to treat both domestic sewage and large amounts of food processing wastes.

Mission Mill was incorporated in 1964 as a museum.

In 1964 Kent Mathewson resigned as city manager and Doug Ayers was appointed.

Vern W. Miller was mayor from August 1, 1965 through 1972. Chemeketa Community College was established in 1969.

In 1968 Doug Ayers resigned as city manager and Bob Moore was appointed.

In 1971 the city's Stayton Island water system was expanded with a second slow sand filter giving the facility the capacity of producing 66 million gallons per day of high quality drinking water.

Salem's population in 1970 had swelled to 68,725.

In 1971 voters in Salem approved a bond issue to build the Civic Center consisting of City Hall, the Library, and Fire Station #1. In 1972 construction was completed on the new Civic Center and the old City Hall at High and Chemeketa was demolished.

Robert E. Lindsey was mayor from 1973 through 1976. The Thomas Kay Woolen Mill was placed on the national register of historic places.

In 1976 a major improvement was made to the Willow Lake Wastewater Treatment Plant with a large capacity increase as well as a significant decrease in discharged pollutants to the Willamette River.

Before becoming mayor, Dr. Lindsey, a dentist, led the city campaign to fluoridate the city's drinking water in 1964. Dr. Lindsey had observed the high percentage of tooth decay in young people and knew that fluoride would greatly decrease this problem.

Kent L. Aldrich was mayor from 1977 through 1982. The city purchased in 1978 an additional 62 cfs of 1856 water rights from Boise Cascade.

Bob Moore, longtime city manager retired effective May 31, 1978. Ralph Hanley the city's fifth city manager started to work June 1, 1978. Hanley developed an urban growth management system that was approved by the City Council in 1979.

The afternoon newspaper, the *Capital Journal,* suspended publication in 1980. The morning newspaper was renamed, the *Statesman Journal*.

Salem's population in 1980 grew to 89,233.

In 1982 the City of Keizer was incorporated much to the disappointment of the City of Salem and the objectives of Salem annexing all the land within the urban growth boundary.

Susan Miller was mayor from 1983 through 1988. Miller was Salem's first female mayor.

Ralph Hanley retired in 1983 as City Manager and Russ Abolt was appointed City Manager. Abolt had been Hanley's assistant city manager. In 1987 Abolt was fired by the City Council and Larry Wacker was appointed interim city manager. In 1988 Gary Eide was appointed city manager.

In 1985 the city purchased an additional 55 cfs of 1856 priority water rights from Boise Cascade after the water right transfer was challenged by the City of Stayton and Santiam Water Control District.

Salem established sister city relationships with Simferopol in the Soviet Union and Kawago in Japan.

Salem was named an All American City for the second time.

In 1984 the city purchased 22 acres of prime riverfront property from Boise Cascade. Later the voters of Salem in a citizen initiative rejected the city's plans to build a riverfront hotel there.

Thomas Nielson was mayor in 1989 and 1990. Tokyo International University opened a campus in Salem as part of Willamette University.

In 1989 the 100th anniversary of Thomas Kay Woolen Mill was celebrated.

In 1990 the Capital Theater closed. It had opened in 1926.

In 1989 and 1990 at the State of the City Address the audience participated with much enthusiasm with the Tom Nielson cheer for the bright future of Salem.

R.G. Andersen-Wyckoff was mayor in 1991 through 1994. The North Santiam watershed was given much greater protection for water quality after President Clinton, Vice President Gore, and the Secretaries of Agriculture and Interior met in Portland in 1993 and mandated a new federal forest plan. The new forest plan greatly benefited Salem's watershed, the North Santiam River.

Andersen-Wyckoff chaired the new Water/Wastewater Task Force that was charged with examining the need to modernize the Geren Island water system and the Willow Lake Wastewater Treatment Plant that would later produce soaring water and sewer rate increases.

Gary Eide resigned as city manager under pressure because of possible inappropriate travel expenses. Larry Wacker was appointed the new city manager in 1993.

Roger Gertenrich was mayor in 1995 and 1996. Both the North Santiam and the Pringle Creek watershed councils were created in 1995. Gertenrich actively participated in the formation of the North Santiam Watershed Council. Salem became a member after much controversy that the "big city" would dominate the Council.

In 1996 the modernization of Geren Island was initiated.

The Riverfront Park Phase 1 was completed in 1996.

Mayor Gertenrich initiated the concept of converting an old Boise Cascade acid storage ball tank as the Eco-Earth globe. The globe was completed in 2003 with donations from the community.

In February, 1996 a major flood on Mill Creek created major damage to many properties and public infrastructure. The flood also created major erosion in the North Santiam River which affected Salem's water supply for several months.

Mike Swaim was mayor from 1997 through 2002.

The modernization of Geren Island neared completion in 2002. Soaring water and sewer rates challenged the City Council. Annual rate increases of over 8% were approved.

Salem's population in 2000 increased to 128,595.

Courthouse Square, the new downtown transit center opened in 2000.

In 2000 Larry Wacker retired as city manager and Bob Wells was appointed interim city manager. Bob DeLong was appointed city manager in 2001.

In 2002 the City Council approves a downtown convention center in cooperation with VIPS.

The library's Salem History Project was started in 2000.

Voters in Salem approved the requirement that all new annexations be approved by the voters of Salem.

Water, sewer, transportation, and storm drainage system development charges were approved by the City Council to the dislike of the home building industry.

Janet Taylor took office as Mayor on January 1, 2003.

The City Council gave final approval of an agreement with VIPS to cooperate in building a major new hotel and conference center in the downtown adjacent to the Civic Center.

Mayor Taylor's vote for increased water and sewer rates decided the controversial issue in a close 5 to 4 City Council vote. The increased rates were necessary to pay for the modernization of Geren Island and Willow Lake and meet increasing federal and state mandates.[120]

# Appendix B
## Water Development Accomplishments By City Staff, Consultants And Environmental Activists

The information in this appendix is in six sections as follows: first, all the past city managers of Salem and their interest in water development issues; second, past and present public works directors; third, past and present water division managers; fourth, city engineers and engineering consultants working on water development projects; fifth, staff monitoring and managing the watershed; and sixth, environmental activists engaged in preserving the watershed.

### CITY MANAGERS OF SALEM

J.L. Franzen was the city's first city manager. and served from 1947 to 1957. He took a very large interest in the water system and had several conflicts with the City Council about water rates which were insufficient to operate and improve the system. Franzen Reservoir was named after him. Franzen was a registered engineer and had extensive experience both as an engineer and a city manager before coming to Salem. Previously he had been city manager of Oregon City for 20 years. Franzen took a personal and intense interest in the water supply system. He was a strong mentor of John Geren, who became water system manager in 1952 and continued Franzen's passion for developing an outstanding water system.

Kent Mathewson followed J.L. Franzen as city manager in 1957. Mathewson advocated increased revenues for the water system that needed improvements in the 1950's and 1960's due to rapid city growth. Mathewson's policy as city manager was maximum cooperation with citizens and other governments. He was instrumental in creating the regional council of governments which later became the Mid Willamette Valley Council of Governments. He also offered to serve areas outside the city with water and sewer services, thus the East Salem and the Keizer Sewerage Districts were formed. Mathewson had a masters degree from Syracuse University and extensive experience in city government before coming to Salem. He resigned in 1964.

Doug Ayers started his employment as finance director with the City of Salem in 1963. He was appointed city manager in 1964. Ayers had the exact opposite personality of Kent Mathewson. He was not an advocate of maximum cooperation with other governments in the area. He opposed the concept of offering city services to outside areas and insisted that annexation to the city was necessary if city services are provided. A large area in South Salem had been developed to urban density in Marion County with two water districts and a system of individual, county approved septic tanks. The septic tanks of course did not work and the area needed sanitary sewers. Ayers refused to allow the county to contract sewer services with the city by creating county sewerage districts but insisted instead that the entire area be annexed to the city. The area was annexed and the city inherited two water districts with distribution systems made of galvanized pipe that needed to be replaced in its entirety. Ayers policy of requiring annexation to obtain city services was controversial at the time but has been recognized by all later city managers and City Councils as a bottom line policy of the city. Doug Ayers also had a graduate degree from Syracuse University and had extensive experience in city government before coming to Salem. He resigned in 1968.

Bob Moore started his career with the City of Salem in 1964 as finance director. And, yes, he also had a graduate degree from Syracuse University. It seems Matthewson, Ayers and Moore all attended Syracuse at the same time and of course knew each other before coming to Salem. Salem benefited greatly from these friendships because it probably was the main reason the talented Ayers and Moore were attracted to Salem. Moore was appointed city manager in 1968 with the resignation of Ayers. In 1968 the city developed their first water master plan. This plan recommended the city aggressively perfect additional water rights. Several attempts were made to purchase additional water rights and finally in 1978 the city was successful in purchasing 62 cfs of 1856 priority water rights from Boise Cascade. In 1971 the city was successful in funding and building the second slow sand filter at Stayton Island.

Ralph Hanley was city manager from 1978 to 1983. Hanley was hired by the City Council to create a plan to accommodate growth. He responded with a creative urban growth management ordinance that revolutionized who pays for growth infrastructure. Prior to adoption of this ordinance, the utility system paid for all extensions of major trunks and mains. Under the new growth ordinance, the developers became responsible for all infrastructure outside the currently devel-

oped area. Hanley also initiated development impact fees that preceded state approved system development charges. Hanley was bru-
tal with any staff that he believed to be incompetent or simply not
giving a 100 percent effort. Hanley was a shooting star who created a
lot of political enemies and he resigned after a short five year tenure.
Staff who survived under Hanley's iron grip felt they were much better prepared to deal with controversial government issues in the future, including the author. Hanley died in the mid 1990's.

Bob Moore on the right at the dedication of the new Civic Center
(Sorry about the distortion in this photo. Bob Moore's left arm is
not really that long.)

Russ Abolt started his employment as assistant to City Manager,
Bob Moore. He became an assistant city manager under Moore along

with Bob Briscoe. Abolt continued as an assistant to Ralph Hanley and was appointed city manager in 1983 with the resignation of Hanley. Abolt served until 1987 when the City Council terminated his services. Abolt was an energetic manager, a graduate of Wharton School of Management, and an ex-marine. He expected perfection from his staff and scrutinized every document that went to the City .

Russ Abolt

Council. Abolt was city manager when the city, in a very controversial action, acquired the last of Boise Cascade's 1856 water rights of 55 cfs. Abolt stood firm on the city's rights to acquire all of these water rights even though others wanted to purchase part of these rights. In 1985 the city approved an entirely new method of charging water and sewer rates to areas outside the city with the adoption of a cost of service analysis (COSA) that used the utility basis of accounting. It took a Wharton graduate to understand this complex system. With the departure of Abolt in 1987, Larry Wacker, Abolt's assistant was appointed interim city manager. Abolt went on to become a long time and very successful county manager in South Carolina where he is presently employed.

Gary Eide was appointed city manager in 1988. Water and sewer rate increases were controversial subjects for the City Council for the next four years. In 1988 it was known that large capital expenditures would be needed to modernize the Geren Island water facility and the Willow Lake Wastewater Treatment Plant. The City Council at this time hated the idea of raising utility rates and every year it was a very controversial subject. Eide resigned in 1993 after there was publicity and controversy over his expense account.

Larry Wacker was appointed city manager in 1993. Wacker was a career employee with the city and a native born Oregonian. He was a graduate of North Salem High School in Salem and the University of Oregon. He started his employment under Bob Moore as assistant personnel director. He was later promoted to personnel director and as assistant city manager under Ralph Hanley. He continued as assistant city manager under Russ Abolt and Gary Eide. Wacker was a strong city manager and had the full confidence of his department heads, a partnership that is necessary for all successful city managers. Wacker had the bad luck to be city manager when utility rates had to be greatly increased because of the need to spend several hundred million dollars to modernize the water and sewer systems. This need to raise so much money with water and sewer rate increases was due to past City Councils' attempts at keeping the lowest utility rates in Oregon. Under Wacker the City Council finally understood the need and agreed to many years of 8 % utility rate increases. In 1996 the modernization of Geren Island was initiated. I'm sure shepherding the raising of utility rates would not be Larry Wacker's wish for a legacy, but this was only one of many accomplishments of this talented city manager. Wacker retired in 2000. Bob Wells, Wacker's hard working assistant and financial wizard was appointed interim city manager.

Bob DeLong was appointed City Manager in 2001 after a nation wide recruitment and a town hall type hiring process that left only DeLong standing, a testament to his staying power. On October 20, 2003 DeLong announced his retirement in the face of what was rumored to be a very negative performance appraisal. DeLong's retirement date was set as January 2, 2004.

Bob Wells, while not officially a city manager, has been the assistant city manager since 1993. Prior to that he was the city's budget officer. Wells has steered the city through some very troubled financial waters (this water is not potable). He is recognized as the staff leader and a lot of folks are eagerly anticipating the day he becomes city manager.

Larry Wacker early in his career as Personnel Director

## WATER DEPARTMENT DIRECTORS

Cuyler Van Patten was the city's first water system director after the city purchased the system from the private Oregon Washington Water Service Company in 1935. Patten died at age 49 on July 4, 1939 while actively managing the water system. He managed the extremely difficult process of purchasing the water system from the private company, the selection of Stayton Island as the location of the water source, and the construction of the Stayton Island treatment system.

Karl Guenther was the city's second water department director. He served from 1939 to the early 1950's. He was John Geren's boss and mentor. He was the assistant water director under Cuyler Van Patten when the Stayton Island system was constructed. He managed the system after the construction and start up of the Stayton Island treatment system during very lean water system budgets. His contributions were many because of his dedication in a similar way as John Geren's. John Geren followed Karl Guenther as water department director and served as director of utilities managing both the water and sewer systems for the city. His love, however, was the water system. He skillfully managed the system through extremely trying times when system expansions were critically needed and he was faced with a penny pinching City Council who refused to properly fund the expansions and operation of the system. He also was successful in purchasing the highest priority water rights for the system from the Oregon Pulp and Paper Company and its successor, Boise Cascade. Geren was a crusty individual that demanded the best from the staff. Staff had the highest respect for him because of his expertise and commitment to a quality water system. Geren retired in 1974 and died in the early 1980's. Stayton Island was named Geren Island in memory of his outstanding contributions. John Geren's legacy is the outstanding water system that Salem residents now enjoy, and hopefully will continue.

**John Geren at retirement age in 1974.**

B.T. Van Wormer followed John Geren as the department head in charge of the water system. Van Wormer was the long time public works director in charge of the streets, airport, transit system, and drainage system. In 1974 the public works department was merged with the utilities department when John Geren retired. Van Wormer then became the director of utilities/public works. He was very active in obtaining the city's 62 cfs water rights from Boise Cascade in 1978.

Louis McNicoll followed Van Wormer as utilities/public works director in 1979. Lou started the process of modernizing the business and financial processes of the department. His humor, wit, and work ethic was a constant motivator for staff.

Ronald Merry followed Louis McNicoll as director which was now renamed the public works department. Ron served from 1980 to 1987. Ron gave the department professional management and continued the process of modernizing the budgeting and the financial end of public works. Ron worked under the toughest city manager the city ever had, Ralph Hanley, and thrived under his iron fisted style as city manager.

Frank Mauldin, the author, followed Ron Merry as public works director. I was appointed director on June 1, 1988 exactly ten years to the day after starting work at the city as a planning engineer. I was assistant public works director to Ron Merry for five years. An early goal as director was to complete the modernization of the management and budgeting system of the department. After developing program budgets the city manager and the City Council for the first time understood what public works was trying to accomplish each year. Protecting the North Santiam watershed was a passion during my tenure as director as well as completing all the facility master plans and developing appropriate systems development charges. I retired on January 31, 2002.

Tim Gerling was my successor as public works director. Tim served an apprenticeship as assistant public works director for several years and knows the department extremely well. Tim had tremendous talent in representing the department in public forums and had the background and skills to excel as the director. Tim needs to look after that water system! Its easy to ignore, because it usually works so efficiently and I know he will stay real busy, but the water folks are looking for his involvement and encouragement. So, he needs to get out there and show your colors! I know he will.

Floyd Collins was assistant director from 1990 to 1999. Floyd had previously been utilities director in Corvallis where he obtained a wealth of management skills. Floyd represented the department on many state wide committees and much respected in Salem and throughout the state. Floyd left Salem to become public works director in Albany, Oregon where he concluded a very successful career with his retirement in 2003.

Pedro (Peter) Fernandez is the assistant director under Tim Gerling. Peter comes from a transportation background and was the highly successful transportation services division head in public works for several years. Peter is on a steep "water" learning curve but with his ability as a quick learn its almost assured that a lot of new ideas will result from Peter's new position. Peter is also one of the most verbally fluent persons I have ever met (in English and Spanish). But don't talk too much Peter, particularly at Council meetings.

**Frank Mauldin and Tim Gerling in 2003**

## WATER DIVISION MANAGERS

Keith Farrow was water superintendent starting in 1977 and became operations manager in the mid 1980's. Keith gave the water system professional management with his long time experience in the water field. Keith after leaving the city made use of his out going personality, wised up, and entered the real estate business where he has grown rich as King Solomon.

Lyle Huffaker was water source supervisor from the late 1950's to the early 1980's. He had to cope with the large flood of 1964 with a long period of high turbidities in the North Santiam River. He and his operators were able to continue minimum water supplies to the city during this event. Lyle was a demanding supervisor, some say gruff, that always demanded the best from his crew to deliver the highest quality water to Salem.

Bill Light followed Huffaker as water source supervisor. He retired in the later 1990's. Before coming to the City of Salem, Bill was a design engineer with the engineering firm of Clark and Groff who designed Salem's slow sand filters numbers 1 and 2. Bill was the chief designer on these projects and became an expert on the operation of these unique filters. He provided expert operation of the Geren Island treatment system when he started his employment with the city.

Dan Bradley followed Keith Farrow as water superintendent and served from the mid 1980's to the mid 1990's. Dan was a star in the water business and the city was lucky to keep him so long. He went on to manage a large water district in the Portland area.

Rollie Baxter was operations manager following Keith Farrow and served until the year 2001 upon his retirement. Rollie had been the public works director for the City of Corvallis for many years and ended his career there as acting city manager. His huge experience in the public works field was of tremendous value to the City of Salem.

Paul Eckley followed Rollie Baxter as operations manager following a long career with the department as chief utilities engineer. Paul's knowledge of utilities and ability to get things done has been unsurpassed. He is also the nicest person that we have ever known. (Don't be too nice Paul, you need to keep the operations staff on edge and productive.) I see nothing but success for Paul and the water and sewer system under his expert watch.

Sofia Hobet is the current water superintendent following the tenure of Jim West. Sofia when starting with the city followed Bill Light as the water source supervisor and she had some big shoes to fill, which she filled very well. Sofia was promoted to water superintendent in 2001. Sofia is a talent that the department has tremendous confidence in. She has a degree in chemical engineering and has excellent rapport with the "guys" in the water division.

Libby Barg Kidd is water source supervisor and follows Sofia Hobet in this critical position of supervising the staff at Geren Island and being responsible for water quality monitoring and quality. Libby has shown a lot of growth in her positions with the department and is highly respected for her diligence in making sure the water is always excellent.

Tim Sherman is supervisor of operations and maintenance at Geren Island. Tim has been an important member of the water division management team. He has lived through a major modernization of Geren Island from a simple system of slow sand filters to a complex system of a flexible control system for maximum treatment efficiency regardless of river conditions. He contributed valuable operation and maintenance information to the new system designers.

Greg Watson, field supervisor for the water division is one of the main "guys" Sofia has to manage. But Greg is a sweet guy on the inside even though his outside usually has his shirt hanging out which is against department regulations. (Regardless of his undisciplined shirt, I have been an admirer of Greg for many years because of his dedication to quality work.)

## CITY ENGINEERS

Herb Arnold started to work for the city in the early 1970's in the utilities department under John Geren. He had previously been a design engineer with Clark and Groff Engineers in Salem. Herb's title was sanitary engineer and he headed up special engineering studies, planning and rate studies. He made a successful transition from the utilities department to the combined utilities/public works department when John Geren retired. Herb hired me in 1978 and I worked under him for two years until he retired. Herb was very much respected by his peers in private practice and by the city staff. The department lost a huge amount of expertise and institutional knowledge when he retired.

Ed Sigurdson was the long time city engineer in the public works department under B.T. Van Wormer. He retained that title when the utilities and public works departments combined in 1974. He was known by his peers as "Mr. Public Works" because of his knowledge of the city and infrastructure systems. He went into private practice in the early 1980's.

Marlin Brinkley followed Sigurdson as city engineer. He provided considerable municipal experience as the city's top engineer. He left city employment in the late 1980's for greener pastures in Portland.

Karl Goertzen the present city engineer, followed Brinkley. Karl's leadership and engineering expertise has been a major factor in creating a highly motivated and productive engineering staff. Karl has managed all the water system modernization projects plus all the design and construction management of all sanitary sewer, storm drainage, and street projects. He is also one of the few remaining professional engineers that is also a registered surveyor. Department records and surveying are also under his management.

Jim Bonnet is the assistant city engineer and has the water modernization projects as part of his supervisory authority. Jim, an expert managing engineer, has the tenacity to never get discouraged in completing a construction project regardless of the barriers that may be thrown up. Jim has been an extremely valuable addition to the engineering division. A recent accomplishment was his successful negotiations with the City of Stayton to allow the construction of the new 75 mgd water transmission lines through Stayton.

Gary Myzak, Dave Prock, and Sandy Olds have worked under Bonnet as project engineers as part of the water modernization projects started in the late 1990's and still continuing in 2003. Dave Prock is managing the ongoing Water Management Plan. Sandy Olds managed the consultant teams that designed and supervised construction of the Geren Island modernization projects.

## CONSULTANTS

Stevens and Koon Engineers designed the original Stayton Island facilities built in 1937. R.E. Koon was the principal in charge and the project engineer. Koon suffered a huge amount of negative press especially from the *Capital Press*. However, he convinced the City Council and the *Oregon Statesman* that the development on Stayton Island was feasible and would be the city's best water source option.

Clark and Groff Engineers designed both the 1957 and 1971 projects at Geren Island where slow sand filters numbers 1 and 2 were constructed. Lloyd Clark and Gilbert Groff were principals and Bill Light was the project engineer.

CH2M-Hill prepared both the 1968 and 1994 water master plans. Ray Topping was the principal in charge of the *1994 Water System Master Plan* with Bob Fuller being the project manager and Paul Berg being the project engineer.

Black and Veatch LLP, consulting engineers designed and managed construction on the modernization of Geren Island starting in the late 1990's and ending in 2003. Principal in charge and project manager was Randy Krueger. This work consisted of pilot testing slow sand filters in partnership with Thames Water Utilities of London, University of New Hampshire, Oregon State University and Economic and

Engineering Services, Inc. and then designing new slow sand filters numbers 3 and 4. In addition Black and Veatch also designed the twin 75 mgd transmission lines from Geren Island to Franzen Reservoir. Black and Veatch is also designing new and improved fish ladders for the two Bennett dams.

## WATERSHED MONITORS AND MANAGERS

Dave Wiley, a management analyst with the public works department and a graduate forester was the first staff person to monitor and manage the North Santiam watershed on behalf of the City of Salem. Dave reviewed all the U.S. Forest Services (USFS) proposed timber cuts and commented as to the effects on water quality. He was doing this as a rear guard action because the mentality of the USFS was to clear cut as much as possible each year. During this period of early 1980's to early 1990's much of the old growth ancient forest was cut. It was not until the Clinton Forest Plan was adopted in 1993 that much more attention was paid to water quality and endangered species. By the time the Clinton Plan was adopted Dave turned his watershed duties to a new staff person in public works hired as an environmental advocate.

Tina Schweickert started to work for public works in 1991. She was a graduate in environmental science from Willamette University. After working in the department for a couple of years developing a water conservation program and a creek protection program she took on the duties of looking after the watershed in 1993 with the newly adopted Clinton Forest Plan. She constantly advocated on each proposed timber cut the possible short and long term effects of clearcutting and logging in riparian areas. As a result of Schweickert's constant vigil to insure consistency with the Clinton Forest Plan, it became clear that the new sustainable cut policy of the USFS would allow the watershed to recover over the next 20 to 30 years and not be a checkerboard of clear cuts and young Douglas fir plantations. Schweickert in 1999 moved to the community development department as the city's natural resources manager. In 2001 she left city employment in favor of an early retirement.

Sofia Hobet, water superintendent, took over the primary responsibilities of monitoring the watershed and is assisted by Libby Kidd and Hank Wujcik. Wujcik, a Geren Island operator and long time field person inspecting the timber harvesting operations, continues these duties today.

## ENVIRONMENTAL ACTIVISTS

Environmental activism started aggressively in the early 1980's when the USFS tried their best to clear cut Opal Creek, the last low elevation ancient forest in the United States.

Opal Creek was saved from the chain saws because of the efforts of Tony George, a citizen of Salem who understood the value of Opal Creek as an ancient forest; Jim Montiff, Executive Director of the Oregon Natural Resources Council; Chris Maser, author and forest consultant; George Atiyeh, a resident in the Little North Fork area and one of the founders of Friends of Opal Creek; Michael Donnelly of Friends of Breitenbush Cascades; and Mike Swaim, an attorney and resident of Salem who in 1996 was elected Mayor of Salem as an environmental advocate. This group of dedicated environmentalists convinced the Salem City Council that clearcutting Opal Creek was not in the best interests of the city. These intense investigations of the USFS plans and resulting political and national media pressure along with threats of law suits persuaded the USFS to shelve their clearcutting plans. Later, Senator Mark O. Hatfield was successful in creating an Opal Creek Wilderness Area which eliminates any timber harvesting and road building.

In the early 1990's an aggressive attempt was made by a Canadian mining company, Kinross Copper, to develop a huge copper mine in the Opal Creek area. Again environmental activists moved quickly to stop the mine development and the creation of a tailings pile. Al White of Oregon Watersheds and Susan Smith a law professor at Willamette University played a key role in defending the State of Oregon's actions to deny the site because of the Three Basin Rule that did not allow waste discharges into the North Santiam River basin. Bryan Johnston, a Salem area legislator headed the successful opposition to a Kinross proposed legislative bill that would exempt Kinross from the Three Basin Rule.

Regna Merritt, staff person and later Executive Director of the Oregon Natural Resources Council, advocated very strongly in the mid 1990's that the USFS was not protecting the water quality sufficiently with several proposed timber cuts. She provided written testimony and testified at public hearings on the inappropriateness of these timber cuts. In every case she was influential in creating compromises beneficial to the watershed.

Jeremy Hall started his environmental advocacy as a student at Willamette University as part of a Watershed Guardian program initiated by Oregon Peaceworks. Jeremy, after graduation, became a

staffer for the Oregon Natural Resources Council. He continues to review timber cuts in Oregon watersheds with his partner and long time
advocate, George Sexton.

Trygve Steen, Ph.D., Professor at Portland State University has
photographically documented the watershed through its different
stages of clearcutting. Dr. Steen developed a computerized system of
identifying each aerial photo with its exact map coordinates which
has made it possible to compare over time many watershed areas. His
photographs greatly assisted public works staff in explaining to the
Salem City Council and the Oregon Congressional members the impacts of further clearcutting on water quality sensitive areas in the
watershed. Dr. Steen has also educated many students, as well as interested citizens, on the value of the old growth forest in the Opal
Creek Wilderness.

# *Endnotes*

CHAPTER 1: SALEM'S EARLY WATER SYSTEMS
1. Guard, B. Jennifer, *Wetland Plants of Oregon & Washington,* Lone Pine Publishing, Redmond, Washington, 1995, p. 98.
2. Gatke, Robert M, *Chronicles of Willamette,* Binforts and Mort, Portland, Oregon, 1943, Chapter 2. (Gatke's history of Willamette University through 1942 is also an excellent history of early Salem.)
3 Maxwell, Ben, "Mill Creek Interesting in History and Legend," *The Capital Journal*, Salem, Oregon, January, 17, 1953. (Ben Maxwell was a dedicated Salem historian and photographer. He documented Salem during his lifetime with thousands of excellent large format photographs. He donated his photographic collection to the Salem Public Library. His photo collection is now part of Salem Library's web page: SalemHistory.org.)
4 "Mill Creek Watershed History," An unpublished report by Friends of Mill Creek (proposed to be a future watershed council), Salem, Oregon.
5. Maxwell, Ibid.
6. Gangwire, Robert E., "Plank Sidewalks Compulsory Under One of First Ordinances Passed by City Council in 1857," *Oregon Statesman*, Salem, Oregon, March 25, 1951. (This very interesting article gives a very brief list of highlights in Salem history from 1857 to 1951.)
7. Will, Clark Moor, Transcript of a radio interview on March 31, 1957 with David Duniway and John Geren, Salem Public Library records. (Duniway was the unofficial Salem Historian and Geren was the manager of the water department.)
8. Wilkerson, John L., *History of the Salem Fire Department,* Old Time Bottle Publishing Company, Salem, Oregon, 1976.
9. Will, Clark Moor, "How Salem Got Its Water," Marion County Historical Society, Salem, Oregon, 1958.

CHAPTER 2: IMPROVEMENTS ARE MADE
10. Will, Clark Moor, "How Salem Got Its Water," Marion County Historical Society, Salem, Oregon, p.3.
11. Maxwell, Ben, "Waterworks Interesting Part In Salem History,"

*Capital Journal*, Salem, Oregon, January 27, 1954

12. Wallace, J.M.,"Water Company," A one page promotion brochure issued by Salem Water Company in about 1899, Salem History files, Salem Public Library.

13. "Report of the Commission on the Value of Salem Water Company's Plant," Public Works Department water rights files, Salem, Oregon, August 3, 1909.

14. Communication from Salem Water Company to the Salem City Council, Public Works Department water right files, Salem, Oregon, March 12, 1910.

15. City of Salem Ordinance 860 passed on October 18, 1910, City of Salem, Oregon archives

16. Public Works Department water rights files, Salem, Oregon.

17. Ibid.

18. Ibid.

19. "Mayor Vetoes Purchase of Plant. City Cannot Buy the Waterworks," *Capital Journal*, Salem, Oregon, May 9, 1911.

20. " Lachmunds Veto," *Oregon Statesman*, Salem, Oregon, May 9, 1911.

21. Walth, Brent, *Fire at Eden's Gate, Tom McCall*, Oregon Historical Society Press, Portland, Oregon, 1994, p. 181.

22. Maxwell, Ibid.

23. Will, Ibid.

24. Geren, John L., "The Salem, Oregon Water Works System," Unpublished report, Salem Public Works Dept. files, 1937.

## CHAPTER 3: MOUNTAIN WATER, FINALLY

25. City Council minutes of May 21, 1923. Mayor Giesy appointed a committee to investigate city water conditions. The committee was: chairman G.J. Winderoth; and, members- B.B. Herrick, George W. Thompson, A.F. Marcus, Ralph Thompson and L.J. Simeral.

26. City Council minutes of July 2, 1923. The report of the committee was:
"We your committee which was recently appointed for the purpose of investigating water conditions as well as the condition of water mains in the City of Salem, respectively report that your committee has made careful investigation of these matters and is of the opinion that a filing should be made for the purpose of securing the water right that will secure for the city a pure and adequate supply of water for the future use of the City of Salem. We therefore recommend that the chairman of your committee be authorized and directed to file with

the State Engineer the proper application for such a permit as may be necessary for the appropriation of the public waters of the State of Oregon and that the City Recorder be authorized and directed to draw a warrant, payable to the State Engineer, for the sum of $9.00 in payment of the necessary filing fee."

27. City Council minutes of July 16, 1923. Submitted by the special committee on water conditions and a successful motion by Alderman Winderoth to adopt the report. There was, however, no motion to fund the necessary work.

28. Cunningham, John W., "North Santiam River Water Rights for City of Salem, Oregon," Barr and Cunningham Consulting Engineers, Portland, Oregon, February 15, 1932, Public Works Department Files.

29. "Algae Play Important Role In Starting Agitation Here," *Oregon Statesman*, Salem, Oregon, October 24, 1937.

30. "Appraisal and Valuation of Salem Waterworks System as of August 31, 1930," Barr and Cunningham Consulting Engineers, Portland, Oregon, public works department files.

31. "City Has Deed to Water System,"*Capital Journal*, Salem, Oregon, August 1, 1935.

32. "City Water", *Oregon Statesman*, Salem, Oregon, August 1, 1935.

33. "Report on New Waterworks Plant for the City of Salem, Oregon," Barr and Cunningham Consulting Engineers, Portland, Oregon, Public Works Department files.

34. "Council and Board Clash Over Plans For New Water Program," *Capital Journal*, Salem, Oregon, November 30, 1935.

35. Crain, Harry N., "Action of Council Selecting Santiam Brings Opposition," *Capital Journal*, Salem, Oregon, February 18, 1936

36. "Proposes Trap Well On Santiam Island As City Water Supply," *Capital Journal*, Salem, Oregon, February 14, 1936

37. "Water System To Be Failure," *Capital Press*, Salem, Oregon, February 14, 1936.

38. "New Offer on Wells Source Made to City," *Oregon Statesman*, Salem, Oregon, March 11, 1936.

39. "Cost Less Than River Supply Or Pumping From Wells, Claim," *Oregon Statesman*, Salem, Oregon, May 3, 1936.

40. "Canal Will Be Added, Water Source Setup," *Oregon Statesman*, Salem, Oregon, May 8, 1937.

41. Ibid.

42. "Engineer Koon Wants To Dig A $10,000 Ditch," *Capital Press*, Salem, Oregon, May 14, 1937.

43. "Commissioners Should Resign," *Capital Press*, Salem, Oregon,

September 16, 1938.
44. "Increasing Water Supply," *Oregon Statesman*, Salem, Oregon, September 17, 1938.

## CHAPTER 4: WATER RIGHTS THROUGH 1951
45. Letter from J.L. Franzen, City Manager, to State Engineer of Oregon, Public Works Department files, February 1, 1956.
46. Culver, Warren, "Water Rights To North Santiam River and Mill Creek," City of Salem, Public Works Department water rights files, 1955.
47. Ibid.

## CHAPTER 5: THE DETROIT DAM FIASCO
48. All letters in Chapter 5 from the City of Salem and the Corps of Engineers are from City of Salem, Public Works Department water rights files.
49. Stevens, Robert L., "City Refused More Water From Detroit," *Oregon Statesman*, January 28, 1958.

## CHAPTER 6: SUCCESSES AND FRUSTRATIONS 1950-1956
50. Geren, John, "Development of Water Supply, Salem,Oregon," unpublished report, Public Works Department files, Salem, Oregon, 1951.
51. Prange, Conrad, "Uphill Paving Job Near
turner Makes Use of New Techniques," *Oregon Statesman*, Salem, Oregon, June 30, 1952.
52. Rice, Archie H, "A Study of an Auxiliary Water Supply for the City of Salem, Oregon," CH2M, Consulting Engineers, Corvallis, Oregon, December, 1951.
53. Geren, Ibid.
54. Geren, Ibid.
55. Geren, Ibid.
56. Geren, Ibid.
57. "Water Rates and Sewer Charges May be Upped," *Capital Journal*, Salem, Oregon, January 18, 1954.
58. Gangwire, Robert E., "Council Shelves Water Supply Expansion Plans," *Oregon Statesman*, Salem, Oregon, August 17, 1954.
59. Gangwire, Robert E., "Assessment Authority Measure on City Ballot," *Oregon Statesman*, Salem, Oregon, August 24, 1954.
60. "Map Is City's Argument For An Annexation Policy," *Capital Journal*, Salem, Oregon, October 28, 1954.

61. "Bigger Salem Water Supply Recommended," *Capital Journal*, Salem, Oregon, January 23, 1956.
62. "Salem Must Have More Water," *Capital Journal*, Salem, Oregon, May 7, 1956.
63. "Contract For Design of New Water Line Ordered by Council," *Capital Journal*, Salem, Oregon, June 12, 1956.

CHAPTER 7: WATER SYSTEM IMPROVEMENTS 1956-1971
64. Gangwire, Robert E., "Reservoir Named For Franzen - Outgoing City Manager Feted By Testimonials," *Oregon Statesman*, Salem, Oregon, July 19, 1956.
65. Gangwire, Robert E., "Kent Mathewson to Start by July 1, At $14,000 Pay." *Capital Journal*, Salem, Oregon, March 28, 1956.
66. Geren, John L., "Nature Provided Part of Our Water System," *The American City Magazine*, April, 1959.
67. "Stayton OKehs Salem Water Line Plans," *Oregon Statesman*, Salem, Oregon, June 9, 1957.
68. Breraugal, Russell, "Salem's New Water Line One of Top Contracts In Valley History," *Oregon Statesman*, Salem, Oregon, May 26, 1957.
69. "Water Distribution System Master Plan, Salem Metropolitan Area for City of Salem, Oregon," CH2M, Engineers and Planners, Corvallis, Oregon, April, 1968.
70. "Water For Salem," brochure prepared by John Geren for an American Water Works Association meeting in 1968.

CHAPTER 8: WATER RIGHTS PURCHASES 1960's & 1970's
71. Bill of sale, recorded in Marion County, Oregon for $30,000, Marion County Investment Company grants the City of Salem, Oregon 50 cfs of water from the North Santiam River, November 5, 1962.
72. Geren, John L., Letter to Santiam Water Control District, Public Works Department water rights files, January 27, 1956.
73. Drews, David H., Secretary-Treasure of the Santiam Water Control District, letter to John L. Geren, Public Works Department water rights files, February 18, 1976
74. Public Works Department water rights files.
75. "More Water from Santiam," *Oregon Statesman*, Salem, Oregon, August 24, 1976.
76. Public Works Department water rights files.
77. Silver, Paul, "Report of Water Rights on the North Santiam River," City of Salem, Oregon, June 9, 1977.

78. Dickie, Lance, "Salem Buys Boise Cascade Water Rights," *Oregon Statesman*, Salem, Oregon, July 27, 1978
79. "Future Water Source, Supply and Distribution for the City of Salem, Oregon," Steven, Thompson and Runyon, Engineers and Planners, Portland, Oregon, April, 1977.

CHAPTER 9: WATER WARS ALONG SALEM DITCH
80. Merry, Ronald J., "Possible Purchase of a Boise Cascade Water Right," staff report to the Salem City Council, Public Works Department water rights files, December 20, 1982.
81. Woodall, Bill, "Stayton Pursues Ditch Water Rights," *Stayton Mail*, Stayton, Oregon, May 26, 1983.
82. Merriman, Ed, "Stayton Charges Salem with Conflict of Interest," *Statesman-Journal*, Salem, Oregon, March 7, 1986.
83. Public Works Department water rights files.
84. Gustafason, Alan, "Water Rights Deal Assured,"*Statesman-Journal*, Salem, Oregon, July 2, 1986.
85. Water rights acquisitions and sales:
        1. The 1923, 22 cfs water right was applied for in 1923 and issued in 1936. The City of Salem gave 10 cfs of this certificated right to the City of Stayton in 2001 leaving 12 cfs for the City of Salem.
        2. The 60 cfs right was purchased in 1951 from Oregon Pulp and Paper Company.
        3. The 50 cfs right was purchased in 1962 from Marion County Investment Company.
        4. The 62 cfs right was purchased in 1978 from Boise Cascade Corporation.
        5. The 55 cfs right was purchased in 1986 from Boise Cascade.

CHAPTER 10: WATERSHED PROTECTION
86. Ashbough, James G., editor, *The Pacific Northwest Geographical Perspectives*, Kendall Hart Publishing Company, Dubuque, Iowa, 1994, p. 61-63.
87. Alt, David, and Hyndman, Donald W., *Northwest Exposures, A Geologic Story of the Northwest*, Chapter 31, "The Western Cascades," Mountain Press Publishing Company, Missoula,Montana, 1995.
88. Alt and Hyndman, Ibid., Chapter 43, "The High Cascades"
89. Hamblin, W. Kenneth, *The Earths Dynamic System*, Chapter 19, "Volcanism," Burgess Publishing, Minneapolis, Minnesota, 4th Edition, 1985.
90. The information for the "Second Major Event" was obtained en-

tirely from Evangelyn Fleetwood's article "A Successful Failure - The Oregon Pacific Railroad," *Historic Marion*, Marion County Historical Society, Volume 40, Number 3, Fall, 2002.

91. Maser, Chris, *Sustainable Forestry, Philosophy, Science and Economics*, St. Lucie Press, Delray Beach, Florida, 1994, p. 24-25.

92. Maser, Ibid, p. 249.

93. Maser, Ibid, p. 255-257.

94. "A Brief History of the Willamette National Forest," Web Page, U.S. Department of Agriculture, U.S. Forest Service, Willamette National Forest.

95. *Record of Decision* for Amendments to Forest Service and Bureau of Land Management Planning Documents within the Range of the Northern Spotted Owl, April, 1994, p. 3.

96. Schweickert, Tina, "City of Salem Questions Effect of Forest Practices on its Municipal Watershed," *Sixth Annual Water Conference Proceedings*, Lewis and Clark College, Portland, Oregon, May 3-4, 2001.

97. "Evaluation Report - Proposed Storage Reallocation Project," Corps of Engineers, November 25, 1975.

98. Bates, Deigh, et al, *Watershed Management Council Networker*, "North Santiam River Turbidity Study, 1996-97," Published by Watershed Management Council, University of California, Berkley, California, Fall, 1998.

99. Ruffing, F.E., et al, "City of Salem Water Supply - February 96 Flood," 2nd Annual Pacific Northwest Water Issues Conference, 1996.

100. Glassman, J.R., "Clay Mineralogy of Soils and Suspended Sediments within the North Santiam River Drainage," Progress Report, Willamette Geological Services, WGS049704, 1997.

101. *Oregon Watersheds - Many Activities Contribute to Increased Turbidity During Large Storms*, Report to Congressional Requesters, U.S. General Accounting Office, July, 1998.

102. "Rage Over Trees," a video produced by the Audubon Society, 1989.

103. "House Passes Bill to Protect North Santiam," Stayton Mail, Stayton, Oregon, May 26, 1983.

CHAPTER 11: MODERNIZATION 1996-2003

104. *Water System Master Plan* for the City of Salem, prepared by CH2M-Hill, Consulting Engineers and Planners, Portland, Oregon, 1994.

## CHAPTER 12: SOARING WATER RATES

105. "City Water Rate Cut Favored," *Capital Journal*, Salem, Oregon, May 10, 1957. This rate cut was proposed by a committee of eight and was appointed by the City Council. The committee members were; Peter Ganner, Chair, Walter Gerth, James Loder, Gerry Frank, David O'Hara, Lewis Mitchell, Joseph Dodd and Carol Meeks (City Councilor).
106. "Water System Cost of Service Analysis," City of Salem, 1984.
107. Jordan, Johnnie, "Water Rate Increase, Ordinance Adoption," City Council staff report, February 25, 1985.
108. Athon, Anastasia, "City Water and Sewer Rates Go Up May 1," *Statesman Journal*, Salem, Oregon, April 7, 1992.
109. "Use of Franchise Fees For Government Wrong," editorial of *Statesman-Journal*, Salem, Oregon, April 6,1992.
110. Athon, Anastasia, "Salem Reverses Water and Sewer Rate Increase," *Statesman-Journal*, Salem, Oregon, April 28, 1992.
111. Athon, Anastasia, "Salem Water, Sewer Rates to Rise," *Statesman-Journal*, Salem, Oregon, May 5, 1992.

## CHAPTER 13: FISH EXERT THEIR RIGHTS

112. Endangered Species Act of 1973 as amended through 1988 (100th Congress).
113. Rossotto, Michael, "Challenging the 4(d) Rule: Conserving Threatened Species," *Big River News*, Lewis and Clark College of Law, Portland, Oregon, 2001.
114. Bastasch, Rick, *Waters of Oregon, A Source Book on Oregon's Water and Water Management*, Oregon State University Press, Corvallis, Oregon, 1998, p.44.
115. "Endangered and Threatened Wildlife and Plants; Determination of Endangered Status for Oregon chub,"*Federal Register*, Vol. 58, No. 199, October 18, 1993.
116. *Oregon Chub Recovery Plan*, U.S. Fish and Wildlife Service, September 3, 1998.
117. Lichatowich, Jim, *Salmon Without Rivers*, Island Press, Washington D.C., 1999, p. 198.
118. "Endangered and Threatened Wildlife and Plants; Definition of 'Harm'", *Federal Register*, November 8, 1999.
119. *Consultation Handbook*, NMFS, March, 1998.

## APPENDIX A: A BRIEF HISTORY OF SALEM

120. Many of the miscellaneous facts were taken from the online Salem History web site which were supplied by Al Jones, retired journalist and active Salem historian.

# Index of Names*